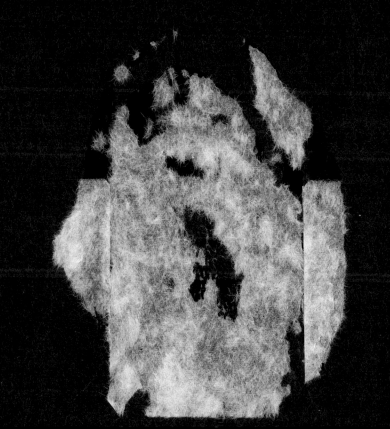

AGING AND SOCIETY

AGING AND SOCIETY *consists of three volumes:*

Volume one: An inventory of research findings
Volume two: Aging and the professions
Volume three: A sociology of age stratification

Under the direction of Matilda White Riley

AGING AND SOCIETY

Volume two: Aging and the professions

edited by Matilda White Riley,
John W. Riley, Jr., and Marilyn E. Johnson

in association with Anne Foner and Beth Hess

RUSSELL SAGE FOUNDATION   NEW YORK

PUBLICATIONS OF RUSSELL SAGE FOUNDATION

Russell Sage Foundation was established in 1907 by Mrs. Russell Sage for the improvement of social and living conditions in the United States. In carrying out its purpose the Foundation conducts research under the direction of members of the staff or in close collaboration with other institutions, and supports programs designed to improve the utilization of social science knowledge. As an integral part of its operations, the Foundation from time to time publishes books or pamphlets resulting from these activities. Publication under the imprint of the Foundation does not necessarily imply agreement by the Foundation, its Trustees, or its staff with the interpretations or conclusions of the authors.

To the memory of
JOHN MADGE
*Friend, scholar,
collaborator*

Contents

Authors and Advisers

Aging and the field of social work

ROBERT MORRIS
Professor of Social Planning
The Florence Heller Graduate School for Advanced Studies in
Social Welfare
Brandeis University

ADVISERS
Walter M. Beattie, Jr.
Dean, School of Social Work
Syracuse University

Ollie A. Randall
Principal Consultant, Programs in Aging, The Ford Foundation
Board Member, National Council on the Aging

Aging and the field of medicine

LOUIS LASAGNA
Associate Professor of Medicine, and of Pharmacology and
Experimental Therapeutics, School of Medicine
The Johns Hopkins University

ADVISERS
Reubin Andres
Gerontology Research Center
National Institute of Child Health and Human Development

Arthur J. Patek, Jr.
Professor of Medicine
Tufts University School of Medicine

DeWitt Stetten, Jr.
Dean, Rutgers Medical School
Rutgers University

OTHER CRITIC
Esther Lucile Brown
Consultant on Psychosocial Aspects of Patient Care

Aging and the field of nursing

DORIS R. SCHWARTZ
Public Health Nursing
Cornell University—New York Hospital School of Nursing

ADVISERS
Faye G. Abdellah
Division of Nursing
United States Public Health Service

Esther Lucile Brown
Consultant on Psychosocial Aspects of Patient Care

OTHER CRITICS
Ellen Fahy
Professor and Dean, College of Nursing
State University of New York at Stony Brook

Frances Cook Macgregor
Research Scientist
New York University Medical Center
School of Medicine

Margery T. Overholser
Professor Emeritus
Cornell University—New York Hospital School of Nursing

Aging and the field of public health

MERVYN SUSSER
Professor of Epidemiology and Chairman of Division of Epidemiology
School of Public Health and Administrative Medicine
Columbia University

ADVISERS
George Rosen
Professor of History of Medicine and Epidemiology and Public Health
Yale University School of Medicine

Frederick D. Zeman
Chief of Medical Services
The Jewish Home and Hospital for Aged
New York, New York

Aging and manpower development

HAROLD L. SHEPPARD
Staff Social Scientist
The W. E. Upjohn Institute for Employment Research

ADVISERS
Geneva Mathiasen
former Executive Director
National Council on the Aging
New York, New York

Walter J. McNamara
Manager Personnel Assessment Programs
International Business Machines Corporation

Charles E. Odell
United States Employment Service
Department of Labor

Aging and financial management

JUANITA M. KREPS
Professor of Economics
Duke University

ADVISERS
Herman B. Brotman
Administration on Aging
Department of Health, Education, and Welfare

Sverre Roang
Judge, Rock County Court—Branch 1
Janesville, Wisconsin

Aging and the fields of architecture and planning

JOHN MADGE
(formerly) Political and Economic Planning, London
Bartlett School of Architecture
University College, London

ADVISERS
Robert L. Geddes
Dean, School of Architecture
Princeton University

Huson Jackson
Professor of Architecture, Harvard University
Sert, Jackson and Associates, Architects

OTHER CRITIC
Glenn H. Beyer
Center for Housing and Environmental Studies
Cornell University

Aging and the law

MERTON C. BERNSTEIN
Professor of Law
The Ohio State University
College of Law

ADVISERS
Max Rheinstein
Professor of Law Emeritus
School of Law, University of Chicago

Alvin L. Schorr
Professor of Social Policy
Brandeis University

Aging and the ministry

PHILLIP E. HAMMOND
Associate Profesor of Sociology
University of Wisconsin

ADVISERS

James M. Gustafson
Professor of Religious Studies
Divinity School
Yale University

Andrew M. Greeley
Program Director, National Opinion Research Center
University of Chicago

Manfred H. Vogel
Associate Professor, History and Literature of Religions
Northwestern University

Aging and the field of education

LOWELL EKLUND
Professor and Dean, Division of Continuing Education
Oakland University

ADVISERS
Ernest E. McMahon
Professor of Adult Education
Dean, University Extension Division
Rutgers University

Thurman White
Vice-President
University of Oklahoma

Aging and mass communication

WILBUR SCHRAMM
Professor and Director, Institute for Communication Research
Stanford University

ADVISER
W. Phillips Davison
Editor, Public Opinion Quarterly

Preface

A great deal is now known about older people in modern American society, yet comparatively little of this knowledge is systematically utilized in the practicing professions. A series of three volumes, entitled *Aging and Society,* aims to stimulate and facilitate such utilization. Volume One, *An Inventory of Research Findings,* selects, condenses, and organizes the body of social science research on human beings in their middle and later years. The present volume, second in the series, draws upon Volume One as a reference work and interprets the Inventory for the several professional and related fields concerned with the well-being of older people and with the prevention or treatment of problems associated with aging.

Designed to serve as one channel through which social science knowledge can flow into the professions, this book is addressed both to practitioners and to students in professional training. It is directed not only to traditional fields, like medicine or law, that are the province of clearly established professional groups, but also to the emergent fields of financial management and manpower development in which a diversity of experts counsel or plan for old age, and to the clearly relevant field of the mass media. The book should be of interest also to public officials concerned with aging, to social scientists designing further research, and to the general reader seeking insight into this universal process.

The substantive chapters that constitute the book are each written from the perspective of a particular field. The authors were asked to identify those findings from the Inventory of highest relevance for their own profession, and to interpret the implications of these findings both for practice (at the clinical, pastoral, or counseling level) and for policy making (at the legislative or administrative level). The original plan was to publish the papers as separate treatises for specialized use in the respective disciplines; but the project was scarcely underway when it became clear that, despite differences in approach, each contributor was as much concerned with the content of the several other chapters as with his own. Accordingly, the papers as finally conceived are by no means discrete entities. All are stimulated by a common body of knowledge. All refer to the same population of older individuals. And all reflect the notable interdependence and the frequent overlapping of boundaries among the different professions, just as aging itself has interpenetrating biological, social, and psychological perimeters. Thus the chapters have been written, as they are intended to be read, to deal with the problems and opportunities in each profession, not in isolation, but within the broad context of aging in contemporary society.

A discussion of this broad context of aging in contemporary America is supplied by the editors in the first chapter of the book, a chapter that serves as a general introduction to the substantive materials. The editors have also written specific introductions to each chapter in order to underscore the common purposes of the volume. Cross references have been inserted to lead the reader of one chapter to related portions of other chapters as well as to the source material in Volume One. (See the Detailed Table of Contents of Volume One on pages 377 to 389.)

Apart from questions of fact, the editors have made no attempt to reconcile any differences of interpretation or emphasis that may appear in the various chapters. Nor do the chapters necessarily reflect the views of the editors. Each one stands on its own merits.

The several chapters have been read critically by practitioners and educators in the respective fields, as well as by generalists in social gerontology, all of whom have made valuable suggestions to authors and editors both on content and on effective utilization of the material within the professions.

Acknowledgments The program of study that has produced these volumes was made possible by a grant from The Ford Foundation to Russell Sage Foundation. The foresight that initiated this program and the enthusiasm that has sustained it are attributable in large part to Stacey H. Widdicombe, Jr., and Ollie A. Randall of The Ford Foundation and to Donald R. Young and Orville G. Brim, Jr., of Russell Sage Foundation.

Countless other persons have helped to bring this second volume to completion. At the outset, leaders from government, universities, and professional agencies, who were themselves working toward the development of curriculum materials on aging, attended a conference aimed to avoid duplication and to maximize the combined effort. Representatives of the several fields included in the book aided in the intensive search for authors who could meet our criteria of distinction as professionals and excellence as writers. Specific assistance at critical points was provided by Robert Gutman, Abbott A. Leban, Geneva Mathiasen, Mary E. Moore, Mary Patek, and Stephen A. Richardson.

The staff of editors for the book, headed by Matilda White Riley and Marilyn E. Johnson of the Sociology Department at Rutgers University, and by John W. Riley, Jr., Vice President and Director of Social Research for the Equitable Life Assurance Society of the United States, were ably assisted at every stage by Anne Foner and Beth Hess, also Rutgers sociologists. Research and technical work has been effectively and skillfully provided by Mildred G. Aurelius and Sallie Smith, who verified the bibliographical references; and by Margaret Scott, who prepared the indexes. The typing of the manuscript through successive revisions was handled by Marion Erhart, Dee Maltese, and Ellen Enhoffer.

To all these persons and agencies, the editors express their profound appreciation.

M. W. R.
J. W. R., JR.
M. E. J.

AGING AND SOCIETY

1

Introduction

The gradual aging of the population in modern industrial society has wrought profound changes within the constituencies served by the practicing professions. In the United States, as the number of people aged 65 and over has multiplied fivefold since 1900, so too the numbers of older people in church congregations, hospitals, or mass media audiences have multiplied. These changes arise not only from growth of the entire population, but also from especially rapid increases in older age groups: Over the century, the proportion of the total population who are aged 65 or older has risen from 3 per cent to nearly 10 per cent, and the proportion who are aged 45 to 64 has grown from 10 per cent to 20 per cent. Thus there has been a continuing rise in the likelihood that the physician or nurse must treat the chronic ailments and disabilities associated with senescence, that the architect must provide housing for older couples or widows living alone, that the social worker must deal with persons no longer absorbed in occupations or other socially valued roles, or that the lawyer must advise on the estates of persons who can expect to live well beyond the age of retirement.

This long-term intrusion of aging and its concomitants into the clientele of the professions has been gradual, subtle, and often unremarked by persons engaged in practice or in preparing others for practice. Many a physician has been surprised at the number of geriatric cases among his patients, for example; many a community planner has come unexpectedly upon the extensive need to house family units that do not consist of young parents and dependent children; and many a financial adviser has been confronted by the fact that nowadays not merely the favored few but the great mass of workers must make provision for retirement.

In the chapters of this book, however, the impact on the professions of the changing age composition of the population becomes strikingly clear. Available knowledge has been codified in *Aging and Society: An Inventory of Research Findings* and summarized in Chapter 1 of that volume. Utilizing this knowledge, the several authors of the present volume assess the characteristics associated with the growing numbers of older people, define the needs and the potential of the aged, and discuss programs and policies to meet these needs and develop this potential for both current and future generations of older people.

The authors have approached in diverse ways their mandate to write interpretative essays on the implications of social science knowledge of aging for their respective fields. The chapters vary both in content and in scope, depending upon the situation in a given profession as well as upon the interests and perceptions of the particular interpreter. In Chapter 2, on social work, Robert Morris treats a wide range of topics, setting the stage for much of the discussion in the ensuing chapters. A number of concerns touched upon by Professor Morris are expanded in Chapters 3 through 5, which examine the health fields. While Louis Lasagna and Doris Schwartz deal with the various issues arising in the treatment of aged patients by the physician and the nurse respectively, Mervyn Susser explores the entire social environment of older people to assess its impact on their state of health. Certain aspects of the broad economic problems of labor force participation and income maintenance are investigated in Chapters 6 and 7 by Harold Sheppard and by Juanita Kreps. In Chapter 8, John Madge examines the challenge to architects and planners presented by the needs of older people for appropriate housing and service facilities. Economic, health, and housing problems are then set into a wider framework in Chapter 9, in Merton Bernstein's far-reaching discussion on the legal implications of an aging society. In contrast, Chapters 10 through 12 concentrate more on the social-emotional aspects of old age, as Phillip Hammond surveys the role of the church in the lives of older people, Lowell Eklund stresses the potential of continuing education, and Wilbur Schramm suggests the possibilities of the mass media for involving older people in society and for facilitating the aims of specialists in all fields dealing with the aged.

Different as these chapters are in specific detail, they all consider in one fashion or another three fundamental questions that cross-cut the boundaries dividing professions and emphasize the interdependence of professional concerns. First, what *can* be done about the condition of older people? What possibilities for professional service are suggested by social science knowledge about aging as a process and about the meaning of age for the individual's psychosocial adjustment and his position in society? Second, what, if anything, *ought* to be done about the condition of older people? How can social science knowledge be brought to bear in selecting and evaluating programs and in allocating resources? What standards and values are implicit in the plans and goals of the several professions? And third, *how* can the desired changes in the condition of older people be accomplished? How can a balance be struck between the needs of increasing numbers of older people and the availability of services? What changes may be indicated in professional training or in the structure of the professions?

Present versus potential condition of older people

One major principle emerging from the Inventory is relevant for any assessment of professional services to older people. This principle stresses the importance of differentiating between the present condition of older people, who are in some ways disadvantaged, with the potential condition of older people in the future, provided that increased scientific understanding leads to appropriate action by professional groups. Thus a basic distinction must be made among the state of being old, the process of becoming old, and the changing prospects of successive cohorts (sometimes loosely called generations) of the aged. In programmatic terms, the existing ills of people who are old today call for *therapy*, whether through individual treatment or through manipulation of the relevant environment. But the future ills of persons not yet arrived at old age still allow the possibility of *prevention*, whether through deliberate action or as an indirect consequence of existing trends.

THE STATE OF BEING OLD

It is clear from the Inventory that, in certain respects, older people are at any given time deprived relative to younger people. Accordingly, the essays note at various points the professional implications of older people's comparatively higher rate of morbidity, their relative economic impoverishment, and their lower levels of educational attainment, labor force participation, and social participation in general.

To be sure, such relative deprivations must not be overemphasized (as they have been overemphasized in numerous fallacious interpretations noted in the Inventory). The old do not differ from the young in every respect, nor are the differences always to their disadvantage. Older people, by virtue of their longer years of life, have acquired both experience and, perhaps, wisdom; they appear quite as adequate as the young in performing various aspects of their familial, occupational, religious, and political roles. Furthermore, the majority of older people hold a positive self-image that does not stress unfavorable comparisons with the young, and thus they may not perceive themselves as deprived even though objectively disadvantaged.

It is not surprising, therefore, that a common theme of these essays is a general rejection of the traditional view of old age as a situation of utter and inevitable disadvantage. By pointing to the many areas of independence and to the lack of serious physical disability among the majority of today's aged, each essay contributes to the erosion of some aspect of this negative stereotype. Moreover, discussions of the relative deprivation of the older population as a whole are balanced by examples of the relatively salutary status of specific segments of this population. There are many older individuals who enjoy high education, good health, and adequate income. There are also many older individuals who exhibit high levels of adjustment, of morale, and of interaction with their fellows. Such examples serve importantly both to deny the intractability of the current problems of the elderly and to suggest areas in which ameliorative effort is likely to produce needed solutions.

THE POTENTIAL FOR DEVELOPMENT

In rejecting both the completely negative image of old age and the notion that the invidious features of aging are inevitable, the authors stress instead the potential for change and adaptation, noting the older person's demonstrated ability to learn, to develop, and to adjust to new circumstances and new roles. Here the contributors to this volume are developing a second perspective emerging from the Inventory, one which focuses upon the aging process rather than upon the current status of the aged. Very little is yet known about aging as a process, either about the extent of the individual's capacity for change or about the conditions for fulfillment of this potential. Yet, several of the proposed programs and goals proceed on the assumption that not all age-related ills are intrinsic to aging and are thus preventable through intervention at earlier stages in the life course.

For example, the unrealized abilities of the aging individual is a basic premise of Eklund's essay on education. If man has an almost unlimited capacity for learning and educational achievement, the aim of any educational system, Eklund insists, must be to produce individuals with motivation for continuous learning. Such an aim obviously requires implementation of programs at early ages as well as the creation of a system of continuing education for adults. In a somewhat similar vein, the criterion of unfulfilled potential is clearly, if not explicitly, invoked by Schramm, who raises the provocative questions of how the mass media might operate more effectively not only to maintain the link between older people and the larger society, but also to provide appropriate and compelling programs for the continuing development of the older person. Further, the importance of continued learning in the form of retraining is enunciated both by Sheppard and by Bernstein in their discussions of devices for maintaining employment among older workers. Ideally, such retraining must start at the early stages of work life, for, as Bernstein notes, rapid technological advance creates the necessity for "periodic retooling." Consequently, a person no more than forty may already be classified as an "older worker."

Belief in the potential for continuing personal growth is further illustrated by numerous suggestions for new roles that might be assumed by the elderly. Whether proposing new occupational arrangements, new civic and volunteer activities, or new ways of using leisure time, the authors seem convinced not only that the aged display a capacity for development, but also that such development may be an important key to a satisfying old age. Moreover, in discussing ways of training and socializing people to new roles, the authors underscore the importance of implementing programs well in advance of the onset of old age. Thus Morris proposes that employers and unions support auxiliary organizations (even "spin-off corporations") for the early practice of semi-retirement and for the anticipatory acquisition of hobbies and skills of various kinds, including the organizational and administrative skills required for independent business enterprises or for important civic roles.

The potential of the middle years as preparation for old age is also emphasized by contributors concerned with early planning and counseling. Whether the authors are dealing with personal health care, adjustment to retirement, potential accumulation of savings, estate planning, or preparation for changing housing needs, they tend to concur in the proposition that many of the negative features of old age may be avoided by "anticipatory socialization" and, when necessary, by professional intervention at earlier stages in the life course of the individual.

One difficulty, however, that arises from assumptions of potentiality involves the definition of *limits* to capacity for development in specific respects. Particular authors may assume these to be finite and measurable or infinite and unmeasurable, but the supporting evidence is rarely available. Susser handles this problem in his discussion of the unfulfilled health potential by indicating a *minimum margin* for improvement. Analyzing the potential for gains in longevity and for avoidance of age-related organic deterioration, he explores the difficulties of distinguishing inevitable biological effects of aging from environmental effects which may be susceptible to manipulation. The evidence required for making a clear-cut distinction is not at hand. Nevertheless, a minimum margin for improvement may be established, not upon a definition of what might be possible under ideal conditions, but upon empirically observed variation in disease and mortality rates, with the lowest known rates providing a standard toward which public health programs may be directed. At the level of individual therapy, similar notions underlie the chapters on medicine and on nursing, where Lasagna and Schwartz respectively note the possibilities of improving the health of those with apparent "chronic" ailments through earlier attention and care on the part of health professionals.

PROSPECTS FOR THE FUTURE

Quite apart from the possibilities of professional intervention in the environmental and institutional context of older people or in the process by which individuals age, broad social changes are continually taking place that affect the preparation for old age of successive generations of individuals. Many of the essays converge in accenting, as a third perspective emerging from the Inventory, the importance of such social changes for estimating the future prospect of older people.

It is quite clear, for example, that husbands and wives today live together independently for a longer period of time than was the case even several decades ago. The implications of such a fact for housing needs, family roles, income maintenance and insurance coverages, leisure activities, and myriad other aspects of the lives of older people cannot be ignored.

Other societal trends, such as urbanization, increased geographic mobility, and the growth of suburbs must be taken into account in the planning and location of housing and service facilities. Moreover, such changes in the spatial distribution of the population, both old and young, will affect the social and political attitudes, the patterns of consumption, and many of the activities of older people.

Important changes are also occurring in the educational attainment of the population. The differences between old and young in the level of formal education, though striking at the present time, may perhaps be less pronounced when the better educated younger generations of today become the aged of the future. At the very least, tomorrow's aged will have had more years of formal schooling than their present-day counterparts. Programs designed for the future must give attention not only to this rise in educational level but also to the broad consequences for the situation, behavior, and attitudes of individuals.

Equally profound resultants of social change are associated with increases in the productivity of the economy. The long-term trend has been toward declining labor force participation and earlier retirement of the older population. If such a trend continues, it can alter drastically the organization of work and leisure, the supporting values, and the total role complexes of individuals at all ages. Although such possible alterations are difficult to estimate, they must receive serious attention in the creation of programs for future cohorts of aged.

Not only are the long-term effects of broad changes difficult to estimate, but the impact may not always be beneficial or may have differential effects on various age groups. Thus it is not entirely clear that future cohorts of old people will have fewer problems or be better off in every respect than those now old. For example, Kreps points out that, although tomorrow's aged may experience increases in real income as a result of continued economic growth, their position *relative* to other age groups may not improve or may even deteriorate. Eklund makes a similar point with regard to education. The negative effects of relative deprivation, though differing in kind, may be as severe as those of absolute deprivation. Lasagna provides a further illustration when he questions the social costs of prolonging the lives of large numbers of aged who are especially subject to disabling chronic ailments. And Susser's analysis of public health problems, though pointing to advances on certain fronts, notes the possible deleterious effects of certain aspects of the urban environment, such as increasing air pollution.

Thus, changes in the attributes of future cohorts of aged and in the general societal context of aging are of fundamental importance to a full consideration of the needed professional services. However imprecisely the implications can be currently foreseen, it is very clear throughout these chapters that the forces of social change are not only constantly intervening in the aging process, but are also bringing new influences to bear on the situation and characteristics of persons who are old.

When the problems of aging are seen in this dynamic perspective, the relevance of a common theme of these essays becomes apparent. By focusing on the distinction between the present condition of older people in contrast with what the status of future cohorts might be, these essays suggest the possibilities of professional intervention for meeting the challenge of both individual potential and social change. Intervention, however, is not contingent solely upon knowledge of the situation of the aging, as this may be supplied by the Inventory or by further scientific research. Such action also requires policies and programs. Thus the authors of these essays propound for their respective professions a wide variety of long-range goals and practical procedures that involve basic questions of standards and values.

Standards and values

Any determination of what ought to be done to reduce the deprivations of older people or to enhance their potential strengths requires evaluative judgments. The substance of professional policy can be formulated only with reference to immediate aims and ultimate goals, and such ends are invariably derived, even if not explicitly, from basic notions about what is good or desirable or aesthetically appropriate. Thus countless questions of standards and values underlie the professional solutions discussed in these essays.

On some issues, there is near unanimity of value position among the several authors. One after another of the contributors asserts the desirability of keeping older people in the community rather than in institutions, and of discharging to the community the maximum feasible number of old people currently institutionalized. Indeed, so strongly entrenched is the aversion to institutional living that there is little exploration of the possible benefits of such arrangements except as an alternative of last resort.

There is consensus also on the importance of freedom of choice, as this freedom might be fostered by a diversity of programs for older people. Considerable attention is paid in the essays to the wide variations among older individuals in education, rates of aging, or preferred activities. There are frequent warnings that programs aimed at stereotypic images of the aged can have little chance of success. Instead, the authors recommend arrangements that would maximize choice, and propose information or referral systems that would make older people aware of available alternatives.

Despite important areas of agreement among the professional fields, there is considerable heterogeneity in the normative prescriptions and standards of evaluation utilized in the several essays. The normative issues involved range from specific judgments about minimum standards to the raising of inscrutable moral dilemmas.

STANDARDS FOR ALLOCATING RESOURCES

Proponents of particular programs for providing older people with a more adequate fraction of the nation's scarce supply of goods and services employ several different criteria of adequacy, including minimum standards that are arbitrarily set and proportional standards that would guarantee to older people a "fair" share.

Minimum standards Minimum standards are discussed at some length in regard to housing, for example, as Madge lists specifications that would protect older people against various hazards. Several authors stress the necessity of minimum standards for nursing homes and geriatric care facilities. And Kreps discusses the desirability of income transfers that would maintain above some prescribed level of adequacy the financial integrity of those older people who are extruded from the labor force and can no longer claim a share in the nation's increasing economic productivity.

As the phrase implies, minimum standards define the status of the aged and the professional services rendered them not in terms of what is possible or ideal, but according to arbitrary criteria of what seems acceptable in the opinion of some particular person or group. The value of what is to be provided is not itself explicitly assessed. Rather, desiderata such as good health, good housing, or financial security are simply taken for granted, and the professional aim becomes one of supplying these desiderata to the aged in accordance with established criteria of adequacy. One difficulty of this approach, of course, is that minimum standards can change over time as conditions in the general society change. For example, if the income of the population as a whole shows improvement over time, support programs based on earlier definitions of a minimum standard may no longer be adequate.

"Fair shares" A second type of standard against which goals for the aged may be set demands a fair share relative to other age groups in the distribution of goods and services. Studies of the relatively deprived status of older people are often utilized to show the need for redress of imbalances as, for example, when Morris points

out that the elderly are underrepresented and underserved by various welfare agencies, or when Kreps analyzes the inferior economic status of the aged, and Sheppard examines their relatively unfavorable employment situation.

A somewhat similar method of evaluation takes as its standard of fairness, not younger age groups, but earlier stages in the individual's own life. Here the goal is to minimize the difference between the middle years and the later years in the life course through the preservation of the aging individual's health, for example, through the smoothing out of income differences between the two stages, through continued employment, or through maintenance of preexisting friendship and kin relations.

It might appear at first glance that some such standard of proportional sharing of scarce resources would find little opposition in the context of the American value system. Nevertheless, there is a major difficulty with such a standard, formulated by sociologists in their theories of distributive justice, which often leads to alternative bases of assessment. The norms of a society regarding the fair or just allocation of resources do not always prescribe a simple proportional distribution of goods and services, but recognize certain special claims of some groups. Distributive justice in a particular society may require, for example, that the young should receive a disproportionately large share of health services and support. Indeed, in some societies, the aged and infirm are left alone to die. By such a standard, it would be regarded as "unfair" if the chronically-ill aged were to command an ever-increasing proportion of the medical dollar.

Underlying the precepts of distributive justice is an insistence upon the differences among various groups in their needs or in their social contributions. For example, the argument is sometimes offered that older people do not need as high an income as younger people or that older people do not deserve as high an income because they no longer contribute to production. Such assertions lead away from the aims of redressing the relative deprivations of older people or of smoothing the flow of resources over the life course, and tend to imply goals couched in terms of minimum standards of adequacy.

ETHICAL STANDARDS

In addition to practical problems of setting minimum standards or determining equitable allocations of resources, certain ethical dilemmas arise. Some of the chapters are concerned with decisions that transcend specific questions of allocative standards and deal with what is "right" or morally defensible according to prescriptions embedded in professional codes and in the society at large. Such dilemmas arise when the consequences of contemplated action, though judged beneficial according to one set of values, are perceived to be in conflict with other, equally compelling, ends.

The question of death   A notable instance is the discussion by Lasagna of the patient's legitimate claim to a dignified death. Here the dilemma for the physician lies in the tension between the ethical strictures to preserve life and those to relieve suffering. Many patients are themselves capable of taking action and many do, in fact, contribute to their own deaths by removing intravenous feeding devices, failing to take prescribed medicines, or otherwise thwarting the efforts of medical experts to prolong their lives. Are these patients to be considered suicides? Shall physicians be indicted for malpractice or manslaughter if they contribute to such actions or withhold treatment from such patients? Who is to decide when and when not to terminate treatment of any given patient? These are the kinds of predicaments confronting doctors and nurses, patients, and patients' relatives as they contemplate the meaning of death vis-à-vis the meaning of life.

Individual versus society   Another set of evaluative questions ask whether a given program or policy is designed to foster the well-being of the aged individual or of the society as a whole. Often the two aims coincide. Thus provision of jobs for older people in sectors where there is a shortage of personnel can redound to the good of the entire economy. Similarly, as Morris and Susser attest, programs that make older people feel useful and adequate can at the same time ease strains within the family.

Nevertheless, some programs designed for the benefit of society may work to the disadvantage of the individual. Institutionalization of the older person, for example, may be convenient for the family or other social groups but may constitute a great deprivation to the individual.

Moreover, some programs designed to benefit older people may prove to be of questionable social utility. Thus Lasagna questions the advantage to society of diverting millions of dollars for the treatment of certain comparatively rare disabling diseases afflicting the aged. And Kreps contends that federally sponsored programs for maintaining retirement incomes may not always be compatible with broad national policies concerning economic growth, full employment, or price stability.

In parallel fashion, certain programs designed to benefit the young may have detrimental consequences for older people or for society at large. Thus the improvement of health programs for infants can allow increasing numbers of individuals with organic defects to survive into senescence. Or encouraging the early retirement of still competent older workers in order to give their jobs to the young can at once curtail the occupational rewards to the displaced individuals, add to the dependency burden on the society, and waste the potential human resources thus displaced.

The balance between needs and services

Despite certain unresolved issues of value positions, the authors in the several fields proceed to discuss pragmatic approaches toward implementation, at either the clinical or the policy level, of particular programs that bring into conjunction knowledge of what *can* be done with notions of what *ought* to be done about the condition of older people. An overview of these programs and approaches suggests certain areas of discrepancy between the emerging needs of older people and the professional services available. Constructive planning might help to redress this imbalance through establishing priorities among the needs that are to be met, through developing interdisciplinary approaches to the performance of certain functions, through filling gaps in the present structure of the professions, and through modification of existing curricula in the professional schools.

PRIORITY OF NEEDS

One serious difficulty that becomes apparent from the series of essays is the present lack of clear priorities as to which services to older people should command the scarce resources at hand. Among the many programs for the aged proposed by the different professions, which are the more worthy?

To a great extent, of course, choices among programs will be made on the basis of comparative costs and other practical considerations. Beyond this, attempts to establish priorities among the needs to be filled must rest both on value judgments and on understanding of the facts. Thus whether the need for friendship should have precedence over the need for income may be in part a question of basic social values. Most authors set at least as high a premium on the psychological satisfaction and morale engendered by a program as on its filling of tangible needs.

Once value decisions have been made, however, other questions may be answerable through understanding of the relevant facts and their causal connections. For example, if it were to be established that good health derives from a high standard of living, then it might be argued that income maintenance must be accorded a higher order of priority than the expansion of health services. That is, if one area of need is found to result from another area, then both will be served by attacking the area of primary causation. Unfortunately, the available evidence often fails to establish the causal connections among important areas of need and many of the required answers must await the future execution of carefully controlled research studies.

In the absence of more compelling alternatives, a number of practitioners would hope to establish priorities in the light of older people's own preferences and desires and the relative importance to them of their varying needs. This position stems from the commitment to preserve freedom of choice for the aged in the creation of special programs to serve them. Here too, however, the evidence is all too often either absent, conflicting, or patently unreliable. For example, is it important to older people to be integrated into age-heterogeneous neighborhoods or housing units? The evidence suggests that, although older people consider age-heterogeneous kinship relations to be of primary importance, they also tend to choose age mates as friends; and, as Madge points out in assessing the success of segregated retirement communities, there is some reason to believe that the aged may desire a degree of separation from younger people. What actually is the case? Or, to take another example, are social-emotional needs more important to older people than instrumental needs? Hammond suggests this in discussing the ministry of the church, and a similar implication underlies Eklund's notion that one very important aim of adult education should be the enhancing of the enjoyment of leisure. In contrast, however, Sheppard's treatment of manpower development seems to assume that the instrumental need for continued employment may be the more crucial one. Again, what actually is the case? Further research on such points would clearly be useful, not only because general tendencies to choose one or another alternative may be revealed, but also because systematic differences among older people in their preferences may be specified. Such specifications should be of considerable value in developing a range of alternatives within which older people may satisfy their needs.

Research can be useful too in providing insights into possible unanticipated consequences of professional attempts to fill particular needs. What future ramifications can develop, both for older people and for society, from pressures to keep alive more and less healthy individuals? Or to retain more and less healthy individuals in the labor force? An understanding of such latent possibilities is important to the rational establishment of priorities in serving the needs of older people.

NATURE OF AVAILABLE SERVICES

In addition to revealing various uncertainties about the competing needs of older people, even in some instances an unawareness that priorities must be set, the essays also afford considerable insight into the professional procedures and structures designed to satisfy these needs.

Levels of approach   Attempts to meet the needs of older people are undertaken at various levels: at the individual level, through professional attention to the individual; or at the social level, through reform of institutions or through changes in public policy and legislation. Although it might be anticipated that most authors would discuss programs addressed to both the individual and the institutional or policy-making levels, it is significant for the current status of the professions that solutions of the latter type seem to command the major emphasis.

With respect to income maintenance, for example, although individual responsibility and initiative continue as central values, both Kreps and Bernstein stress the necessity of programs at the governmental and corporate levels. Regarding social work, Morris insists that the elaboration and administration of social welfare as an institutional sphere is of greater importance than the development of professional competence in individual counseling and therapy. In assessing the ministry, Hammond suggests that, while pastoral counseling and other expressive concerns may be central to the church's role vis-à-vis the aged, a restructuring of religious institutions is required for effective enactment of such a role. In the field of architecture, Madge devotes more attention to the provision of suitable postretirement housing than to the preparation of individuals for their own later-life housing needs. In discussing manpower development, Sheppard, while concerned with individual betterment through retraining and employment service counseling, aims also at the provision of suitable job opportunities for older people through programs for job redesign and legislation against age discrimination in hiring. Indeed, the underlying rationale of a majority of the solutions proposed in this volume seems to be reflected in Bernstein's emphasis upon the special significance of the lawyer's function as architect of the law. To be sure, lawyers practice in a variety of roles in relation to the aging; but, he insists, the changing age composition of the population and the accompanying profound social changes present the lawyer with the primary task of establishing new legal arrangements.

Even though the essays express major concern with policy matters, they are replete also with exhortations for more sophisticated treatment of the individual. Social workers are taken to task for their failure to recognize the developmental capabilities of older people; nurses are castigated for allowing unnecessary depersonalization of aged patients; educators are chided for overlooking the significance of the learning potential in continuing education; ministers are scolded for their uncritical acceptance of the belief that people become increasingly religious as they grow older; and architects are called to account for their lack of strategy for dealing with the living requirements of the bereaved spouse. New norms and procedures of many kinds are demanded by the essayists: clear guidelines for dealing with the dying patient, public health techniques for identifying susceptibilities in older individuals, feasible aids to estate planning for persons at all income levels, facilities for occupational guidance of retired persons, and creative utilization of the mass media to link the isolated older person to the larger community.

Organization of services　When the several professions are viewed as a whole, they appear to duplicate or compete with one another in some of the services they now provide or contemplate providing. Thus churches and government may both sponsor housing for the aged. Architects, social workers, and health personnel may each wish to decide the location of health services. Social workers and nurses may each aim at developing and staffing referral services and at providing administration of residential institutions. Physicians, lawyers, social workers, and personnel managers may all lay claim to special competence in counseling on problems of work and retirement. Professional educators, specialists in mass media, and practitioners in various substantive fields may all think it their peculiar function to regulate the content of adult education and the utilization of mass communications to implement desired ends!

To a certain extent, of course, such overlapping may be only apparent, reflecting the separate contributions of the professions to different facets of a problem. In the field of health, for example, it is well recognized that special contributions are required from the physician, the nurse, and the public health official. To these professions must be added many others who also deal with the health of older people: the architect or planner in designing hazard-free homes and the location of health facilities, the educator and the mass communicator in providing health care information, the social worker in identifying and referring cases to proper health agencies and possibly in administering health facilities, and both the financial expert and the social worker in insuring that the cost of health care is not beyond the means of the elderly. Beyond this, various other professionals not directly concerned with health, such as the chaplain or the family case worker, make frequent contributions to the scope of professional practice within health institutions.

To the extent that efforts of this kind lack integration, however, there is a danger that scarce resources may be wasted through duplication or through competition for administrative influence and control. Coordination by means of interdisciplinary structures can forestall such dangers as well as foster the emergence of new and imaginative solutions to many problems. Appropriate interdisciplinary approaches also could help to facilitate decisions concerning the relative competence of agencies to perform needed functions, establish priorities among competing needs, and point to gaps in existing services. Such coordination may require a conceptual approach that would look upon welfare services as a single system rather than as a collection of separate institutions and agencies.

Gaps in existing services   If in some areas several professions are performing similar services to older people, there are other areas in which the structures of existing professions have not yet adapted to meet developing needs. The economic requirements of older people present one glaring instance: There are no clearly established professions devoted to matters either of retirement or of income maintenance. A range of specialists, from government officials to personnel managers, concern themselves with selected aspects of the older worker's participation in the labor force or his withdrawal from it. Similarly, advice on financial management is proffered by a number of specialists, including bankers, lawyers, investment counselors, and life insurance agents. Yet, there is typically no single source of unified advice for the individual who is planning whether and when to retire or who is attempting to understand the intricacies of social security, pension benefits, insurance and annuities, real property, and other assets. This gap becomes increasingly apparent as the mass of today's workers confront the necessity of planning for retirement. Thus the question arises whether the striking growth in the proportion of potential clients may not encourage the emergence of a new financial management profession and the development of personnel managers trained to deal specifically with the occupational and retirement potentials of persons in middle and later life.

The possibility that entirely new categories of professional practice may emerge in response to the rising needs of the aged calls attention once again to the wide-ranging consequences of social change, not only for the aged as the client population, but also for the very structure of professional services. As institutions in society, the professions are not more immune to the impact of change than are the clients they serve. Thus the authors of this volume are acutely aware of the necessity to consider the future from the double perspective of aging and the professions. They point to numerous ways in which social change is affecting professional practice and its institutional settings. For example, the joint survival of the husband-wife pair and the tendency for older couples to maintain independent households have forced changes in the traditional functions of old age homes. The proliferation of insurance-based programs for income maintenance, both private and public, may in time free public welfare departments from their current preoccupation with financial assistance. The ever greater specialization and differentiation of the entire social structure, including the professions, have resulted in many appeals to the professions for integrative solutions. Perhaps one of the most difficult problems awaiting solution is how to resolve strains between the demands for neighborhood location of service facilities and the centralizing tendencies of increasingly complex institutions. One emergent trend is toward decentralization of services within centralized administration. Further experience with such an arrangement should indicate whether it represents a solution or merely creates additional strains in the provision of services.

Thus the writers of these chapters set forth many policies and programs to meet the needs of older people, but they also highlight many questions of professional standards, organization, and training. As they are aware, it will not always be simple or easy to arrive at answers to such questions. In particular, they foresee a future of continuing social change in which the professions must be capable of adapting to new circumstances. Accordingly, they emphasize the need for new kinds of professional training that will stress administrative, organizational, and coordinative skills. Their strong plea is for practitioners, both those now in training and those already established, who are flexible enough to meet the immense challenges posed by the aging population.

2

Aging and the field of social work

ROBERT MORRIS

Professor Morris argues in this chapter that the failure by social work to recognize the potential for personal growth and success- ful adaptation of old people—and the consequent low priority often given their needs—conflicts with professional beliefs in the continuing developmental capacity of adult individuals, and over- looks the scientific knowledge upon which these beliefs rest. He delineates new opportunities for social work as a profession, and social welfare as an institution, to close this gap between belief and practice in dealing with older people. Such opportunities are found, for example, in reinforcement of, or substitution for, fam- ily relationships; elaboration of meaningful social roles for the aged through leisure-time and work activities; expansion of health services and facilities; improvement of income main- tenance programs; integration of welfare services through co- ordinated referral systems; and planning for the appropriate location of services.

Professor Morris concludes with a special caveat for his col- leagues. He states that, if social work is to assume responsibili-

ties in these areas, the structure of social work education can no longer be restricted, as at present, to individual or group treatment and counseling but the curriculum must be expanded to develop a cadre of administrators and planners for the complex welfare organizations and systems of the future.

Advisers for this chapter were Dean Walter M. Beattie, Jr., School of Social Work, Syracuse University; and Ollie A. Randall, National Council on the Aging, New York, New York.

ON THE RELEVANCE OF VOLUME ONE

Much of the social science knowledge about older people as set forth in Volume One is relevant for the social worker concerned with the individual in his environment. The several chapters in Part One, for example, describe the society as it provides the setting for the aging individual, defines the roles he can play, and is, in turn, affected by the aging of its collective members. Part Two deals with the state of health of older people, with their anatomical and physiological condition, and with age-related behavioral changes in perception, motor skill, intelligence, memory, and learning. Part Three outlines the relevant research on the personality characteristics and basic attitudes of the aging individual as he reacts to the circumstances of the later years, begins to define himself as old, takes a positive or negative view of that self-image, and in some instances succumbs to mental illness or suicide. Finally, Part Four is concerned with the various roles— political, economic, religious, familial—available to persons in their middle and later years, including such additional roles as retiree, widow, or (on occasion) inmate of an institution.

Social work is both a profession and a field of social organization. As a social institution it is called social welfare, and as a profession it is called social work; but, since both institution and profession are in the early stages of formal development, the boundaries of neither are wholly clear. The charitable impulses of philanthropic individuals, kin, and neighborhood groups have evolved into complex formal organizations requiring specially trained staff and governed by a body of principles and ethics. Yet, despite the demands of industrialization and urbanization, earlier informal structures and practices persist.

Professional aims have been based on a holistic philosophy. From its inception, social work has been concerned with the individual in his environment—with biological, physiological, psychological, social, cultural, economic, and political factors all intertwined in a single assessment at the nexus of man and society. It has tried to grasp the whole of man's functioning as one unseamed web of interaction.

However, the evolution of social work institutions has occurred through discrete, incremental steps. As points of friction developed between individuals and their environment, pragmatic, *ad hoc* forms of social organization and specialized institutions were created to deal with specific cases of social distress. This in turn has led to specialized professional practices, concerned with dependent, neglected, and sick children, with adults lacking income because of illness or lack of training, with the physically disabled, with immigrants, and with the delinquent.

The varied institutions and the staff to serve the several groups have developed in substantial isolation from one another, only loosely linked together by an abstract concern for the adaptation of the individual to his social, economic, and cultural environment. As many pre-existing institutions failed to change their policies and programs to meet changing needs, new organizations have arisen. Each new addition has had little direct effect upon the body of policies and operations of earlier welfare programs, however. Special purpose institutions have proliferated, but there has been little overall planning. Hence there has been insufficient updating or expansion of older organizations, and insufficient development of the new institutions needed to fill gaps in service or to bring the total spectrum of services into alignment with a professional holistic philosophy.

In this process, the aged have, for a number of reasons, received limited attention. Old people have not been a sufficiently visible minority in the total population; a tradition of family and filial responsibility has pervaded welfare thinking; the aged have constituted an insignificant fraction of the service population of hospitals, family service agencies, recreational facilities, and other existing institutions. Moreover, they have seemed an unpromising group, relative to other groups in the population, for the investment of scarce resources. As society in general has been late to admit responsibility for the living conditions of the elderly, so has that comparatively new profession of social work.

It is now clear that research in aging has produced knowledge, as summarized in Volume One, which materially affects the customary practices and concepts of social welfare organizations and of their professional staffs. The burden of much of this chapter is that new knowledge about older people has introduced pressures for change in the responsibility of social workers, in policies of agencies, and in the treatment of individuals. These pressures are not limited to a few agencies serving only the aged, but ramify throughout the social welfare structure.

The reevaluation of the status of older people rests on a new understanding of the profound social and economic processes at work. Studies of cohort populations moving through the life cycle have illuminated the extent to which experiences, opportunities, and behavior in early and middle adult life influence life in later years. Early family functioning is, in turn, seen to be affected by the provisions made for aged family members. Health and medical services emerge as heavily weighted by the needs of greatly increased numbers of surviving aged persons. The entire distribution of rewards and benefits in our economic system is affected by the demands for economic security of an older population not required in an active labor force. In sum, the pressures of an aging population now have implications for the entire social work enterprise, and cannot be contained by specialized activities created in isolation from all others.

The impact on social work can be seen in two directions: (1) in the professional practices of individual social workers confronting individual clients or patients, and (2) in the evolution of programs and policies for aggregates of both the elderly and the American population as a whole. Although profession and institutions are intertwined, this chapter will concentrate on the second, on the organization of services, relying on the comparatively measurable data about institutions now available. The implications of the cumulated research findings will be traced through discussion of such topics as the gap between professed aims and behavior; provisions for strengthening family relationships; opportunities for diversifying social roles; provision of health, medical, and community services for the handicapped and disabled; income maintenance; organization of service structures into centralized, decentralized, or coordinated forms; and the educational bases for social work training.

The development concept: contradictions between professional belief and behavior

Social workers profess strong belief in the developmental ideal that the experiences of early childhood and of adolescence affect adult behavior, and that—given the proper combination of will, insight, or means—adults can change or adapt. Yet such a general tenet carries no necessary guidelines for action and, indeed, practice has often lagged behind belief.

Examples of this lag pervade the field. *Family service agencies*, as one instance, underserve the aged as a class,[1] despite the accumulation of social risks and hazards with age. Old people constitute on the average less than half of 1 per cent of the caseload of such agencies, but at least 10 per cent of the population purportedly served. In general, most family service agencies serve only those aged whose needs interfere with the well-being of grown children or grandchildren in an extended family. Although a few agencies offer comprehensive service to the elderly themselves, the most common help is referral to other service programs such as homes for the aged, senior citizens' centers, and hospitals.

As another example, *homes for the aged*, the earliest welfare service for the elderly, have until recently merely provided congregate shelter representing terminal existence. Once admitted, for whatever reason, the aged residents entered into a final way of life. Experience over time, however, has led the staffs of these institutions to the discovery that growth and change do not end in the middle years. To be sure, many have now added programs designed to enrich life within the institution—medical rehabilitation, recreational and occupational therapy, sheltered workshops, and the like—but the congregate or total environment still remains as the setting for such programs. [*Cf. Madge, Chap. 8 in this volume.*]

In *medical and mental health services*, where social work is typically asked to arrange for alternate care when active clinic or hospital care is to be terminated, much of the effort seems shrouded in fatalism. Despite the nominal search for alternatives to continued active treatment, the sick elderly continue to accumulate in commercial nursing homes and in mental hospitals. Those who end up in such congregate facilities differ from others of like age and disability mainly in income and quality of preexisting family relationships, a fact which strongly suggests inattention to the potential for alternative choices which could be offered many of the elderly. [*See Vol. 1, Chap. 25.1, pp. 579–583.*]

Rehabilitation services, which generally aspire to help all persons regain the maximum function of which they are capable, in fact have offered relatively little to the aged. Older disabled workers referred by the Social Security Administration to state rehabilitation agencies are most likely to be evaluated as "unfeasible," meaning that scarce resources can be used to better advantage for the young or that

---

[1] Dorothy F. Beck, *Patterns in Use of Family Agency Services* (New York: Family Service Association of America, 1962), Chap. 6, p. 6.

work opportunities are not available anyway.[2] Pioneer exceptions to this practice, by some public and voluntary rehabilitation centers, point to future possibilities rather than present realities.

In regard to *income maintenance programs*, social work has been most fully identified with Old Age Assistance rather than with social security viewed as an insurance system. Staff in Old Age Assistance, more than in most social agencies, has tended to rely on the presumed capacity of the recipients to fend for themselves once a modest income is assured. This tendency has more often resulted from preoccupation with administrative detail than from professional philosophy. Overlooked by agency staffs is the fact that the aged public assistance beneficiaries run a much higher risk of ending up in nursing homes than do others, when age and medical diagnosis are controlled.[3] [*Cf. Vol. 1, Chap. 25.1.b, p. 580.*]

For many of these programs (especially Old Age Assistance and the long-term care institutions), the staff all too often lacks the necessary training, either of the full professional or even of the journeyman-apprentice or in-service variety. The absence of a basis—in philosophy, values, knowledge, or skill—for serving the elderly reflects a lack of commitment by the profession to the older person.

Nor is it clear that professionalization of services alone can alter the situation. Among family service agencies, the class of social work agency most fully professionalized, services to the aged are still too limited (taken as a total or as a proportion of all services) to afford much guidance.[4] Most likely, an increasing employment of professional manpower will have to be accompanied by changes in professional thought and education as well.

Closing the gap between belief and behavior

The gap between professional belief and behavior is sometimes justified on grounds of insufficiency of current knowledge, lack of qualified staff, or lack of resources available to particular agencies or classes of

[3] George Goldin, "The Functioning of Statistical Reporting Procedures in The State Rehabilitation Agency" (Ph.D. dissertation, Florence Heller Graduate School for Advanced Studies in Social Welfare, Brandeis University, 1962).

[3] Howard E. Freeman, Arthur Richardson, and Robert Morris, "The Role of the Nursing Home in the Provision of Care for the Aged," Final Report for Community Health Project No. 23–12, Public Health Service (Washington, D.C.: Government Printing Office, 1967).

[4] A few agencies, such as the Community Service Society of New York, the Jewish Family and Counseling Service of Long Island, and The Benjamin Rose Institute, Cleveland, Ohio, represent exceptions to this generalization in that they seem to have closed the gap with wide use of professionally qualified help.

agencies. Yet a careful review of available evidence suggests that these explanations, however valid in the past, have now become mere rationalizations for avoiding difficult tasks.

Major gains in knowledge, codified in Volume One of this series, have served to counter stereotypic views of the aged through rediscovery of an almost infinite capacity for individualized adaptation to the "points of passage" which aging represents. Life offers a variety of challenges which cluster around major transition points in the human cycle, and individuals display varied patterns of behavior and preference in negotiating these transitions. This diversity suggests that the gap between belief and behavior, on the part of both institutions and professions, may be closed by greater attention to the problems of expanding the alternatives available to the aged in modern society. A bridge between fragmented social organization to meet human needs and the ideal holistic view of each individual lies in increasing the variety of opportunities for choice. Choices should be made available, feasible, and salient to the aged through a coordinated network of services, for individual choices depend on structural supports that permit the individual to select from an array of services in order to match his requirements.

NEW PERSPECTIVES ON AGING

Aging is not merely an indeterminate recession from social and physical existence, and the stages of adult passage through life do not end with the coming of parenthood. Definable transition points include, at the minimum: the departure of the last child, retirement from vocation or occupation, the onset of irreversible and limiting handicap, and the loss of spouse or close kin and friends. The middle-aged adult confronts an entirely new way of living when children establish their own households, whether near or far away, a change which opens up the opportunity for a new utilization of time. Physiological changes in the middle years often produce a reexamination of one's life pattern as a "last chance" opportunity to "do something different with one's life." And as the 60th birthday approaches, the individual faces retirement from occupational activity, which deprives him of those associations and responsibilities which govern, by and large, the daytime hours of most adults. The risk of forced change in way of life imposed by illness or disability increases enormously in the upper years [see Vol. 1, Chap. 9.2, pp. 204–218], and the shift to a life of full or partial dependence upon others may become a reality. Although there are few rites to herald these changes (save perhaps the ceremonial retirement party), the fact of passage into a new stage can well be understood on an individual case basis.

These stages, though encountered by most adults, are not fixed by clear-cut boundaries of age or by uniform modes of response. Early life experiences lead to diversified responses as each individual, in his own unique fashion, works over his private heritage of genetic constitution, family experience, education, intellectual capacity, and occupation. The effects of genetic inheritance and early experience on later behavior are apparent in many respects. For example, the positive relation between long-lived subjects and their long-lived forebears has been frequently pointed out. [*See Vol. 1, Chap. 8.2, pp. 189–190.*] Moreover, the income and class status of aged persons tends to be associated with the educational and income attainment of their parents. Income or education, in turn, seem to be associated with differing attitudes to retirement among older people, differing levels of personal morale, differing ways of utilizing leisure time, and differing ways of adapting to physical disability. [*See Vol. 1, Chap. 15, pp. 341–359; Chap. 18, pp. 421–462; Chap. 22, pp. 511–535.*]

These examples of the developmental links between earlier and later stages of each individual's life suggest programmatic interventions which might perhaps be introduced early in the life cycle to reduce the likelihood of difficulty in later years. Thus, for the adult with limited formal education, introducing certain social experiences may alter his subsequent capacity for self-maintenance. Or a change in diet in the individual's early life may perhaps alter the chance of disability in his 70's.[5] The construction of urban neighborhoods today in order to facilitate social and civic interaction among all age groups at the neighborhood level may in the future reduce age and income segregation. An assured retirement income, adequate for transportation, clothing, recreation, and the like, may reduce progressive risk of social isolation and psychological deterioration as age advances.

Of equal importance to such insights derived from examination of the effects of early experience are the insights to be gained from knowledge of the widely varied developmental and adaptive capacity of particular individuals. Many aged individuals continue to "work over" their heritage until the very end of life, displaying a capacity to change despite early experiences. Individual variations in ability of the aged to negotiate the passage of retirement, illness, or loss of friends are

[5] See Alfred Washburn, "Influences of Early Development Upon Later Life," in James E. Birren (ed.), *Relations of Development and Aging* (Springfield, Ill.: Charles C Thomas, Publisher, 1964), 29–40.

not perfectly associated with precedent conditions. Some persons with limited education or income, for example, desire and are able to continue employment; others show remarkable ability to resume learning, or to have new social experiences after living routine adult lives. Although cognitive capacities tend to decline with age, on the average, the ability of many older people to learn anew does not disappear. The aged may concentrate on certain subjects rather than others; they may take a little longer than most younger people or may prefer to work less vigorously, but learn they do.[6] [See Vol. 1, Chap. 5.4, pp. 116–119; Chap. 11.3, pp. 255–257; Chap. 18.C.4, pp. 453–459.]

In similar fashion, many older people show competence in coping with social or physical hazards. The aged can often learn to manage well on reduced incomes; they can learn to live with artificial hips or legs; they can care for themselves physically although bedridden or wheelchair-bound; they can learn new social skills, such as running organizations; they can conquer new technical tasks, such as survey interviewing or inventorying historical monuments; they can develop unexpected forms of artistic expression which are valued by art lovers as well as by their friends. [Cf. Vol. 1, Chap. 15, pp. 341–359; Chap. 22, pp. 511–535.]

Such adaptive capacities involve more than a reaction of a fixed personality to changed environmental conditions. There is growing evidence that development of personality itself occurs, or can occur, throughout the full life cycle. Peck, Birren, and Neugarten,[7] among others, have reexamined some of the evidence on which it is commonly assumed that there is a necessary deterioration in personality function with age and a negative psychological reaction to losses experienced by individuals. They make the counter-suggestion that there may be two separate processes at work: the "intrapsychic," which may alter ego function, perception, affect, or emotional response; and the socio-adaptive, which may alter competence to manage adult social roles. Intrapsychic changes may occur without affecting social competence, and social competence may be affected (as with illness)

[6] Leonard Breen, "The Aging Individual," in Clark Tibbitts (ed.), *Handbook of Social Gerontology* (Chicago: University of Chicago Press, 1960), 152–154; Jack Botwinick and James E. Birren, "Mental Abilities and Psychomotor Responses in Healthy Aged Men," in James E. Birren *et al.* (eds.), *Human Aging*, Public Health Service Pub. No. 986 (Washington, D.C.: Government Printing Office, 1963), 97–108.

[7] Bernice Neugarten, "A Developmental View of Adult Personality," in James E. Birren (ed.), *Relations of Development and Aging* (Springfield, Ill.: Charles C. Thomas, Publisher, 1964), 176–208; Robert Peck, "Psychological Developments in the Second Half of Life," in John E. Anderson (ed.), *Psychological Aspects of Aging* (Washington, D.C.: American Psychological Association, 1956).

without deterioration in personality dynamics. [*Cf. Vol. 1, Chap. 12, pp. 275–287.*]

In practice, then, aged persons *may* find a new assessment of their worth as individuals despite loss of work roles. They *may* transcend their body concerns and their worry about illnesses. [*See Vol. 1, Chap. 13, pp. 289–313; Chap. 14.1, pp. 317–323.*] Their reactions at 80 *may* differ from their reactions at 70 or 60.

NEEDED PROFESSIONAL AND INSTITUTIONAL RESPONSE

Conversion of the *possibility* of individual development in old age into the *probability* of such development depends upon more than the appropriate behavior and attitudes of old persons; it depends also upon the creation and intervention of appropriate social institutions. Thus, developmental knowledge forces attention to the end purposes of social and professional action. It is no longer necessary to assert that a particular constricting social or personal condition must be accepted as inevitable, when some feasible social action at an earlier time could have altered this condition. Despite the remaining inadequacies of the present state of knowledge, the goal of attempting to reshape social conditions seems worthwhile in view of the potential for preventing future human distress.

To act on this knowledge, however, requires a major change in welfare priorities. Though there have never been sufficient resources in manpower and dollars to support all that is desired by agencies, the welfare community must be persuaded that services for the elderly require a fair share of these resources; that expenditure on the elderly is not a dead-end gratuity but an essential aspect of man's progress through a limited life span; and that growth and adaptation is possible and valued at all times. Institutional and professional conviction regarding such beliefs would in itself represent a shift in priority.

This change in outlook is utopian unless social agencies are prepared to substitute the development of community policy for agency policy as the guide for resource and professional allocation. Agency policy as the determinant means acceptance of the present status, the defense of present allocations of staff and resources to carry out present purposes. Existing agencies tend to believe that their current specialized aims and methods are as good as circumstances permit; for evaluation is likely to be in terms of the population already served, not the population that might be served.

Once social work effort is evaluated against the changes it brings to major population groups, then the first step has been taken toward community planning and policy. What happens to old people as a group, in their ways of living and in their family and social relation-ships, is more important than the elaboration of professionalism or the maintenance of 100 per cent occupancy of particular institutions.

Suggestions about how such a *reorientation in value and organ-ization* could be carried out in several key areas are outlined in the sections to follow.

Family relationships

A fundamental goal in social welfare has been the strengthening of family life. Recent evidence makes it clear that a program for family life must be sensitive to the total condition of an urban industrial America, with its highly mobile population and complex organiza-tional and technological structure. Exposure of social workers to se-lected categories of older people, however—to the most isolated, lonely, or handicapped—has blurred perception of what has been happening to the majority of American families.

NEW CONDITIONS OF FAMILY LIFE

Systematic studies of population have begun to reveal new demands on the family, deriving from the nature of modern American society. The modern family, as a primary social institution, has had to cope with an enormous increase in the numbers and proportions of aged members who now survive into the seventh, eighth, and ninth decade of life. Life expectancy at birth has risen from 54.1 years in 1920 in the United States, to well over 70 years in 1962. Since the nineteenth century, the proportion of the total American population over 65 has increased from 4 per cent to 9 per cent, of which nearly a third are more than 75 years of age. [*See Vol. 1, Chap. 2, pp. 15–37.*]

At the same time, the mobility of the American people may raise barriers to maintenance of traditional family ties. Between 1955 and 1960, for example, half of the population changed its abode. [*See Vol. 1, Chap. 6.C, pp. 143–155.*] Although geographic mobility is much greater for young families than for the aged, the effect in either case is spatial separation of adult children from their parents. There is little evidence to suggest, however, that mobility necessarily weak-ens affective bonds between family members, or represents a rejec-tion by the young of their aged parents. The majority of old persons do maintain their own households, but most seem to prefer it so. [*See Vol. 1, Chap. 7.B.2, pp. 171–175; Chap. 23.B.1.f, pp. 549–550.*] Eighty-four per cent of older persons with living children still live either in the same household with one of their children or less than one hour away from one of them [*see Ex. 7 · 12 in Vol. 1, p. 169*], and interaction between family members persists at a high level. [*See Vol. 1, Chap. 23, pp. 537–560.*]

Thus the increase in surviving aged has resulted in a three-generation family which may be conceived as two parallel sets of two-generation families—one with small children and parents, the other with adult children and aged parents. Both families are likely to be related by bonds of affection or at least association, but each may be burdened by problems—of finances or of health, for example—requiring social service.

NEEDED WELFARE RESPONSES

In this situation, social welfare needs to redefine the sectors of family life that demand social welfare attention. Social work practice has been confused by the inconsistency between a belief that families should bear primary responsibility for the care of their aged members, and a realization that many aged individuals require social as well as private family care.[8] Piecemeal reactions to emergency needs, moreover, have produced a professional stance that equally supports pension benefits or insurance for the aged, on the one hand, and deplores the erosion of family responsibility, on the other. A solution would be to adopt the view that social welfare should stand as a family surrogate or as a complementary family device for certain categories of aged persons, as it has stood in the past for certain categories of children. This solution requires the abandonment of the view that social work is only a residual function, to be called upon as a last resort—a view that fosters a reliance upon family and individual resources even under wholly inappropriate circumstances.

Illness of aged parents   A very large share of the problems that plague families are produced by serious illness of parents, especially as they reach their 70's and 80's, when the risk of major disability is especially great. [*See Vol. 1, Chap. 9.2, pp. 204–218.*] Counseling agencies need to understand the realities of such illness, in order to help families over the pain they may confront as a parent suffers irreversible physical or mental injury. Knowledge about physical illness and the resources for its care are as essential as knowledge about the psychic and emotional stresses in family relationships. Conversely, if social support in illness is to be effective, physicians

[8] For a review of the problem of filial responsibility, see Alvin L. Schorr, *Filial Responsibility in the Modern American Family*, Social Security Administration (Washington, D.C.: Government Printing Office, 1960).

and other health workers need to be equally conscious of the relevant social dimensions.

Full care of aged family members, if extended over months or years, exceeds the capability of the normal family, which can neither mount the requisite nursing care nor afford to purchase it. Such care, if attempted, could destroy the viability of the nuclear family itself, damaging young children and adult children alike. When long-term care is required, it should be provided by special health agencies. For this reason, the trend toward conversion of congregate homes for the aged into facilities for long-term nursing care should be encouraged. [Cf. Susser, Chap. 5, and Madge, Chap. 8 in this volume.] Social welfare organizations need to support the extension of such services without believing that they represent a failure of family responsibility.

Financial support of aged parents   For those aged with family ties, traditional conceptions of income maintenance also tend to be inadequate. Unfortunately, these concepts are often embedded in restrictive state laws which force parents to sue children for support. [See Vol. 1, Chap. 4.D.2, pp. 105–106; and Bernstein, Chap. 9 in this volume.] Old Age Assistance is legally premised on the provision of residual income only after family responsibility for support has been exhausted. The survival of this older view may be more likely to destroy family solidarity than strengthen it, especially if legal steps are taken to enforce support. In an affluent society, with rising levels of expectation supported by the society through pervasive advertising and promotion, few families in the lower and middle income range of economic independence can support two households, one for themselves and their children, the other for aged parents. The solution is a universal grant for all older persons in need, regardless of kin resources. [Cf. the discussion by Bernstein, Chap. 9 in this volume.]

The lone aged person   Although most aged widows or widowers may find adequate social support from their families, a significant proportion of the aged have never been married, have become estranged from families over a very long time, or live far away from them. [See Vol. 1, Chap. 7.B, pp. 167–183.] The concept of social welfare as family surrogate demands that the provision of enriched social opportunities for this category of aged persons be accepted as a major community responsibility.

Cultural variation   Finally, the apparent uniformity of American culture conceals a myriad of cultural patterns. Family organization and behavior varies among such diverse subgroups as the Negro, Mexican, Italian, Jewish, Puerto Rican, or French-Canadian. Respect for these cultural variations demands attention to alternate program offerings and practices. These variations within the national society may require sectarian service programs, or flexibility and variety in mass public programs, or both simultaneously. Just how this diversity of programs is to be handled in highly bureaucratized systems remains to be worked out.

Diversification of social roles

LEISURE-TIME ACTIVITIES

A major welfare effort in recent years has been invested in providing more recreation centers, more information centers, and more volunteer welfare opportunities for those elderly who are pushed by retirement into years of impoverished and limited social activity, feared by the aged themselves. But various difficulties have been encountered in recruiting elderly volunteers for conventional or routine tasks and, despite repetitious use of several programs by a core of aged, in extending leisure or educational services to more than a small fraction of all the able-bodied aged. Special clubs reach only some 1 to 5 per cent of older people; fewer than 3 per cent of the aged enter adult education classes compared with 8 per cent in the general adult population. [*See Vol. 1, Chap. 5.4.a, p. 116; Chap. 21.4, pp. 508–509.*] The conclusion that existing services are inadequate does not explain their failure to broaden the base of their initial appeal. Do the aged really want and need so much service, or are the services poorly conceived?

The gap between program and consumer Most programs are modeled along lines understandable to a recently educated staff: a more or less formal structure of organization, officers, committees, and the like. But participation in such formal activities is positively related to educational attainment, and only one-third of the present aged have achieved as much as an eighth-grade education. Moreover, about 20 per cent of the elderly were born in a foreign culture, compared to 5 per cent foreign-born in the total population. [*See Vol. 1, Chap. 5.1, pp. 112–113.*] Thus a culture gap may well exist between program and consumer. It is likely that the significance of this gap has been minimized in the past because of a belief that differences would eventually disappear in an equalitarian and open society. Although it is true that the educational, occupational, and income levels of each new generation seem to be higher than those of the preceding generation, it is also true that the ceiling for achievement in each generation has risen as much as the floor. While the next generation of older people may attain a high-school education, on the average the number of youths who continue to college or to a postgraduate level of education will also increase. The chances are, then, that generational differences will persist on more dimensions than age alone.

Variations in retirement activity If the gap between program and consumer is to be closed, stereotyped planning derived from an abstract model of the "typical" retiree must be replaced by planning for a more diverse population in which complex factors explain different behaviors. The elderly bring a variety of skills, fears, and handicaps to retirement, and these must be recognized in the creation of welfare services.

Studies vary in the degree to which the aged population is reported to remain vigorously active. [*See Vol. 1, Chap. 17, pp. 408–420.*] In one instance, little reduction in social participation was observed as individuals retired. [*See Vol. 1, Chap. 18.C.4.e, pp. 457–458.*] Among retiring government workers, about one-seventh actually increased their organization memberships; and in some samples over one-twentieth of the retired devote at least three hours a day to volunteer action. In other studies, however, old people are found to reduce their membership in organizations on retirement, or to give less time weekly to organization business now than when they were younger. [*See Vol. 1, Chap. 21.1.e, p. 506.*] While some studies report a heavy attendance at leisure-time and club activities, others report serious difficulty in recruiting and sustaining older persons in persistent or systematic types of activities.[9]

Some of this variation may be explained by the evident association of higher education and income with greater social activity. Those older people with high education, high income achievement, or high social class position have greater flexibility in adapting to new leisure than those in the lower socioeconomic strata, who have more difficulty in affording new activities or in learning the new roles required for participation in formal community and leisure-time associations. Physical disability is another factor interfering with the satisfying use of leisure time; and many older people suffer from the combined disadvantages of low status and poor health. [*See Vol. 1, Chap. 17.4, pp. 416–418.*] Moreover, the societal trend toward living in urban or suburban locations—the latter of which may lack accessible

---

[9] Camille Lambert, Mildred Guberman, and Robert Morris, *New Roles for the Elderly* (Waltham, Mass.: Brandeis University, 1965).

transparation and other facilities—and the high mobility of Americans generally, often destroy an older person's established networks of kin, friends, and neighbors. [*See Vol. 1, Chap. 6, pp. 121–156.*]

An additional difficulty in providing satisfying leisure-time activities for the elderly is the fact that retirement is not uniformly welcomed by these persons. Although the average age of retirement is declining [*Vol. 1, Chap. 3.A.1, pp. 40–43*], despite the accompanying loss of income, the proportion of people who say they want to retire as early as 60 is far lower among the over 50's than the under 50's. [*See Ex. 18 · 21 in Vol. 1, p. 443.*] Thus the closer one comes to the reality of retirement, the less attractive it seems to become. Moreover, more than one-third of retired workers report they are forced into retirement by their employer's decision rather than their own. [*See Ex. 18 · 24 in Vol. 1, p. 448.*]

Therefore, it may be questioned whether the major welfare stress on recreation, leisure, and family provides a powerful enough alternative to work. The combination of earlier retirement with the reluctance of many to leave the labor force suggests that a sizable proportion of workers would perhaps choose to alter their work activities without relinquishing them entirely, giving up a routinized or very familiar schedule for one less rigorous, more varied, or more flexible.[10]

THE DEVELOPMENT OF NEW ROLES

Social work focus might then invest major effort in the production and stimulation of many more varied roles for older persons to perform. These efforts might include the opening up to the aged of clearly important volunteer activities in social agencies, rather than limiting older people to mere routine chores; the restructuring of some social work duties for part-time employment of older persons; the pressure for employment of older persons, as volunteers or at pay, to perform many civic tasks that could enrich the nature of city life, such as staffing information centers, reporting on public services, surveying attitudes, or monitoring social problem areas of the city.

To be effective, such a program of role development needs to meet several criteria:

1. Roles must be widely diversified to accommodate the range of interests, capacities, education, and cultural backgrounds of the entire aged population.

[10] An alternate explanation is that early retirement is a function of earlier illness, the existence of which is concealed in survey interviews.

2. New roles should be productive. Most older persons will find their way, self-selectively, to available activities, but will resist "make work" roles created out of mere charitable impulse.

3. A minimum service structure is useful to assure that those who are socially inexperienced have an opportunity to learn new kinds of activity. In many cases, the need for these learning experiences can be anticipated and opportunities introduced in the middle years of life.

4. The aged themselves should be able to share fully in the administration of any service mechanisms created to further these ends.

5. Programs containing opportunities for the elderly can be more effective if directed generally, without age limits, to community service activities.

Opportunities for preventive effort Any such development of new roles would present social work with an extraordinary opportunity to launch a major experiment in prevention. Most research suggests that behavior in the later years is in part conditioned by earlier life experiences. Thus it should be possible, after defining a variety of roles for the aged, to estimate what prior conditions and experiences would be significant for confident and successful entry into particular later-life roles.

For example, the civic roles often suggested as appropriate for the elderly may require expertness in managing a formal association such as a membership association, experience with the political structure of the community, and some knowledge about civic affairs. Unions or organized employee groups in large industries help to meet such requirements by bringing together large numbers of adults in organized activities. A part of this organized energy, now devoted mainly to economic self-protection and recreation, might be channeled into some civic activity for workers, and facilitated by benign employer and union encouragement. Such opportunities are already often given by industry to executives; and social workers who now concentrate on personnel problems and recreation could help in introducing similar opportunities to other classes of employees.

Similarly, identity-sustaining activities for both active and retired members have been organized by some unions, such as the United Automobile Workers of America and some corporations, such as the Bell Telephone System and Polaroid. These are, however, limited in scope and in accessibility. A less unusual example can be found in the hobby interests of many workers, often encouraged by management through hobby shows and the like. Vital organizing experience for later life could be acquired if major industries supported the creation of spin-off employee corporations or associations to foster hobby and craft talents, to locate market interests, and to organize marketing outlets for hobby products. Such corporations might be staffed in part by workers still employed, and in part by workers who continue in the roles after retirement.

Participation by elderly in program development   This issue of role diversification can not be wholly separated from the responsibility of older persons to share in such development. Numerous projects have been started by the efforts of senior citizens, usually retired business executives, to locate productive activities for themselves. Major social work activities have not yet been directed to the employment of older workers in large numbers as a matter of manpower policy, however, nor have the aged been given program and policy development roles comparable to those offered adolescents and young adults. This is explained in part by uncertainty as to the amount of time the elderly wish to devote to such activity, in part by the newness of the idea. Social work has made a major contribution in general to the idea of participation, and to the importance of assertively offering stimulation in order to elicit creative reaction from others. What is required is the same commitment to participation by the elderly in shaping their later years as is now urged for the poor and the social minorities in attacking urban poverty.

Opportunities for second careers   A further channel for preparing older people in advance for diversified roles in later life is suggested by the increasing numbers of persons in their 40's and 50's who have retired once and seek a new middle-years career, a number that includes many thousands every year from the Armed Forces alone. Here social work can pioneer in confronting a new reality in industrial society. Though shifts in work have conventionally taken place along a single industrial or professional career path, via the promotion ladder, changes in the economy suggest the potential for horizontal as well as vertical shifts in work careers, through which adults in their middle years enter new and enriching activities which require manpower. In particular, the human resources industries (schools, social welfare, health) afford such opportunities.

Experimental efforts to provide second careers can be made by social work employers themselves, in their own welfare institutions, without relying on pioneer ventures by commercial employers. Second-career seekers might well help to fill the staggering social work manpower shortage estimated to reach 100,000 in the next few years.[11] This would undoubtedly require a restructuring of social work

[11] U.S. Department of Health, Education and Welfare, *Closing the Gap in Social Work Manpower* (Washington, D.C.: Government Printing Office, 1965).

tasks to allow performance by a diverse social work labor force; but such restructuring seems inevitable in any case if the demands made on the profession are to be met. Such an effort by social work could also serve more generally to throw light on the problems of middle- and late-life retraining; on the time and interest preferences of older persons; and on the potentiality for phasing employment time in the later years as a step-by-step move to retirement rather than the present abrupt change within twenty-four hours from 100 per cent work to 100 per cent retirement. [*See Bernstein, Chap. 9, and Sheppard, Chap. 6 in this volume.*]

Health services

Another area in which social work is under pressure from the mounting numbers of older people is health. Only 9 per cent of all social workers have been identified as employed in medical, psychiatric, or rehabilitation occupations, although estimates indicate that at least one-third of total public and private expenditures for health, education, and welfare are devoted to health services.[12] These figures confirm the long-recognized underrepresentation or maldistribution of social work manpower through the health system. The long-term tendency for medicine (in both its general and psychiatric forms) has been to organize itself within hospitals to carry out specialized therapeutic activities which assume that patients can resume normal functioning on departure from the hospital. Thus social work, identified with community functioning more than with in-hospital practices, has remained peripheral to the health system, despite the creative work of some institutions and of many individual medical social workers.

The demand for a more equitable distribution of health services in the population, the growth in concepts of preventive medicine, and, above all, the increased need for treatment and care of the long-term ill associated with an aging population have introduced new impetus for change. One consequence is the pressure for more numerous and varied arrangements for the handicapped and sick outside of active treatment in general and psychiatric hospitals. [*See the health essays by Lasagna, Schwartz, and Susser, Chaps. 3, 4, and 5 in this volume. See also the related discussion by Madge, Chap. 8 in this volume.*] While general hospitals are seeking to reduce the length of stay, mental hospitals seek to return to the community those patients

[12] *Ibid.*, based on 1960 data; and U.S. Department of Health, Education and Welfare, *HEW Trends* (Washington, D.C.: Government Printing Office, 1964), Table 1.

who can respond to active treatment over relatively short periods of time. [*See Vol. 1, Chap. 16.A.3.f, pp. 382–385.*]

This trend has not yet produced clear results. Since 1940, the total volume of institutional facilities has increased by some 150 per cent, although the population of older people 65 and over has increased by less than 100 per cent.[13] Much of the expansion of facilities is attributable to the increase in proprietary nursing homes; but it is not clear whether these represent a real addition to the nonhospital choices open to sick persons, or merely the substitution of less professional institutions for the hospitals whose costs have risen steeply. [*Cf. Vol. 1, Chap. 6.B, pp. 128–142; Chap. 7, pp. 157–184; Chap. 25, pp. 577–596.*]

The trend to nonhospital care is accompanied by demand for qualified staff to negotiate and manage the shift back and forth between hospital and community. Can social work and its institutions respond to this demand, or must new arrangements be devised? The answer is critical and will affect the nature of homes for the aged, family service agencies, public assistance departments, home nursing services, and hospital social work departments.

IN-HOSPITAL ORGANIZATION

Social work in hospitals has undergone an uneven development, with only 25 per cent of all American hospitals currently employing a social worker of any kind. Even in the most progressive medical institutions, shortage of personnel has restricted social work services to the securing of access to limited resources on some preferential basis for indigent patients among the aged. If, however, hospitals are led to assume greater responsibility for posthospital care, the demand may vastly increase for social workers who can coordinate hospital with nonhospital arrangements.

Management of the transition between hospital and home is most difficult for the elderly patient with a long-term illness or disability, especially if in addition his income is limited. He is particularly likely to linger in the hospital, to be discharged to a public institution, or to end up in a nursing home. [*See Vol. 1, Chap. 25.1, pp. 578–583.*] If his income is marginal, the simple matter of maintaining a home during the hospital interlude is taxing, the more so if the patient lives

[13] This estimate is based on the volume of hospital, nursing home, and other long-term institutional beds reported in the U.S. Bureau of the Census, *Historical Statistics of the United States, Colonial Times to 1957* (Washington, D.C.: Government Printing Office, 1960); and in the U.S. Department of Commerce, *Statistical Abstract of the United States* (Washington, D.C.: Government Printing Office, 1964), Tables 42, 92, 96, 372.

alone. Although medical insurance (Medicare) will give low income families an improved chance to have private physician care in hospitals and also to pay for some extended care beyond the hospital stay, neither circumstance will in itself bring into being the array of posthospital care facilities necessary to meet the new demands. Hospitals can, may indeed be forced to, assume leadership in the development of such care facilities, to take responsibility for altering the posthospital environment into which patients are discharged.

One illustration of such hospital extension has been the organization of coordinated home medical care programs, in which hospitalized patients are transferred back to their homes after an acute emergency, with integrated major nursing, social, and medical care delivered into the home. Social work has played a leading role in urging and in organizing such programs, although social work represents only a small portion of the services used.[14]

Another example is the neighborhood comprehensive health service, financed by the Office of Economic Opportunity, and often organized by a general teaching hospital. While these programs concentrate on treating employable youth and adults, they often offer a full range of family health services for all ages.[15]

Parallel to the extension of medical facilities is a growing attention to the need for community-wide health planning in which the range and volume of facilities, and the relationships among facilities, will be guided by social policy and by comprehensive health planning organizations. Thus an expansion in hospital functions can be expected in a number of directions:

a. Increase in the number of departments of social medicine, to enlarge clinic programs functioning outside of the conventional hospital framework.

b. Extension of hospital-based home medical care programs, to deliver a full complex of hospital services to patients physically cared for in their own home.

c. Increase in hospital medical and social services to nursing homes administered by the hospital or (through contract) by independent operators, so that patients may receive uninterrupted medical attention as they move into long-term facilities.

[14] See, for example, George Silver, *Family Medical Care: A Report on the Family Health Maintenance Demonstration* (Cambridge, Mass.: Harvard University Press, 1963); Peter Rogatz and Guido Crocetti, "Home Care Programs—Their Impact on the Hospital Role in Medical Care," *American Journal of Public Health,* 49 (1959), 441–454.

[15] See Victor Geiger, "The Columbia Point Health Services Proposal" (unpublished; Tufts University Medical Center, 1965), 17.

d. Proliferation of outpost medical services opened by hospitals in deprived areas of the inner city, where relatively complete medical services can be provided to low income families in their neighborhoods of residence. These can have especial value for the aged, whose mobility is often limited. It is worth noting, however, that a similar extension has seldom taken place into suburban areas, where a confrontation with the private practice of medicine would be more acute, though the elderly living in suburban areas are numerous and access to health services is at least as difficult for them as for residents of central city areas.

Most of these extensions of the hospital, largely demonstrative or experimental in character, have been managed by physicians—less often by social workers—who have solved pragmatically and through experience the problems that are confronted in organizing and administering any social resource. If hospitals accept responsibility for these broadened services, then the allocation of responsibility to hospital staff becomes a central issue. It is not at all clear whether, in the long run, physicians, nurses, or social workers will be best equipped to staff these extensions, since all will be required and all will be in short supply. The need is for skilled manpower in the organization and administration of community resources. This need will doubtless be filled by those professions that decide to alter their training programs to produce manpower best equipped for such enlarged tasks. If social workers are to undertake such tasks, the focus of their education must be altered materially by a new stress on planning skills. Since others beside social workers can be similarly trained, the intensity of social work interest will determine the scope of the profession's role in future health services.

SPECIAL MENTAL HEALTH CONSIDERATIONS

The problem of the tie between hospital and community for the mentally ill is similar in many ways to that confronting the physically handicapped, but some additional considerations arise. [*See Vol. 1, Chap. 16, pp. 361–406.*] Though social work functions in the mental hospital and in the general service hospital are similar, the role of the social worker in the mental hospital is more clearly defined and more universally accepted. In the mental hospital, there exists the uncertainty about the patient's capacity to exercise reasonable judgment, which complicates decisions about his discharge to community living. Mental hospital responsibility for the posthospital period is thus greater than that of the general hospital, and the social worker has functioned as the extension arm of the hospital for this purpose.

Nevertheless, there has unfortunately been a long-term tendency for aged patients to accumulate in mental hospitals with minimal or no special treatment. Yet the conviction has been growing that not all of these cases require institutional care and attention. (In fact, many of them may remain in institutions because of the undesirable effects of the institutional care itself.) There have been numerous demonstrations, beginning with the pioneer work of the New York State Department of Mental Health and extended on a large scale by the Veterans' Administration, that established the feasibility of treatment and community care of older mentally ill patients who had experienced long years of hospitalization.[16]

Residence in the community As with the general hospital, once serious attention is given to the potential for community living by mentally disturbed older persons, the mental hospital itself is significantly affected in two directions. First, the attitude and frame of reference of the entire staff must be reoriented toward the impermanence of hospital stay and away from the present attitude of long-term hopelessness that surrounds much of the existing hospital care for the aged. Second, the potential for return to normal community living can become a reality only with an elaboration of the hospital staff to extend the hospital into the community.

In view of the shortage of general community facilities that can be drawn upon, the hospital must take leadership either in providing special services for its own patients or in stimulating overall community services in sufficient volume for patients from many hospitals. Moreover, continuity of attention must be supplied by psychiatrists, psychologists, and social workers to support the continued adjustment of mentally disturbed older persons. Where close and affectionate family ties persist, reinforcement of family capability may be all that is required. However, a large number of older persons under long-term care in mental hospitals either lack such family ties initially or have lost them over the years. As a result, substitute community facilities for such released patients must be provided in the form of group homes, boarding homes, or foster homes.

The Veterans' Administration has demonstrated that such homes can be located in normal community settings, that public fear and anxiety about the reception of the mentally ill can be overcome, and

---

[16] William T. Appel *et al.*, " 'Independence' Prepares Long-Term Patients for Discharge," *Hospitals*, 38 (1964), 36–37; R. F. Boquet, "The Community Placement Ward," *Mental Hospitals*, 15 (1964), No. 6; Hester Crutcher, *Foster Care for Mental Patients* (New York: Commonwealth Fund, 1944); Samuel Nadler, "The Adjustment of Psychiatric Patients on Trial Visit" (lithographed; Pittsburgh: Veterans' Administration, 1962); Veterans' Administration, *Annual Report* (Washington, D.C.: Government Printing Office, 1966).

that relatively stable community living situations can be re-created. The price, however, is a dispersion of these facilities over wide geographic areas, and a continuous investment of staff time to reinforce the substitute home situation. Since these requirements are costly in manpower, it remains to be seen which of the care professions will be capable of producing sufficient skilled personnel. At the present writing, it would appear that social work will be capable of meeting this need *only* if its professional staff functions in an evaluative and administrative capacity, supervising a much larger network of subprofessional social work aides.

Protective services   Mental disturbance further creates a need for what has come to be known as protective services. Preliminary studies by the National Council on the Aging,[17] not yet projected on any quantitative basis, suggest that, although a considerable number of persons are capable of continued residence in their own communities, this capability is affected by periodic interruptions of mental functioning. Periods of gross absent-mindedness, aberrations in the management of funds, and neglect of minimal personal safety crop up especially among the very isolated persons, those without families, and those who have sustained organic brain damage. These aberrations, though not necessarily continuously dangerous, require protective care. In addition, when older persons living alone are hospitalized for physical illness for long periods of time, maintenance of their homes demands that someone pay rent, bills, and look after the premises until the medical absence comes to an end.

It is now agreed that protective services can undoubtedly prolong normal community residence for such persons, provided only that there be regular and continuous surveillance in order to locate and identify the aberrant period, arrangements for quick and immediate introduction of protective personnel if needed for relatively short periods of time, and availability of necessary legal services to permit protective action by guardians over either person or property. [*See Bernstein, Chap. 9 in this volume.*] Such a program would intervene only for the periods of time required, by contrast with the present situation in which the aberrant individual is removed to institutional care, with a complete abdication of normal community living.

Firm studies are not available to demonstrate the viability of this approach, although its reasonableness is suggested in the mild degree of deterioration among many patients in homes for the aged, and in the belief of institutional staffs that many of these patients could

[17] Virginia Lehman and Geneva Mathiasen, *Guardianship and Protective Services for Older People* (New York: National Council on the Aging, 1963).

live outside of such homes.[18] The alternative to such an approach is a continued accumulation of this population in nursing homes and other congregate institutions.

The Social Security Administration has taken steps to protect the confused older beneficiary by authorizing payment of his insurance benefits to a representative. The selection of this representative payee, and the protection of the beneficiary against payee mismanagement, are handled by appropriate administrative as well as legal mechanisms.

Major service agencies, such as family service societies, departments of public welfare, or hospitals, might take the responsibility for organizing the peculiar network required in the provision of full protective services. Alternatively, a completely new organization might be created, with staff to take personal responsibility as well as to mobilize judicial, legal, social welfare, health, or psychiatric services as needed. In either case, the insights and services from the several professions (medical, nursing, legal, social, psychiatric) would require coordination. This coordination may prove to be as important, and as difficult to achieve, as the allocation of service resources for this difficult-to-care-for segment of the population.

NONMEDICAL COMMUNITY ARRANGEMENTS

The most extensive array of posthospital facilities have no organic relationship to either the hospital or the health system. The most common posthospital setting is the patient's own home. The concept of organized supports for home health care is sustained by the belief that patients may be better cared for, from a medical point of view, in their own homes, despite the shrinking capability of the American family to undertake personal care and responsibility toward ill members.

Although the picture of home health services is not entirely clear, current evidence suggests the main outlines of the problem. It would appear that the older person can still draw on the emotional support of his family regardless of mobility and consequent curtailment of intergenerational family responsibility, employment of women, and activities of teenage youth outside the home. Such trends make neces-

[18] Saul Kaplan, *Report on Services to the Aged* (mimeographed; Chicago: Jewish Welfare Federation, 1966); Marjorie Lowenthal, *Aging and Mental Disorder in San Francisco* (San Francisco: Jossey Bass, 1967). See also Margaret Blenkner, "Prevention or Protection? Aspects of Social Welfare Services for the Mentally Impaired Aged" (presented at the First Workshop on Comprehensive Services for the Geriatric Mental Patient, Washington, D.C., 1967); Margaret Blenkner, E. Wasser, and M. Bloom, *Protective Services for Older People: Progress Report, 1966–67* (Cleveland: Benjamin Rose Institute, 1967), 82.

sary, however, the introduction of supplementary physical care facilities upon which the family may draw if older members are to be retained in family settings.

Some of this home care is now provided by the visiting nurses' associations; and, since most of the care does not require nursing, social agencies have also developed housekeeper and homemaker services of varying degrees of complexity. Unfortunately, very few of these latter services have an adequate association with the medical care system.

The major nonmedical social work resource for home health care is the department of welfare. Reorganization of the federal Department of Health, Education and Welfare in 1967 separated the administration of income maintenance from the provision of socially necessary services.[19] It is expected that this may, over time, encourage local and state departments of public welfare to develop into centers of public social services, with the capacity to mount large-scale service programs such as those of homemakers and home health aides.

Needed changes in public welfare   Such development must cope with two issues, finance and service organization. Although public welfare services have historically been limited to persons who are financially dependent upon public support, the Social Security Act Amendments of 1965 extended the concept of public service to those aged who are economically self-supporting save for their major medical needs. One advance has been assurance of payment for some home health services through health insurance for the aged (Medicare). A second has been the widening of public welfare responsibility, bringing many publicly dependent aged within reach of funds for home health services. This widening of eligibility might, in time, reach at least half of the aged population, so that the requirements of the elderly might well be the means for a dramatic transformation of the entire public welfare system.

Financial support, though necessary, is not sufficient, for home health services must be so organized and staffed as to be realistically accessible. In the past, departments of welfare have been concerned mainly with controlling payments of small grants and rechecking eligi-

[19] Executive orders issued in August, 1967, established the Social and Rehabilitation Service, bringing together the functions of the Welfare Administration, Vocational Rehabilitation Administration, Children's Bureau, Administration on Aging, and the Mental Retardation Division of the Bureau of Health Services. The recombination separated administration of income maintenance programs from other service programs and gave authority to the Administration on Aging for services to the aged on Public Assistance as well as to other groups of elderly.

bility or indigence. Recent trends oppose this limiting approach and encourage development under public auspices of the community servives themselves. Whether the public welfare system, with its accumulated history of control and limitation, can make the transfer is yet to be established. However, the potential exists for converting the department of public welfare into a general, community-wide service program, constituting a true utility as a department of social services. In time, this department could broaden its services to include all persons requiring extended home health care, regardless of age. In this sense, the public service could become a resource not only for hospitals but also for programs of social insurance, aid to the permanently and totally disabled, workmen's compensation, and the like.

Even if no such far-reaching change in public welfare departments is achieved, one major alteration in current performance is urgently needed in that public assistance, preoccupied as it is with doling out small stipends and constantly guarding against ineligible claims, seems to have lost sight of the end result of its work. The most glaring example is seen in the management of health needs of Old Age Assistance beneficiaries. OAA programs have produced so large a population living out their terminal years in proprietary nursing homes that almost one-fourth of all OAA payments are made to vendors of nursing home care. OAA beneficiaries are much more likely to end up in nursing homes than are aged persons with comparable physical disability who are not on public assistance. To be sure, nursing home care might possibly be better than that given in a person's own home, but the past record of average nursing home standards makes this doubtful.

If income source is a major determinant of whether a person lives in his own home or in a nursing home, then public welfare departments must confront openly the fact that their practices in OAA seem to channel the sick aged into institutions. The public payments for institutional care are substantially higher than those given to the aged maintaining their own homes, even though the effects of long-term institutional care may be deleterious. The balance should, apparently, be redressed between per capita public expenditures for care in own home and in nursing home. Such a balance might take the form either of more equitable cash payments to beneficiaries in the two situations, or of increased supplementary home care services. Nowhere is the link between public practice (or policy) and a person's life outcome more clearly discernible, and nowhere is the need for corrective action more clearly spelled out by available evidence.

If any such extension in public welfare responsibility is to take place, a vast increase in subprofessional manpower will be required, as well as a major redirection in the training of professional man-power, toward administration and management rather than personal counseling. It seems clear that the pressures to provide adequate posthospital and community care will produce new forms of organization. Whether or not social work will be the profession to train the manpower for that purpose remains to be seen.

NONMEDICAL INSTITUTIONS

Still another major resource for care of older people includes the nursing home and the home for the aged—though the distinction between the two is blurred. Although few nursing homes are administered by social workers, many homes for the aged are so administered and are conducted as social services.[20]

Homes for the aged   Homes for the aged, especially the non-profit homes, were originally evolved to provide food and congregate sheltered care for those with limited incomes and with some disability, but capable of managing their daily physical needs. However, the increased tendency of physically competent older persons to maintain their own residences (with support from the social insurances and public assistance) has pushed most homes for the aged either (1) into caring for the physically ill and handicapped whose average age is 80 to 85, or (2) into providing accommodations similar to private residences, with some supplementary services added.

Where homes for the aged have chosen the second course, the exclusive provision of residential accommodation is sometimes carried out by the home itself, and sometimes by a satellite corporation performing only a residential function while the parent institution maintains a service for the disabled.

Although homes for the aged have not matched the commercial nursing homes in the proportion of aged sick cared for,[21] a few have pioneered in providing comprehensive health and personal care services. Such homes may combine rehabilitation, leisure-time, and medical services for the ill. By providing these comprehensive services, they have been in the position to pioneer in the rehabilitation of older persons, in the extension of self-care following serious illness, and in

[20] Definitions by function of these institutions are not consistent and are confusing, so that accurate data about volume and distribution is difficult to secure. The two are distinguished here mainly by auspice—proprietary and nonprofit. It is the non-profit institutions that can be counted among social work institutions. Nevertheless, the growth of proprietary institutions is likely to attract more and more social workers both for residential service and for administration so that the distinction between the two types will be further diminished.

[21] According to analyses of the U.S. Public Health Service, 80 per cent of all nursing home beds are provided by proprietary nursing homes.

the maintenance of vigor and vitality even in the lives of very old persons.

Those homes for the aged that have elected to care for the sick find that their health services require an association with the basic medical and hospital system in the community, thus becoming a major social work service in a medical care system that is increasingly widened to encompass both medical and social resources. The homes for the aged which have chosen this path, especially the voluntary nonprofit homes, are a counterpart of commercial nursing homes in the race to produce adequate nonhospital facilities for the sick aged.

As homes for the aged have been pushed more and more in the direction of providing nursing care, they have at the same time been made aware of an additional gap in community services: The commercial market for housing has never satisfactorily provided adequate housing at low income for older persons [*cf. Madge, Chap. 8 in this volume, on Architecture and Planning*]. The impact of the social security program and the provision of relative economic independence for the vast majority of the elderly population has forced the homes to re-think their functional responsibility for those older persons seeking strictly residential accommodations. The vast bulk of retired persons, even though they may be living on submarginal incomes, are still capable of opting against congregate living in which rooms must be shared with strangers, and choosing instead private housing (even if substandard in quality). Many institutions for the elderly, concerned with this problem, have begun to develop modern forms of nonprofit housing in which the desire for privacy is satisfied through independent apartment-house living for older persons with modest incomes.

The borderline between the old congregate living and the new apartment-house residence is still in the making, and constantly being adjusted. Nevertheless, substantial numbers of church groups and homes for the aged have established corporations for the construction of apartment-house dwellings in which privacy is assured for the older resident. These homes for the aged have also recognized the higher risk of disability to which older persons are subject, and they have therefore introduced supplementary services for home care. These pioneer institutions have become new centers for the elaboration of home health services, competing with older family service and home nursing agencies, and have shown an especially vigorous growth in recent years.

Proprietary nursing homes   The demand for improvement in services and the increasing rigor of public health licensure and standard setting have begun to convert many proprietary nursing homes—

though not ordinarily considered to be social welfare agencies—to quasi-service facilities into which various social services are being introduced. Among these services are provision of leisure-time and recreational activities for long-term residents, more active rehabilitation suited to the potential of older disabled persons, and improved screening so that family ties are not unduly disrupted. Since these are all functions normally fulfilled by social workers in health institutions, it is possible that at least the larger nursing homes may seek the employment of professionally qualified individuals. Whether social workers will be produced in sufficient volume to fill this need is problematical. It is more likely that manpower of less skill or training will be employed, with administration or consultation provided by social workers who are attached to city-wide centers such as hospitals or departments of health or welfare.

One clear result of the demand for more extensive services in proprietary nursing homes is to force out of business the small, family-run nursing homes and to replace them by much larger institutions run along corporate lines. These larger institutions have sufficient residents to justify the employment of a larger and more varied team of specialists; but the physical plant is more costly, and the problem of retaining a personal and humane touch in the care of residents becomes more difficult. This circumstance argues in favor of introducing formally into the bigger institutions staff whose main concern is to foster friendly relations and kindly attention in times of stress.

In sum, then, both nursing and residential facilities, especially the nonprofit institutions, are tending to develop as multiple purpose organizations. There is an emerging consolidation under a single administration of services and facilities that may include intensive nursing care, rehabilitation, sheltered employment, private residential accommodation, recreation for a neighboring noninstitutional population, personal care in an individual's own home, general community counseling on care of the elderly, and even temporary day or night accommodations in cases of family emergencies.

Income maintenance

In the early days of social welfare, the provision of supplementary income for families in need was considered primarily a social welfare function, but since 1935 it is no longer exclusively the responsibility of social workers. Social work as a profession retains significant interest in income maintenance programs and policies, however; and the public still assumes that social work has responsibility for managing such institutions, even though the actual staffing is largely in the hands of others.

The major social welfare policy question introduced by current knowledge concerns the relationship between public pension and insurance payments (social security) on the one hand, and public welfare support based on the determination of individual needs, on the other. The general drift of American policy has been in favor of universal provision and away from case determination. Social security has steadily replaced public assistance as the major income source of retired persons, although some two million older persons still receive full or partial support from case-determined public assistance programs. Even these latter are in many states subject to only occasional checking of eligibility, however, so that public assistance in fact tends to become similar to a lower level pension program.

Economic data introduced by Sheppard and by Kreps, Chaps. 6 and 7 in this volume [*and in Vol. 1, Chap. 3, pp. 39–68; Chap. 4, pp. 69–104*] suggest that older persons as a group are sufficiently removed from the operations of the labor market to justify the general and public provision for income support incorporated in the social security program. However, this program is based in large part on lifetime earnings in the labor force and, like any income maintenance program based upon wage-related pensions, inevitably introduces inequities. Some, albeit a diminishing proportion, of the retired population have insufficient wage-related earnings to provide a minimally decent livelihood.[22] Particularly those aged persons with serious health problems or with serious physical and mental handicaps are likely to have insufficient wage-related pension income for all needs. Moreover, the long-term rise in cost of living, which depresses the value of fixed incomes, suggests that a gap between benefits and requirements may persist indefinitely.

Although social work is committed to the ideology of a universal program, the profession's daily practice derives from individual case determination. Indeed, it is this attention to individual case variations which suggests that some residual program for income or service supplement will be necessary no matter what universal system of retirement insurance is developed. The level of economic support due the aged requires adjustments so as to cover more than food and shelter alone. Income should, for example, provide a sizable margin of com-

---

[22] In 1965, 6.9 per cent of all social security insurance beneficiaries received public assistance payments in addition; although this proportion declined from 13.4 per cent in 1940, it has increased slightly since 1960, from 6.7 per cent to 6.9 per cent.

pensation for the reduced mobility of the aged. Their food may cost more since comparative shopping is difficult. Their rent may be higher since high, walk-up apartments are unsuitable. Income should also be provided for suitable transportation for visits to family, friends, or centers of social activity. Finally, it would seem reasonable to urge that income be sufficiently high to permit a telephone and the purchase of small, reciprocating gifts to insure maintenance of social ties and bonds.

Although it cannot be argued that the responsibility for such residual or supplementary income will rest upon social work in the future, it is clear that whatever universal program is evolved should at least facilitate access to the various social services dealt with in this chapter—leisure, health, and sociability—at modest charges appropriate for low-income families.

Service coordination and integration

The transformation of America's income maintenance programs, from case determination to insurance, forces social work not only to reconsider its relationship to insurance systems, but also to reassess the linkage among multiple welfare systems generally. Whatever linking arrangements are adopted, social workers, who have long functioned at the margins of several service systems, are likely to play a major role in insuring client access to services that are usually in short supply and difficult to locate in a modern city.

It is not clear whether general insurance programs provide the best setting within which social workers may establish linkage with non-income service programs, or whether some other mechanism should be developed within the social service system. While social work as a profession has had little contact with insurance-based income programs, the Social Security Administration has experimented with numerous devices for dissemination of information about social services. Its network of regional offices constitutes a heavily used resource for distribution of service information to its beneficiaries, who represent 750 out of each 1,000 elderly. The Administration already sensitizes its staff to this community function in a widespread in-service training program. This resource is much more extensive and more widely used than many independent information and referral centers created by urban social planning councils. Insurance organizations may be loath to deflect attention from their primary insurance function, however, in which case some other equally acceptable and widespread information service must be developed.

The need for service information will persist even if the income floor for all elderly persons becomes adequate to permit the aged consumer to purchase his social services wherever he wishes, or even if some services, such as health, are made available to all as a public utility. In either event, the aged consumer of social services will require some guidance system, whether advertising or referral services, to locate services he wants, and he will demand some freedom of choice in selecting the service he desires from among several alternatives.

An alternative to a referral system is an open-market situation in which clients find agencies without the mediation of any referral system. In such a case, income maintenance and services would be even more separate than is true today, and the organizational character of social work would depend upon consumer behavior more than on any other single factor.

Such alternatives are clearly oversimplified. The fragmentation of all social services has produced a demand for integrating the felt need and the proper service for its relief. The scores of "possible" resources in any city are hedged in by restrictive eligibility requirements: age level, religion, place of residence, income level, to name only a few. Names of agencies seldom provide clear description of the services actually provided, and publicity seldom penetrates to persons before they reach a crisis. To these difficulties is added the overall shortage of many facilities. Thus the search for help must be conducted through a puzzling, and frequently frustrating, maze.

Since the elderly constitute a subgroup of the general population which uses selected social services in large volume, information centers might be incorporated into existing services without the creation of separate institutions. Hospitals constitute one such service, to which an extensive network of facilities for health-related needs is already attached. Although relatively few older persons are in hospitals at any one time, a larger proportion use hospital facilities over the course of the average year. Thus a redefinition of hospital responsibility might result in hospital centralization of information about home health services (an added function which would, to be sure, require a substantial expansion of social work staff or the training of subprofessional aides).

An alternative source for information and referral services is found in the local departments of public welfare, which are in communication with over 2 million, or about 117 out of each 1,000, older persons. However, this agency, for the most part preoccupied with establishing financial eligibility for service rather than with extending help where needed, is hampered by the negative attitudes with which many of its clients regard it. If, over a generation, the department of welfare could be shorn of its investigatory functions and converted into a department of public social services, it might well serve as a major agency for identifying social and health needs of the elderly and for providing information to individuals on request.

The local department of public health has frequently been considered a suitable centralizing resource; but, while this department does have competent medical orientation and may collect data about large numbers of older persons through special survey methods, it could not easily serve as a center for dispensing information about available services.

Whatever form of referral system emerges (through income maintenance or health agencies, or through a general consumer population), it seems likely that social work services will become specialized resources reached through cross-referrals from other agencies, rather than becoming the central resource to which individuals initially turn directly.

The location of service facilities

The need for service information may be intensified by the gradual abandonment (except for some settlement houses, senior citizen programs, and branch libraries) of neighborhood locations for social services. Most social services expect consumers to travel to central offices, or, as in the case of many hospitals, are content to serve only those elderly who live within a half-mile radius of the institution. A candid appraisal of centralized services from the viewpoint of the aged raises a major policy issue. Older people may be hampered by physical limitations that restrict movement over long distances, may find it difficult to use inconvenient public transportation or expensive to travel by automobile. In addition, a proportion of older people find it difficult to deal with large organizations with their formalized procedures.

A counter-movement to this centralization has set in recently, with a more aggressive "outreach" on the part of agency staffs. There is a revitalized interest in working in the core city ghettos through outpost stations, storefront offices, and home delivery services. This counter-movement has been largely concentrated in the poorest areas of the city, however, not yet penetrating into the more dispersed suburban fringe.

The nature of urban planning and design calls for a closer partnership between those who plan transportation and buildings and those who plan the human services. Together they can bring the urban design and human needs into reasonable balance. [*See Vol. 1, Chap. 6, pp. 121–156, and Madge, Chap. 8 in this volume.*] Attention to the elderly thus constitutes a model on which to test out the larger issue of community-wide design.[23]

Urban service delivery systems can take either of two courses to deal with the reduced mobility of the elderly. Neighborhood service delivery units might be organized in a widely dispersed though dense network, tied together by some city-wide administrative system; or special travel and communication networks might be built to bring aged consumers to central service units. Urban planning has not yet taken into account the fact that the elderly not only tend to cluster in their living; they also cluster in the services they use. Hospitals and major social agencies such as social security offices, settlement houses, and welfare departments are natural gathering points. Thus a varied range of service units built around such natural collecting points could reduce the amount of travel.

A pragmatic approach to comprehensive urban planning would require a searching-out of concentrations of older persons living in normal community settings, followed by an adaptation of the special services believed to be necessary in such geographical areas of the city. Complete coverage need not be assured, but the largest aggregates of older persons might be viewed as "populations at risk" in planning the organization of health, protective, leisure-time, and social services. Three major loci for integrating physical and social planning design can be identified: (1) low-income residential concentrations of the aged in the city center, in public and commercial low cost housing units; (2) major service delivery facilities for the aged, such as hospitals, recreation centers, and social security offices; and (3) new retirement communities for the more affluent aged. Services of all kinds for the aged might be usefully centered in one or more of these concentrations.

Such an approach might also simplify the problem of information and referral services to assist consumers and their families in utilizing the intricate urban network of social services. Instead of general community information services designed to give everybody in the metro-

[23] *Vide* the multi-purpose Neighborhood Service Centers and the Neighborhood Health Services Centers, established by the Office of Economic Opportunity and by the U.S. Public Health Service. See also Bernard Frieden and Robert Morris, *Urban Planning and Social Policy* (New York: Basic Books, Inc., 1968).

politan area prompt access to all services, it would become possible to develop specialized information centers related to the requirements of particular population groupings.

The educational base for social work: individual treatment and social policy

The pressures for change that new knowledge about aging has introduced are nowhere more evident than in education for social work. Knowledge about the behavior of the aged and about development in the later years has already been disseminated in some schools, through courses in human growth and development and through service descriptions. This diffusion must spread to all curricula, so that social workers everywhere will have a deeper understanding of the reality and the potential throughout the entire life cycle, an understanding comparable to that now claimed for the pre-adolescent years.

Still more important structural changes in education are on the horizon. A social and community orientation requires that social work educate a body of social workers capable of planning, organizing, and administering large service complexes and systems that employ other professional workers (such as physicians, nurses, and teachers) and many nonprofessional social and health aides. Yet this type of education is nowhere offered by schools of social work. Unless they adapt their curricula to such ends, the management of major social welfare institutions will devolve upon other professional groups who do have access to such training. An encouraging sign is seen, however, in the recent rapid growth of education for community organization in schools of social work. The number of social work students concentrating in community organization doubled between 1965 and 1967, rapidly accelerating a trend that began in 1950. A continuation of this trend may provide the field with the manpower necessary for new responsibilities.[24]

A consequence of changing social work education may be a further separation of the profession, and of social welfare institutions, into two major channels, one concentrating on treatment of individuals, the other on policy and management of services. If these channels remain

[24] Between 1950 and 1960, the percentage of all social workers employed primarily in community work increased from 3.6 per cent to 7.3 per cent. In 1964, 8,000 professional community workers were assisted by 23,000 community aides recently employed through the Office of Economic Opportunity. See Council on Social Work Education, *Annual Reports* (New York: Council on Social Work Education, 1965 and 1967); and U.S. Department of Health, Education and Welfare, *Closing the Gap in Social Work Manpower* (Washington, D.C.: Government Printing Office, 1965).

interdependent the two classes of professional skill will be intertwined in most social welfare institutions. If, however, the channels diverge, the consequences may be a separation of counseling and individual therapy from social agency constraints, and the emergence of an independent counseling profession, free to sell its services at a fee or at a salary.

If the policy recommendations set forth at various points in this chapter are to be implemented, the service delivery institutions will require major restructuring of tasks to permit many types and levels of workers (professional, subprofessional, assisting, nonprofessional) and also several levels of professional performance. Manpower for clearly sanctioned social services cannot be provided solely by a single level of professional recruitment and training at the postgraduate level. Educational opportunities of many kinds are required to assure an adequate supply of manpower at all levels—high school and pre-baccalaureate as well as at graduate levels. These levels should be so linked that some reasonable career path is open throughout the social work structure.

Whichever path of evolution or revolution is followed, the schools of social work can hardly refrain from a major diversification of their educational offerings for therapists, administrators, planners, and scholars at the professional end of the scale; and, at the least, they must provide leadership in the training of subprofessional and assistant categories of workers at the other end of the scale.

Attention to the needs of the elderly in society would seem to rule out the small, homogeneous, tightly-knit profession. In its stead must emerge a richly diversified profession, with many types and levels of associated workers whose numbers exceed the professional core. Conscious effort to create such a pool of manpower and such an organizational structure should better equip social work and social welfare to translate their view of man *in* society into a reality of continuous development of individual potential through all stages of the life cycle.

3

Aging and the field of medicine

LOUIS LASAGNA

Doctor Lasagna calls special attention in this chapter to a variety of special difficulties confronting the physician who treats aged patients. The uncertain boundary between intrinsic aging and environmentally produced disease, the unknown potential for extending life expectancy, and the wide variability in aging processes among individuals all complicate decisions regarding appropriate therapeutic response. Drawing upon selected aspects of the body of social science knowledge, Doctor Lasagna also isolates two further problem areas. One concerns various social-psychological barriers that impede optimal care of the senescent patient. These obstacles are found in attitudes and practices of both physicians and the society at large, as well as in the facilities available for care of the elderly. Another set of problems stems from the physician's need to deal with predictable and imminent death and even to make decisions as to when a particular death does, in fact, occur. Though increasingly problematic, issues surrounding the definition of death and the prolongation of life cannot be avoided. "There is no place for the physician to hide." Doctor Lasagna is persuaded that, if solutions to present

*difficulties are to be found, there must be a broadening conflu-
ence of both knowledge and practice among the medical profession, other agencies in the society, and the social sciences generally.*

*Advisers for this chapter were Reubin Andres, Gerontology
Research Center, National Institute of Child Health and Human
Development; Arthur J. Patek, Jr., Tufts University School of
Medicine; and DeWitt Stetten, Jr., Dean, Rutgers Medical School,
Rutgers University. It was also reviewed by Esther Lucile Brown,
Consultant on Psychosocial Aspects of Patient Care, San Fran-
cisco, California.*

ON THE RELEVANCE OF VOLUME ONE

*Although mortality rates increase steadily with age, no inherent
process of aging has yet been isolated, independent of the
cumulative assaults of the environment. Nor has a clear line
yet been drawn between biological and social aging. Even if such
distinctions were possible, the vast body of empirical studies in
the varied fields dealing with age-related changes in the human
being, as these are summarized and illustrated in Volume One,
would still be of importance to the physician. Not only do these
studies indicate the nature of the psycho-social adjustment that
must be taken into account when treating patients in middle and
later life, but they may also point to possibilities of preventive
treatment with younger persons.*

*In addition to the more general material in Volume One on
the socio-cultural context of the older person, his personality,
and the roles he plays, Chapters 8 through 11 of that volume
summarize a wide range of findings on the physical condition of
the organism. Prepared by a physician who is also a social scientist, these chapters cross-cut specialized medical fields. Chapter
8, for example, reviews studies of the relationship to aging of
such phenomena as autoimmunity, stress, and diet. Chapter 9
culls from the literature on age-related variables associated with
mortality and morbidity; while the full range of anatomical and
physiological changes frequently noted in older people is described in Chapter 10. Research on age differences in perception,
psycho-motor skills, intelligence, learning, and memory is presented in Chapter 11 which also summarizes studies of age patterns in sex activity and such health-related behaviors as drink-
ing and smoking. Investigations of the mental disorders of older
people are surveyed in Chapter 16.*

Despite the considerable interest in, and research on, the biology of aging, there is still no general agreement on the basic nature of the phenomenon. Indeed the definition is intrinsically a statistical and group definition, rather than an individual one. Senescence can be defined as the gradual series of changes which result in a decreased capacity for survival. It is by death that aging as a process is measured—the increasing probability of death with increasing chronological age in the members of a population. [*Cf. Susser, Chap. 5 in this volume.*]

Intrinsic aging versus environmental assault

A fundamental controversy in regard to human aging is whether the process exists per se as distinct from the impact of multiple assaults, recognized and occult, from the environment. [*See Vol. 1, Chap. 8, pp. 187–194.*] Aging is not biologically inevitable; "natural death" does not occur among unicellular organisms; and certain protozoans, bacteria and yeasts, where the individual and reproductive cells are one and the same, can survive indefinitely. Indeed, certain human tissue culture lines, such as the HeLa cells, might be said to be immortal.

THE EXAMPLE OF ESSENTIAL HYPERTENSION

The difficulty in distinguishing inevitable "wear-and-tear" phenomena from accidental pathological change is illustrated in some of our most common and important diseases. [*See Vol. 1, Chap. 9.2, pp. 204–218; Chap. 10, pp. 221–239.*] "Essential" hypertension, for example —the diagnosis in the great majority of people with "abnormally high" blood pressures—remains a disease whose very diagnosis is beclouded by the imprecise distinction between "normal aging" and "disease." Cross-section population studies have long been known to show an increase in mean blood pressure—both systolic and diastolic[1]—in the older age groups. What, then, should be the criteria for diagnosis of hypertension? Even if one excludes those with elevated systolic pressures only—generally considered to be individuals suffering "only" from a less elastic arterial tree—there still remains a substantial number of older individuals who do not have the astronomically high level of diastolic pressure that is so frequently the

---

[1] Systolic pressure is the first figure given in blood pressure readings, diastolic the second. Thus 150/90 indicates a systolic pressure of 150 and a diastolic of 90 mm. of mercury.

harbinger of vascular catastrophe but whose blood pressures are nevertheless beyond the range accepted as normal for younger people.

Recent studies have begun to shed light on both the phenomenon and the implications for the medical profession. Studies of individuals and cohorts followed for a period of years suggest that the development of hypertension is not a gradual and inevitable consequence of aging but the unlucky fate of a few individuals at special genetic or environmental risk. Controlled and uncontrolled therapeutic trials also suggest strongly that *any* increase in diastolic blood pressure is deleterious to the organism and that treatment with drugs and other measures which lower the pressure can reverse the trend toward early disability or death. At present, therefore, informed opinion would hold that hypertension is abnormal, is not a concomitant of aging, and that its occurrence at any age should evoke a therapeutic reflex from the physician.

DIABETES MELLITUS

Diabetes mellitus provides another example of the difficulty in distinguishing "normal" aging from environmental accident. It is recognized that there is a high incidence of abnormal glucose tolerance tests in the elderly. If one utilizes the "normal" standards derived from data on young adults, approximately one-half of aged subjects will be judged to have diabetes. If, on the other hand, separate standards are to be applied to different age groups, one is then assuming that deterioration in glucose tolerance with increasing age is "physiological" or "normal." Which attitude is correct? No scientific answer is possible, in the absence of an independent test for diabetes, and in the absence of reliable information on what percentage of, and which, people at different ages will develop "overt" clinical diabetes (as distinct from "chemical" diabetes) or will develop those diseases known to be highly associated with diabetes (such as myocardial infarction) or will die at an early age.

ARTERIOSCLEROSIS

Arteriosclerosis was once considered irreversible in its onset and progression with age, while today such changes in blood vessels are more popularly considered as due to environmental factors like diet and stress. Studies at the Philadelphia Zoological Garden, for example, suggest that coronary artery disease in mammals and birds is less associated with age than with some of the social changes contingent on attempts to assemble and maintain breeding stocks, with the introduction of new captives, the proximity of males or females of the same species, or the interaction of the animals with keeper personnel.[2] In humans, it appears that atherosclerosis is accelerated in patients with diabetes or myxedema or nephrosis, independently of age. A "composite" picture by Doctor Alan N. Howard of Cambridge University, while satirical, summarizes many of the factors currently thought to be important:

> The person least likely to get atherosclerosis is a hypotensive, bicycling, unemployed, hypo-β-lipoproteinemic, hyper-α-lipoproteinemic, nonsmoking, hypolipemic, underweight, premenopausal female dwarf living in a crowded room on the island of Crete before 1925 and subsisting on a diet of uncoated cereals, safflower oil, and water.

SENILITY

The unfortunate word "senility," with its implication of inevitable mental deterioration in the elderly, has proven a semantic trap for both physicians and patients. Senility is often used as a substitute for thorough diagnostic and therapeutic measures, and can be employed to cover everything from a true dementia secondary to vascular lesions of the brain or to neuronal atrophy, to frailty and drug intoxication. [See Vol. 1, Chap. 16.A, pp. 363–392.] The elderly, for example, not infrequently suffer from melancholia, which may have various causes. Some of these depressions yield to companionship, hope, or friendship; others require nourishment, treatment of somatic conditions, or anti-depressant drugs. Still other patients need to have sleeping pills or other medication stopped. No depression will respond to the therapeutic nihilism that accompanies the diagnosis of senility.

Potentials for life expectancy

Is it realistic to expect medical science to extend man's life substantially beyond its present expectations? [See Vol. 1, Chap. 2.3, pp. 24–35; Chap. 9, pp. 195–220.] Doctor Robert R. Kohn has estimated that if people could be kept from developing cancer, or if all cancers could be cured, the life expectancy of adults would be increased only by one to three years.[3] He estimates that freedom from atherosclerosis would provide about seven more years of life. [Cf. Vol. 1, Ex. 9 · 8, p. 203.] Such figures are of course highly speculative, since diseases

[2] H. L. Ratcliffe, "Age and Environment as Factors in the Nature and Frequency of Cardiovascular Lesions in Mammals and Birds in the Philadelphia Zoological Garden," Annals of the New York Academy of Sciences, 127 (1965), 715–735.
[3] Robert R. Kohn, "Human Aging and Disease," Journal of Chronic Diseases, 16 (1963), 5–21.

are not necessarily discrete entities, but may be interrelated processes. An old person saved from atherosclerosis might be more susceptible to death from other causes, without a net gain in longevity. It may be more reasonable to anticipate not a major stretching of life span—but the enabling of more people to live the "maximum" life span already enjoyed by some.

"SPARE PARTS SURGERY"

One area of great interest at present and which provides some hope for an augmentation of both comfort and longevity is that of "spare parts surgery." Some species are remarkably adept at replacing individual parts that are lost or wear out; man is capable of such regeneration for some tissues, such as the blood, or skin, or the lining of the gastrointestinal tract, but he cannot replace some of the organs most essential to his well-being.

The miracles of modern cardiac surgery have prepared us, however, for more dramatic accomplishments, and widely publicized experiments are under way to determine how feasible it may be to replace even the diseased human heart with nonliving pumps or with transplanted hearts. Livers, kidneys, intestines, lungs—all are the subject of scrutiny today as surgeons seek to leap farther into the unknown and provide new benefits for old ailments—benefits far surpassing the now commonplace use of donor skin, blood, cornea, or bone.

CURRENT LIMITATIONS

Attempts to correct gross abnormalities are limited both by our ignorance and by the remarkably complex and efficient mechanism that the human body is. Classic approaches to the evaluation of man as a machine determined "efficiency" from the ratio of work performed to energy spent. By such calculations, normal man turns out to have something like 20 per cent efficiency, a performance between that of the steam and gasoline engines.

But such calculations ignore the muscular work that expends energy but does not do work in the "force $\times$ distance" sense, and the secretory work of the glands, and the homeostatic maneuvers which regulate so beautifully the acidity and alkalinity of the body, its temperature, its metabolism. Nor can one measure, in this older sense, the work done by an organ such as the liver, which makes, stores, excretes, extracts, and detoxifies with extraordinary competence and versatility. And when one thinks of the miracle of miniaturization and computerization that is the human nervous system, the task of replacing or improving upon it in any mechanical way seems preposterous.

Nor is it sufficient to attempt to comprehend the working of any one organ in isolation. For it is in the extraordinary coordination of its parts that the human body excels, and we must beware lest tinkering with some part inflict unpredictable damage on the entire apparatus, as Aesop recognized: "They found that even the belly, in its dull quiet way, was doing necessary work for the body, and that all must work together or the body will go to pieces."

INDIVIDUAL VARIATION

One important aspect of aging apart from the continuity of the process, is the variability among individuals in the rate of "physiological decline." Factors as different as heredity and diet seem to affect longevity [see Vol. 1, Chap. 8, pp. 185–194], and it is commonplace to observe how one person looks "younger than his years" while another seems "prematurely aged." These facts make it clear that scientifically there is no basis for automatic retirement at any fixed time of life. Schemes which utilize cut-off points of 60 or 65 may or may not be desirable on the average in specific societal activities, but such inexorable retirement ages must be recognized to have no basis in gerontology. [Cf. Sheppard, Chap. 6 in this volume.] Even a superficial view of music, art, politics, religion, and the law indicates the losses a culture must endure if it ignores the potential contributions of older people. [Cf. Vol. 1, Chap. 18.B.2, pp. 435–437.]

The case of retirement Nevertheless, the retirement phase of life is inevitable for most people who live into their 70's [Vol. 1, Chap. 3.A, pp. 40–51; Chap. 18.C, pp. 442–459], and the physician should play an increasingly important role in helping his patients prepare for this time. The doctor, though he often joins forces with professionals from other fields, is the one individual who is both most likely to have some sort of regular, advisory, "consulting" function in relation to the aging person [Vol. 1, Chap. 14.3.b, p. 327], and also best able to evaluate the physical and psychological strengths and weaknesses of his patient.

The task is not an easy one. To begin with, some of the most capable, imaginative, and successful men seem incapable of planning rationally for a time of retirement. Others, despite waning physiological powers, try to preserve the illusion of unflagging capabilities, instead of realistically functioning at a generally lower level of activity or giving up some activities so as to preserve others at full vigor. For too many, a forced retirement can become the signal for a retreat into trivial, frivolous, and unsatisfying activities that make a travesty of leisure. [*But cf. Vol. 1, Chap. 22, pp. 511–535.*]

Since by no means all superannuated individuals are incapacitated, society in general might well consider what positive steps it might take to recruit "retirees" into active jobs. It might begin by looking at occupational gaps—positions that are characteristically hard to fill or to keep filled. [*See, for example, suggestions by Morris, Schwartz, and Bernstein, Chaps. 2, 4, 9 in this volume.*] Teaching, nursing, hospital work—how many problems could be solved by a flexible approach to hiring the aged, coupled with a revision of our Social Security Act, which is drawn up to encourage planned human obsolescence? In part, at least, society will get what it expects from the aged. The history of education has shown that even the young can accomplish a great deal more than we used to give them credit for. In times of war or other disaster, the energies of men surpass the performance expected of them in their ordinary lives. If we *expect* people to fall apart at 65, many of them will obligingly do so. If the cultural milieu, on the other hand, expects continued productivity, advice, and wisdom from the elderly, it is much more likely that society will reap a fuller intellectual harvest from them. [*Cf. Eklund, Chap. 11 in this volume.*]

Barriers to good medical care

There are a number of formidable barriers to the provision of optimal medical care for the aged. To be sure, certain of these have their source in the attitudes of older individuals to disease. Many tend to take their ailments for granted, or to put little faith in medical science, or to feel that they understand their health problems and needs better than anyone else. [*See Vol. 1, Chaps. 14.1 and 14.2, pp. 317–325.*] Other barriers, however, have their locus in attitudes and practices of members of the medical profession or of the society at large, and in the facilities available for care of the geriatric population.

THE DOCTOR'S LACK OF INTEREST OR OF SENSITIVITY

One obstacle is the disinclination of many doctors to be interested in the patient with a chronic illness not likely to yield dramatically—or at all—to therapeutic maneuvers. Doctors wish to see patients improve as a result of their efforts, and they want to be liked and appreciated by their patients. Neither wish is gratified when caring for a chronically ill patient frustrated by his slow progress.

For many doctors, the common chronic diseases such as strokes, congestive heart failure, diabetes, etc., are less "interesting" than more dramatic illnesses in younger patients, even when the illness in the young is refractory to treatment.

MULTIPLE DISEASES AND COMPLICATIONS

The doctor also has to remember constantly that rules which hold for young adults may be completely inappropriate for the geriatric population. In medical diagnosis, for example, doctors are usually well advised, in the younger age groups, to use Occam's razor—the principle that one should not invoke any more assumptions or entities than the minimum necessary to explain a situation. This philosophical rule-of-thumb, dating back to the fourteenth century, has been viewed over the years as reflecting such diverse forces as God's will, aesthetic principles, and laziness, but its appeal to the physician is simply based: It seems to work well in most acute medical problems. In the aged, however, Occam's razor may serve only to cut the patient's lifeline. Such patients rarely suffer from only one medical condition, and to insist on one diagnosis to explain all the symptoms usually means missing an important facet of the problem.

Doctor David Seegal, Professor of Medicine at Columbia University's College of Physicians and Surgeons, has written on "The Trap of the 'Pigeonholed' Diagnosis":

Picture the physician as he arrives late at his office after a busy period at the hospital clinic. There are two new and three old patients awaiting him. After making apologies for his tardiness, he sees the old patients first since he assumes that their requirements can be met quickly. Unless he is presented with a new set of symptoms, the clinician, by habit, will mentally relate the patient and his name to his labelled disease. This transference becomes increasingly established with time. When he greets Mrs. Chronos, he visualizes her pigeonholed diagnosis of hypertensive vascular disease; when he shakes Mr. Longterm's hand he is thinking of the pigeonholed diagnosis of diabetes mellitus; and when he smiles dourly at Mr. Senior's unfunny joke, he is wondering whether the new drug has helped this patient with the pigeonholed diagnosis of gout. It is only natural that the physician's thinking about each of these long-term patients is directed to the documented disease. Unless overt symptoms or signs of a new disorder appear, it is likely that the physician will spend no more time than is necessary to respond to the demands of the established illness.

. . . the trust given to him by the long-term patient demands a vigilance beyond that of managing the original illness. Although his diagnosis on the first few visits was correct and the therapeutic regimen exemplary, over the years the busy doctor may be lulled into a comfortable acceptance of the status quo of the diseases in his charge. The disciplined phy-sician of record, however, will avoid many of the traps of the pigeonholed diagnosis by adopting realistic methods for the detection of the subtle beginnings of new disease in the chronically ill under his care. Perform-ance of this duty may benefit the patient and prevent the bitter experi-ences which each of us has known in the past while hibernating with the original diagnosis.[4]

Elderly patients are more likely than younger patients to develop complications in the hospital, and the doctor must be on the alert to prevent or treat them. Studies have shown that as many as three-fourths of geriatric patients develop such complications, especially respiratory infections, which are often fatal.[5] Pneumonia in the elderly is often undramatic in onset—perhaps only a poor appetite, or pallor, or a slight rise in respiratory rate, or a little fever. Other problems include urinary tract infections, drug reactions, and injuries sustained from falls.

DEBILITATING EFFECTS OF DIAGNOSTIC PROCEDURES

In the doctor's efforts at health care he must not gamble with the vitality of the elderly patient by quickly subjecting him to more tests and treatments than he can tolerate with reasonable safety. Doctors are apt to forget how debilitating a rapid-fire X-ray work-up can be, for example. A patient is admitted to a hospital with a vague story of belly pain. The physician, rightly concerned with making a diagnosis as soon as possible and keeping hospital costs down for his patient, orders a long list of X-rays: a gall bladder series, X-rays of the esopha-gus, stomach, upper intestine, and kidneys, a barium enema, possibly even a series of films of the lower small intestine. Most of these procedures have deleterious effects on the elderly. Some require restriction of food, drink, or both for as long as thirty-six hours be-fore the procedure. Some require castor oil and "cleansing enemas" before the X-rays, and similar measures may be required to clean the barium out of the intestine after the films are taken. On the day of each X-ray examination, there is usually little or no intake of food or liquid while the patient waits—often for many hours—for the films to be taken, and then for additional hours until the pictures are completed. It is not unusual—even if all the films are "satisfactory"

---

[4] David Seegal, "The Trap of the 'Pigeonholed' Diagnosis in Management of the Long-Term Patient," *Journal of Chronic Diseases*, 17 (1964), 389–390.

[5] A. J. Rosin and R. V. Boyd, "Complications of Illness in Geriatric Patients in Hos-pital," *Journal of Chronic Diseases*, 19 (1966), 307–313.

and no "repeats" are needed—for a patient to go the better part of a week in a state of relative dehydration and starvation. Even a healthy young patient suffers discomfort; the sick oldster whose circulation, heart, kidneys, or brain are barely compensated in the best of circumstances may be pushed over the brink into insufficiency of one sort or another.

COMFORT VERSUS CURE

At the same time, it is not necessary for the physician to deny the elderly patient the benefit of needed therapy for serious conditions. The operating-room schedules of all major hospitals are filled with aged patients in their 60's and 70's, and even octogenarians and nonagenarians can successfully undergo major surgery. There are no absolute age limits to surgery, although the *physiological* age of the patient seems important in predicting risk. What the aged do need, however, is meticulous preoperative preparation, experienced and judicious surgery and anesthesia, and diligent postoperative care. With a smoothly working team of medical and paramedical personnel aware of the special problems of the aged, surgery need not be a fearful or dangerous experience.

One of the lessons the doctor must learn, however, is to be humble in the goals he sets for his geriatric patient. Alfred Worcester described the problem beautifully:

In the first year of my practice I undertook the care of a rich old man, misshapen by *arthritis deformans.* I made notes of his history; I examined his body and his excretions; and then I ordered for him the treatment that in those years was according to Hoyle. As his pulse was irregular I cut off his tobacco. I did not allow him even the meats that he depended upon; and in place of his gin I gave him nauseous draughts of salicylates. When a few days afterwards he complained that he must have relief, I cruelly answered that I should make my visits only as often as I thought necessary, and that either the treatment I had ordered was to be continued or another physician could be summoned. The old man managed to live through the winter. Before he died he gave me this lesson. He had called for my help, he said, because of his suffering, not because he expected or even wanted to be cured. In spite of his confession of life-long dependence upon alcohol, I had taken that away and also the comfort of even his pipe. I had changed his diet from what he liked to what he loathed, and worst of all, when he wanted the encouragement of frequent visits, I had refused him even that boon. He was too proud, he said, not to obey his physician's orders, but he wanted me to know how much more miserable I had made the last year of his life. My only atonement has been in never again making just such an egregious blunder; and I report it in the hope that my younger brothers will never make the mistake of treating their aged patients as if their rejuvenation were possible.[6]

INADEQUATE GERIATRIC FACILITIES

The older patient, with his multiple and recurring problems, has a great need—at present rarely met—for continuing, integrated medical care. His hospital experiences are not usually isolated, self-limited illnesses, and the urgency of his health needs will vary tremendously. There must therefore be a smoothly geared mechanism for rapidly admitting the chronically ill person to a hospital for "acute" medical care as well as for quickly facilitating transfer to the home, or a rehabilitative facility, or long-term custodial care as the needs change. This requires a much closer liaison between general hospitals, "chronic" hospitals, halfway-homes, nursing homes, and home care programs than now exists.

Hospitals　"Acute" general hospitals are often poorly equipped to handle chronic disease problems. A stroke patient admitted there may rapidly develop fearsome bedsores or limb contractures because the doctors and nurses have little experience with the needs of such patients. Chronic hospitals, on the other hand, are all too often third-rate custodial facilities with staffs that are badly deficient in numbers, quality, or both; where patients become pathetic vegetables waiting to die, as remote from imaginative attention as they are from the outside world. [*See Vol. 1, Chap. 25, pp. 577–596.*]

Nursing homes　Many of our nursing homes pose serious problems because of low standards of care. There has been a lot of jockeying for position by different organizations in attempts to remedy the situation, but little real progress in the establishment of adequate criteria for accreditation. Since there are over 13,000 nursing homes listed by the American Nursing Home Association and many more unlisted, and since it has been estimated that over 1,000,000 citizens have need of their services, the health of vast numbers of chronically ill is at stake.

In 1962, tentative standards for nursing home accreditation were approved by a Joint Commission sponsored by the American Hospital Association, the American Medical Association, the American College of Surgeons, and the American College of Physicians. The AMA subse-

[6] Alfred Worcester, *The Care of the Aging, the Dying, and the Dead* (Springfield, Ill.: Charles C Thomas, Publisher, 1961), 10–11.

quently vetoed the plans, however, and joined the American Nursing Home Association to set up a separate accreditation service. Recriminations filled the air. The AMA was accused of selfish motives, the AHA of dictatorial rigidity. The tragic splintering meant inevitable fragmentation, increased cost, and decreased quality of patient care, because of the elimination of the AHA from meaningful interaction with the doctors and the nursing homes. What the impact of Medicare will be on the nursing homes is not as yet clear, although some experts lugubriously predict that as many as half of our nursing homes may fail to meet reasonable standards.

Whatever the standards, and whichever the appropriate accrediting agency, the standards will still need to be implemented. This will require many people—for example, doctors with talent, experience, imagination, dedication, and energy to coordinate the acute, chronic, rehabilitative, and home medical services appropriate to the patient's wants. The community must find and hire these physician-administrators, and the latter must be able to achieve working relationships between agencies, groups, and individuals that may appear superficially incompatible. They must be of a caliber, in background and performance, to command the respect of both the profession and the lay community. In addition, however, many other persons will be needed —specially trained nurses, administrators, social workers, architects, industrial engineers—indeed any group potentially capable of contributing to the team job so urgently required. [*Cf. Morris and Schwartz, Chaps. 2 and 4 in this volume.*]

Hazards of private homes   It is not only hospitals and nursing homes that are poorly designed to care adequately for the aged. Our homes are a serious threat to the older person. [*Cf. Madge, Chap. 8 in this volume.*] Most fatal accidents in the home involve people over 65 years of age. Burns and falls are responsible for many of these, and much of the trouble could be prevented. Our staircases are too steep, without adequate handrails, and badly lit. Chairs are often too low, and lack easily grasped arms. Floors are too polished. Beds are not the right height. Bathrooms are too slippery, lack steps and built-in handles for getting in and out of the bath. Toilets are too low and lack nearby handles to provide support. Kitchen shelves and cupboards are either too high or too low. Devices are needed to prevent pans from being knocked off the stove and for taking hot dishes out of the oven and transporting them to the table. Most of these hazards are neither mysterious nor difficult to prevent; what is needed is a public awareness of the problems and a desire to solve them.

Death

It is extraordinarily difficult to define some of the most important phenomena pertaining to the human condition, such as love, pain, or sleep. Death, at first consideration a remarkably unequivocal event, is another phenomenon that eludes precise limits.

WHAT IS DEATH?

The World Health Organization defines death as the permanent disappearance of life, without the chance of resuscitation. But at what precise moment does this occur? Because we can now breathe with machines for a person who lacks spontaneous respiratory activity and can even pump the blood for those whose hearts have stopped, and because we ordinarily equate meaningful life with a functioning central nervous system, attention has shifted to the brain as the indicator of the presence or absence of life. When brain function ceases, the electroencephalogram shows flatline recordings. But no one, however expert he may be in reading electroencephalograms, is able to say exactly when the brain is destroyed, that is, how long the EEG tracing must be a straight line before a person can be declared dead.

Traditionally, scientific dogma has maintained that the brain can survive only three to five minutes without blood flow, but recently a young California woman who had sustained a ruptured heart in an auto accident recovered rapidly and completely following emergency surgery, despite the fact that twenty-one minutes of complete circulatory arrest had elapsed. Clearly, it is impossible to be exact in these matters, and one can only speculate as to what will be considered death in A.D. 2000, when for all we know that bizarre trick so beloved of science fiction writers—exchanging one brain for another—may be technically possible, no matter how chilling the prospect.

THE DOCTOR AND THE DYING PATIENT

In years past, preparation for death was an accepted and sober act, usually taking place at home and more directly concerned with religious faith and one's family than with hospitals or physicians. Today, however, the physician has become for many the one authoritative figure who is inevitably concerned with death and dying. Unfortunately, there is no evidence that a medical education provides adequate training to deal with the various complicated problems connected with death. Physician surveys reveal that very few doctors feel that their approach to the patient with terminal disease or who is about to die owes anything to medical training. Furthermore, there is evidence of marked discrepancies between doctors concerning what such patients should be told. There is also considerable difference between the way physicians would like to be treated if they were themselves dying, and the way they treat their patients.

The majority of doctors usually do not inform patients that they are facing a terminal illness, despite the pious pronouncements by many of them to the effect that one cannot lie to patients about such matters and that most patients either know they are dying or welcome the opportunity to discuss the problem. In a Chicago survey, however, most doctors wished to be told if *they* were ill, because "I am one of those who can take it" or "I have responsibilities."[7] (Interestingly, most of the doctors said that they were neither more nor less likely to tell physician-patients than other patients.) These doctors also indicated that their policies would not be swayed by research on these questions, and some felt that no research into this area should even be done! Although various studies indicate that 70 to 90 per cent of doctors favor "not telling the patient," they also reveal that 77 to 89 per cent of patients would wish to be told if they were dying.

The meaning of death [*Vol. 1, Chap. 14.6, pp. 332–337*] will naturally affect one's attitude toward leaving this life.[8] Although it is often assumed that the fear of death is almost universal, it seems not unreasonable to wonder whether or not such a fear, where it does exist, actually results from our society's attitude toward death. Since we are impressed from youth onward that life is a beginning and death an end, it is not surprising that many view death as a horror and a void. Paradoxically, it often appears that the prospect of death may be least grim for those who believe firmly in an afterlife, and for atheists—while those with a lukewarm, wishy-washy attitude toward religion may have the most difficult time.

Some individuals, those who assess life in terms of accomplishments and fulfillment, may find the prospect of death stressful because they have not been successful in their own eyes or in the eyes of their survivors or of God. Almost everyone will want a dignified death in which the significance of the individual is not lost, much as Willy Loman's wife in *Death of a Salesman* insisted that Willy was dying psychologically, bit by bit, and that "attention must be paid."

[7] D. Oken, "What to Tell Cancer Patients: A Study of Medical Attitudes," *Journal of the American Medical Association*, 175 (1961), 1120–1126.

[8] [For recent discussion of attitudes toward death see John W. Riley, Jr., "Death and Bereavement," in David L. Sills (ed.), *International Encyclopedia of the Social Sciences* (New York: Free Press, 1968), IV, 19–26; and John W. Riley, Jr., "Old Age in American Society: Notes on Health, Retirement, and the Anticipation of Death," *The Journal of the American Society of Chartered Life Underwriters*, 22 (1968), 30–32.—Editors' note.]

Although systematic studies of the dying have been limited, enough has been done to show that in both children and adults with fatal disease, there are problems in regard to apprehension, depression, and other symptomatology that need more attention than they have received up until now. Patients who are dying are usually willing to discuss freely their awareness of dying, often without great emotional disturbance. Those who are suffering physically are more likely to be disturbed than those who are not, thus emphasizing the importance of paying attention to the control of somatic symptoms. During the weeks to months or years prior to death, there may be a good deal of pain or anxiety or other complaints amenable to appropriate therapy, including the use of drugs. The act of dying is itself rarely distressful, because many people lose consciousness for the last hours or days before death.

In Doctor Edward Hammond Clarke's *Visions*, posthumously edited by Oliver Wendell Holmes, the account is given of the death of one of his patients who had arranged to signal by finger movements after he had become otherwise unable to answer.[9] To the very last, after he appeared to have lost consciousness, this patient signaled "No," in answer to Doctor Clarke's questions if he were suffering. (While this story should reassure both patient and doctor, it must also remind the physician to guard his comments at the bedside of a "comatose" patient. Some fervent hatreds have been inspired by careless, thoughtless remarks overheard by a patient who was all too conscious.)

In guiding the patient through his terminal illness, there are a number of important factors that must be kept in mind.[10] [*Cf. Schwartz, Chap. 4 in this volume.*] The doctor must see to it that everything that might reasonably be done to effect a cure and to make the patient comfortable has been done. If other medical or professional talents might be helpful they should be consulted, even if only to reassure the patient during his lifetime and the family after death that all that could have been done was in fact done. At the same time, needless visits to a long list of other doctors or clinics should be discouraged, since the only result is likely to be a series of bills that will impoverish the survivors.

The dying patient must be treated no less individualistically than

---

[9] Quoted in Worcester, *op. cit.*, 43.

[10] See, for example, Hamilton Southworth, "Management of the Terminally Ill Patient," in Hamilton Southworth and Frederick Hofmann (eds.), *Columbia-Presbyterian Therapeutic Talks* (New York: The Macmillan Company, 1964), Vol. 2, Chap. XIII.

the living. A patient with no close relatives who is at the end of his financial resources and is spiritually prepared to die may be more concerned with the quality of the days remaining than with their number. Another patient, with grievous financial responsibilities, may prefer to keep working as long as possible, regardless of the physical suffering involved. A third person may wish only to be kept free of pain, desiring a death that is dignified and not prolonged.

The doctor must honestly communicate to the patient that his estimates are educated guesses based on probabilities, not certainties. How detailed the explanation must be depends on the patient's personality. Some patients wish only the simplest of statements, with a minimum of information, others as full a story as possible. Many patients, having been told the news, will prefer to let the matter drop for all time. Others will prefer to discuss the problem at every opportunity. With all his patients, the doctor must chart a course that avoids false optimism on the one hand and a gloomy pity on the other.

The tendency for the physician to know less than formerly about the patient's family interferes with his capacity to guide the relatives through the difficult last days. Only a careful appraisal of the total family complex, for example, will allow a wise decision as to whether the last weeks or days are better spent at home or in the hospital.

The moment of death is traumatic for all concerned, including the doctor. The family is distraught, emotionally drained, and often physically exhausted. The doctor is also tired and depressed at this point, as well as frustrated by his failure to reverse the pathologic process. Instead of the omnipotent, omniscient authority figure, he is suddenly just another human, powerless in the face of death. His biological training, his storehouse of scientific facts are of little help at such a moment, whereas it counts a great deal how large and warm a soul he has, how much compassion he can share with those who need it.

The doctor will often receive help, however, from the least expected quarter—the dying man. Many individuals manage to meet the end of life in a manner that does great credit to the human species. The famous surgeon William Hunter, in his last words, said: "If I had strength enough to hold the pen I would write how easy and pleasant a thing it is to die." And Cicero relates, in his *De Senectute:*

Just as apples, when unripe, are torn from trees, but, when ripe and mellow, drop down, so it is violence that takes life from young men, ripeness from old. This ripeness is so delightful to me, that as I approach nearer to death, I seem, as it were, to be sighting land, and to be coming to port at last after a long voyage.

Euthanasia versus prolongation of life

One of the most difficult problems facing the doctor is the prolonged existence of individuals suffering from terminal illness. All doctors sooner or later are charged with the care of a patient in coma, with dilated and fixed pupils, incapable of spontaneous respiration, kept "alive" by a mechanical respirator, with fluids and nutrition being pumped in day and night, but with the patient really dead physiologically and legally dead the moment the respirator is turned off. Such patients do not regain the ability to breathe spontaneously, and an autopsy almost always shows advanced degeneration of the brain. Is there any point in maintaining life in such an individual? If not, is there a difference between not starting the respirator at the very beginning and stopping it once it has started?

BASES FOR EVALUATION

Historically, the shortening of a person's life under any circumstances has for the most part been considered undesirable and illegal. Ecclesiastical opinions as far back as the sixteenth and seventeenth centuries have, however, made a distinction between "ordinary" and "extraordinary" means of preserving life. These authorities have stated that individuals are required to utilize ordinary means of avoiding death, but not extraordinary ones. The difficulty arises in the definition of these words. During the centuries in question, the amputation of a leg or the incision of an abdomen was considered extraordinary. With the coming of modern anesthesia and surgery, however, such procedures became "ordinary." Hence what was moral in the seventeenth century became immoral in the nineteenth and twentieth centuries.

Some Catholic authorities have expressed the feeling that persons are bound to use only "natural" aids. Such a position seems difficult to defend, since it would lead to a position wherein modern antibiotics, since they are artificially produced and administered, might be considered unnatural and extraordinary means for preserving life. Modern authorities, while agreeing that something like intravenous feeding is ordinary and not unnatural, nevertheless do not feel that treatment of this sort is obligatory.

The attitudes described in the last two paragraphs lead to the conclusion that the prolongation of human life per se is not an absolute good, but a relative one. They furthermore highlight one of the crucial points, namely the importance of a standard for comparison. If the ending of a life is preferable to continuation, one must ask—

preferable in what way? Can we make such decisions without coming to grips with the problem of the meaning of human life itself, and why ultimately human life must be preserved? And, by the very nature of the question, is it the sort of thing that can be handled by law? Should it not rather be a highly individualistic and flexible decision involving philosophy and religion as well as science?

Legally, there is no way for the physician to hasten death, even if the patient requests it and the family approves of it. Two recent Swedish cases illustrate the dilemma. Both were patients of the same physician. In the first instance, an 80-year-old woman died when the physician stopped intravenous therapy that had been keeping her alive for five weeks following a massive cerebral hemorrhage. The relatives had consented to stop the treatment. In the second case, a 65-year-old woman in coma, the doctor had told the relatives that the condition was hopeless and he had asked for the right to end treatment that was sustaining life. Both cases came to public attention when the son of the second patient accused the doctor of planning to kill his mother. Sweden's Central Medical Board found the physician guilty in both cases, but in court the judge ruled, in a decision that has been termed a big step toward legalizing euthanasia, that the physician had acted properly both times, and that relatives had the moral right to make decisions as to prolongation of life in such hopeless cases.

The ambivalence of society itself is manifest in certain public treatments of the problem. In the early 1950's, a New Hampshire physician injected air into one of his dying patients, but his only punishment was temporary suspension of license. In 1963 a physician was tried for murder in Liege for complicity with a mother in destroying a thalidomide baby, but was acquitted. A bill was actually once introduced (unsuccessfully) in the New York legislature which would have permitted a patient to apply for euthanasia, a certification being required from a physician, and a committee being empaneled to consider the petition of the patient.

The Reverend Joseph Fletcher has suggested a new term called "antidysthanasia."[11] He uses this word for what he calls indirect euthanasia. By direct euthanasia he would consider acts specifically to end life, such as introducing air into a patient's blood to cause a fatal embolism or administering a fatal overdose of morphine. Indirect euthanasia amounts to "mercifully hastening death or at least mercifully refusing to prolong it." Death is considered thereby to be

[11] Joseph Fletcher, "Death and Medical Initiative" (one of a series of lectures on medical ethics given at Yale University, New Haven, January, 1963).

permitted but not induced. By this definition, withholding treatment or stopping it would be allowable, whereas administering an overdose of drugs would not.

Most who are opposed to euthanasia in any form are unwilling to allow the patient to have a say in the matter. It is true that many patients are incapable of giving permission, because they are in coma or otherwise unresponsive, but what of the situation where a patient has indicated his desire? Ingemar Hedenius, a Swedish philosophy professor, has proposed that healthy people be given the right to sign up for *dödshjälp* ("death help") on their health insurance cards. He divides this "death help" into passive and active categories, "passive" death help being equated with the physician's refraining from undertaking treatment vital to maintain life or discontinuing such treatment (Fletcher's "antidysthanasia"). "Active death help" is equated with giving pain-killing drugs in such amounts as to shorten life, or giving such drugs so that death occurs immediately. Professor Hedenius has indicated that he would rather die than suffer immeasurable pain or become a helpless wreck without any prospect of a decent human existence, that he would rather die than usurp a hospital bed with his own meaningless suffering when others might be nursed back to health in that bed, and that he would rather die than have relatives wish him dead in vain and remember him as a distasteful wreck.

The journalist Helen Hill Miller has discussed the same issue as follows:

As younger persons become accustomed to the signs of terminal illness of the very old, what if they, while still in good health and sound mind, wish to instruct family, physician and the institution where they may one day be after an incapacitating stroke or when deterioration has reached a non-reversible stage, that they are not to be maintained in an existence that has lost all significance? Should a properly attested instrument not be accorded the same validity as an individual's last will, likewise prepared in advance with a view to a future contingency?[12]

ROLE OF THE DOCTOR

It seems reasonable for physicians at least to discuss these contingencies and to consider the possibility of committees made up of appropriate medical and nonmedical members (including perhaps representatives of the patient's family) to decide about euthanasia in certain instances. I do not mean to minimize the difficulties involved.

[12] Helen Hill Miller, "Over Sixty-five: Beyond the Merely Bearable," *The New Republic*, 151 (1964), 71.

The taking of life is an awesome business. But safeguards are conceivable which could eliminate dangers arising from the rapacious or guilt-laden relative or the amoral physician. One would have to devise ways of maintaining the individual's dignity as well as the dignity and peace of mind of his family and his physicians, but the task need not be an impossible one.

Those physicians who oppose euthanasia cite a number of reasons for their stand. One is the possibility that a new cure may be discovered at any moment, a notion impossible to rule out, even if it is unlikely statistically. On the other hand, there are more cogent reasons, such as the knowledge that the physician is fallible, and that his diagnosis and prognosis may be incorrect. Also, no one is keen to place himself in that difficult position where one must judge whether the quality of a given life is worth maintaining. The taking of a life is a grievous burden to bear, even when the motives are beyond reproach.

Yet, whether he likes it or not, the physician cannot avoid this judgment. He is in essence making a decision about euthanasia whenever he has to order a life-sustaining medication for a terminally ill patient. When different treatments of potentially fatal illnesses are available, such as surgery or radiotherapy or drugs for malignant cancer, the physician will have to decide whether one form of treatment is to be preferred to another. He may have to judge whether a treatment that provides less physical and mental distress but a shorter life may not be better than one that prolongs life to a greater degree but at the cost of great suffering. There is no place for the physician to hide.

It is of interest that surveys of American physicians have shown that approximately one-third of all doctors feel that euthanasia is justified in the case of a patient in great pain without hope of relief or recovery. (This figure is close to 40 per cent for Protestants and Jews, but only 7 per cent for Roman Catholic physicians.) Similar figures apply to the case of infants born with serious abnormalities and with no chance of a normal life. Indeed many physicians practice at least indirect euthanasia without admitting to it, such as making little or no effort at resuscitation of a child born with the grossest of congenital anomalies.

THE EXAMPLE OF RENAL DIALYSIS

The problems in deciding how and when the ill shall die are demonstrated in a dramatic way by an advance in the treatment of irreversible kidney failure—the so-called chronic dialysis programs. Of the thousands of individuals in the United States who die of chronic renal failure each year, only a small percentage can be sustained alive by the most enthusiastic of these programs. The dialysis procedures are not without difficulty. Patients have usually had to return one or more days a week to the hospital to have their blood cleared of its poisons, and many things may go wrong for the patient. With prolonged treatment, the dialysee may suffer infections, neurological disease, disease of the bones, arthritis, hepatitis, gastrointestinal hemorrhage, pulmonary complications, and the overloading of the system with iron. Many patients, disillusioned with the suboptimal level of life available to them with this treatment, become despondent, and some have committed suicide. But others seem to function beautifully and are restored to a productive life.

The cost of these centers is not inconsiderable. The Veterans' Administration Hospital at Denver estimated in 1965 that per diem costs for treating such a patient come to $70.15, because of the multiple chemical and microbiological procedures required, as well as the needs of the blood bank and the pathology laboratory. The government, realizing the tremendous cost involved, has allocated millions of dollars to support research on this problem and has actually set up units at a number of hospitals.

In every society, however, money is limited, and a decision has to be made about priorities in funding. In fact, millions for dialysis units probably means millions kept out of some other health effort. The Anglican moral theologian Canon G. B. Bentley has made the point in these words: "The person who has the opportunity of having his life prolonged by extraordinary means ought perhaps to weigh in the balance not merely the cost to his family, but also the cost to the society to which he belongs."[13] It is unlikely that this sort of judicious weighing can—or should—be done by a critically ill patient, but the community cannot avoid the ultimate decision.

The establishment of dialysis centers has created logistic and ethical problems for physicians. One problem relates to the very decision as to whether a hospital should undertake to provide such a service. Money is not the only consideration. Space and facilities are required, and personnel as well. Busy and talented researchers have been unwilling for the most part to devote a considerable portion of their energies to the supervision of such units, feeling that society is in the long run better off if their efforts are put toward discovering ways of preventing irreversible renal disease.

[13] G. E. W. Wolstenholme (ed.), *Ethics and Medical Progress: With Special Reference to Transplantation* (Boston: Little, Brown and Company, 1966), 124.

Serious problems exist, however, even after one has decided to undertake such a program: How should one pick the patients, since at present there are more candidates than can be handled? (Legally and ethically, a random choice by lot among those medically suitable would probably be most compatible with precedents in other situations.) Currently, some groups leave the matter to chance on a "first come, first served" basis; others use lay committees representing the community to judge whose life should be saved. On what considerations should the selection be based? Should it be the potential value of the subject to society, the burden he leaves behind when he dies, or what? What happens if the patient after a time no longer fulfills the original criteria?

MEDICINE AND THE PRESERVATION OF THE ILL

An important question for society is whether medicine by its very success in preserving the weak and the defective and the medically dependent is imposing an intolerable burden on society and on its medical services. Will one day all the world become a hospital, as has been predicted, with everyone an ambulatory patient? What will happen if the riddles of atherosclerosis and cancer are solved, and the life-span is prolonged for most people? What plans should society be making for such contingencies?

All the above considerations illustrate that the approaches taken by the medical profession and society to the problem of death are not immutable. The very act of dying has been so altered in recent centuries as to necessitate a reexamination of our system of moral and societal values. Even euthanasia, so long barred from ethical and legal discussions, is now under scrutiny by many thoughtful scientists and laymen. A review of the past suffices to prove that a rigid, dogmatic attitude toward death is historically, scientifically, and morally indefensible. It is a pity, to quote Rostand, that "Science has made us Gods before we are even worthy of being men."

Research and policy needs

The previous discussion underscores the need for socio-medical research on a host of important areas.

1. The separation of physiologic aging from pathologic derangement continues to deserve high priority. As illustrated by the discussion of diabetes mellitus, correct answers await the availability of empiric data.

2. "Spare parts surgery" will unquestionably come in for increased attention. In addition to purely medical research and experimentation, we may expect increased investigation and discussion of social, psychological, and legal aspects.

3. We need to find means to improve the attitudes of physicians toward the aged and chronically ill, and to recruit the kinds of men and women into the health professions who will find challenges and fulfillment in these problems. The administrative arrangements for provision of optimal, continuing medical care for the chronically ill require researching and drastic change.

4. In the medical supervision of the ambulatory patient, there is a need for scrutiny of the "pigeonhole phenomenon" described above by Seegal, a phenomenon which may require regular reassessments by "second" physicians to avoid the dangers inherent in it.

5. In the field of preventive medicine, there are many questions to be asked. How can doctors convince patients to stop smoking or lose excess weight? How can people be encouraged to seek medical advice when symptoms of possibly serious portent first appear? How useful are periodic physical exams? What routine screening tests are worth the time, effort, and expense involved in their performance?

6. The medical aspects of retirement, as well as the social and psychological aspects discussed in Volume One, call for imaginative research and pilot experiments.

7. In view of the obvious inadequacies of home and hospital construction in meeting the needs of the aged, is there enough competent multidisciplinary research going on in the design and testing of better, safer, and more comfortable housing and facilities?

8. Is there enough serious thinking about the problem of euthanasia? The questions involved are of the highest order of complexity, and deserve the attention of our most competent jurists, moral philosophers, social scientists, religious leaders, and physicians.

This survey of aging and the medical profession cannot be said to cover all of the relevant problems, but perhaps enough has been said to illustrate the magnitude and diversity of the problems facing society, the nature of social science knowledge awaiting professional implementation, and the possible types of further research that might help provide solutions.

4

Aging and the field of nursing

DORIS R. SCHWARTZ

*As Professor Schwartz points out, nursing shares with the other
health professions a concern for prevention, detection, treatment,
and rehabilitation. The unique functions of nursing, however,
center upon care of patients in situations in which they lack the
ability or knowledge to care for themselves. A number of special
difficulties impede the development of adequate nursing services
to the elderly: ambiguities in the role of the nurse relative to
that of the physician or other specialists; a nursing literature on
geriatrics that tends to give more emphasis to keeping patients
"happy" than to an adequate understanding of their problems
and potentialities; and professional education that has not kept
pace with the increasing demands placed on nursing personnel
by elaboration of their roles in nursing homes, retirement communities, out-patient departments, and community health centers. In discussing these and related problems, Professor Schwartz
stresses the importance of providing continuity of patient care,
sensitizing student nurses to the realities of bureaucratic structures, preventing the "progressive depersonalization of patients,"*

improving the efficiency of home nursing care, and developing a fuller understanding of the nurse's role in relation to the dying patient.

Advisers for this chapter were Faye G. Abdellah, Division of Nursing, U.S. Public Health Service; and Esther Lucile Brown, Consultant on Psychosocial Aspects of Patient Care, San Francisco, California. It was also reviewed by Ellen Fahy, College of Nursing, State University of New York at Stony Brook; Frances Cooke Macgregor, New York University Medical Center School of Medicine; and Margery Overholser, Cornell University—New York Hospital School of Nursing.

ON THE RELEVANCE OF VOLUME ONE

In common with the chapters on the related fields of medicine and public health, this essay draws largely upon those materials in Volume One (Chapters 8 through 11) that pertain to the aging organism, and to the associated psychosocial condition of aging individuals described in various later chapters. Indeed, as is true of health professions in general, there is no major section of Volume One which does not directly or indirectly carry important implications for the field of nursing. Throughout this essay Professor Schwartz calls attention to the broadening framework of nursing interest, and points out that knowledge from social science is increasingly utilized as an aid to understanding the behavior and needs of both patients and nurses in a variety of settings—hospital, nursing home, geriatric day care center, the older person's own home, and in the community at large.

The concerns of nursing

Professional nursing, no less than other health professions, is concerned with providing care both to individuals and to populations. In any assessment of the nursing needs of the aged, all that affects the health status of the population as a whole must influence our planning, our educational curricula, and the allocation of our manpower. But we are equally concerned with the individual, with how he ages, for example, and how, as an aging or aged person, he responds to care. It has been said that, although we cannot make health care simple when it has become complex, we can and must keep in touch with the person who is in our care, not regarding him merely as a unit to be preserved.

This dual interest of the health professions in the population and in the individual can be described in five stages, although in reality the several stages often operate simultaneously in a given situation. At each stage, nursing has an important responsibility:

1. The first of these stages is a purely preventive one: the *preservation* of existing health, both physical and mental. Many of our public health nursing programs and our school and industrial nursing services have this as their primary aim.

2. The second stage is also a preventive one. It deals with that aspect of the health of a population or an individual which is under *special hazard* for any of a variety of reasons, such as genetic defect, host susceptibility, poverty, culturally derived deprivation, or lack of the facilities, the knowledge, or the motivation for adequate health care.

3. The third stage of health care is concerned with *early detection* of existing problems. Again, we are talking about both physical and mental or emotional malfunctions.

4. The fourth stage is the familiar one of manifest illness, the *acute stage*, to which nursing directs greatest effort. As medical knowledge advances and technology permits saving even a single life by clinical judgment, an increasingly large concentration of our most dedicated and best prepared nurses is found at the side of the very sick patient where heroic measures have become commonplace.[1] Understandably, then, the care of all but the acute case becomes impoverished by the quantity and quality of nursing personnel drained off from the total nursing supply. As Doctor George James reminds us, the horizontal patient nearly always gets more and better care than the vertical patient.[2]

5. The fifth stage, that of *rehabilitation,* is often conceptualized in the abstract as a discrete phase with a unique set of skills and goals. Yet in practice truly effective patient care implies the activation of rehabilitative techniques from the moment an individual is first recognized as a patient.[3]

[1] See reports of the U.S. Public Health Service and any index to the nursing literature, to recognize the sharp increase in workshops, courses, and employment opportunities in such clinical nursing specialties as care of the premature infant, care of the patient in a coronary unit, care of the patient in a recovery or constant care pavilion.

[2] In a workshop for students of nursing at the Cornell University–New York Hospital School of Nursing. See also George James, "Poverty as an Obstacle to Health Progress in Our Cities," *American Journal of Public Health*, 55 (1965), 1757–1771; and Alonzo Yerby, "The Disadvantaged and Health Care," *American Journal of Public Health*, 56 (1966), 5–9.

[3] The very meaning of the term *rehabilitation* implies that the client has been identified as a patient. When he has not been, and a similar plan is made as a purely preventive measure in stages one or two, the term is properly *habilitation*

Since a good deal of health care is necessarily overlapping, with the efforts of several of the disciplines represented in this volume equally directed toward reducing the incidence and duration of illness, the distinctive functions of nursing require description at the outset.

Perhaps the unique task of nursing may be thought of as doing for the patient, or teaching someone to do for him, or teaching him to do for himself, those health care activities (such as proper eating, breathing, ambulating, eliminating, or communicating) that he would do unassisted were he not sick, or had he the necessary knowledge, will, or ability—and doing all these things in such a way that the patient regains independence as rapidly as possible.[4]

Nursing is concerned not only with alleviating unnecessary suffering, but also with helping the patient and his family accept suffering and death when these are inevitable. Although the morale of patient and family is a concern of all involved in patient care, including social workers and chaplains, the fact that the nurse's contact with the patient is likely to be relatively frequent, even continuing, gives her a special responsibility in this area.

In the discharge of these special responsibilities, nurses perform many specific tasks: They carry out medical orders and undertake prescribed treatments of great complexity; they engage in such preventive programs as family planning, prenatal or well-baby care, and immunization against communicable diseases; and they identify referral needs of those patients having untreated social, medical, or other health-related problems. Although diagnosis and treatment often may be the responsibility of a physician or social worker, the competent nurse must make an accurate evaluation of the patient's nursing needs and, in addition, must be an able observer and case-finder in areas other than her primary field of nursing.

Thus, although a nurse most often is charged with assisting the physician and carrying out his orders, she retains independent responsibility in the assessment of nursing needs and in planning to meet them. Yet considerable ambiguity exists over how these needs are to be defined and which directions planning should take. Ida Pelletier, writing on the patient's predicament and nursing function, suggests that much of today's frustration and confusion over nursing roles and objectives is an outgrowth of nursing's attempt to simulate the physician's work while ignoring the opportunity to develop its own

[4] Virginia Henderson, *The Nature of Nursing* (New York: The Macmillan Company, 1966).

distinctive responsibilities. A distinctive role for the nurse, she suggests, "might more easily have been developed if the Nightingale pledge read 'I will endeavor to help the *patient* while the physician does his work.' "[5] George Reader, as a physician, is persuaded that raising the nurse, as well as the social worker, to full partnership in directing patient management can produce a significant alteration in medical care and teaching; as he puts it, "the constant seeking of the nurse to find and fulfill patients' needs and the nondirective approach of the social worker have come as a revelation to the physician."[6]

NURSING ROLES

Difficulties persist in attempts to define and elaborate the professional status of the nurse. One of these, considered in some detail by Hildegard Peplau, is that nursing roles may be defined from a number of different frames of reference and by a variety of agencies within the society:

Many roles are demanded of nurses. Patients cast nurses into roles that seem necessary for meeting a problem as they view it. Nurses define roles in which they wish to function or that are thought to be desirable performances for a nurse. Society has views on how nurses should function and these conceptions vary in communities and economic groupings. . . .

What roles should a nurse fulfill? . . . Who should decide what roles a nurse can function in effectively? . . . What practical difference does it make who decides? . . . Understanding of the factors in these vital questions will provide a basis for designing nursing that is valuable to individuals and to society.[7]

A second obstacle, thoughtfully explored by Ellen Fahy, points to structural constraints on nursing practice:

. . . because of the nature of the hierarchical structure of most general hospitals, combined with the presence of medical practitioners whose actions are largely uncontrolled by the social organization of the bureaucracy, professional nurses are inhibited in the discharge of professional responsibilities for which they are prepared.[8]

[5] Ida Pelletier, "The Patient's Predicament and Nursing Function," *Psychiatric Opinion*, 4 (1967), 25–30.

[6] George C. Reader, "Organization and Development of a Comprehensive Care Program," *American Journal of Public Health*, 44 (1954), 760–765.

[7] Hildegard Peplau, *Interpersonal Relations in Nursing: A Conceptual Framework for Psychodynamic Nursing* (New York: G. P. Putnam's Sons, 1952), 43–44.

[8] Ellen Fahy, "Nursing Education as Preparation for Change," in Elizabeth Maloney (ed.), *Interpersonal Relations* (Dubuque: William C. Brown & Co., 1966), 42.

Despite the lack of clarity in current definitions of both the boundaries of the nursing profession and the specialities within it, a striking proliferation of nursing roles in recent years suggests the emergent shape of the profession and some of the opportunities for future development. In a recent summary of such trends, Doctor Esther Lucile Brown writes:[9]

Physical rehabilitation services, mental health programs, Medicare and Medicaid, as well as public health, all emphasize the importance of continuity of patient care. To a surprising degree nurses with public health experience have begun to be used to establish bridges between the hospital and posthospital care, whether in nursing homes, foster homes, or home care programs. In Portland, Oregon, to note one instance, the Visiting Nurse Association has made the full-time services of a nurse available to each of four large hospitals, and half-time services to three smaller hospitals, as an informal demonstration of the helpfulness to patients and their families, physicians, hospitals and health agencies of more systematic consideration of patients' social and health needs and the coordination of community facilities to meet those needs.

Some years prior to the Portland experiment, a study conducted by the Associated Hospital Service of New York examined the feasibility of providing nursing service at home following early hospital discharge. The report of this study spelled out with exceptional clarity the potential of an interdisciplinary approach to assessment, and the role of the nurse in selection of those patients who could be well served by nursing aftercare. This report led to promotion and implementation of the widely successful "Blue Cross Home Care Program."[10] Doctor Brown's account of recent trends takes account also of several additional aspects:

A second development that warrants attention is the role of the nurse in nursing homes and retirement communities. Many nurses are administrators of nursing homes, where it is progressively required by law that there be a nurse director of the nursing service. As such, she generally exercises large independent judgment about when to call for medical assistance. With the current effort to raise the standards of nursing homes and convert them into active treatment facilities where nursing, the activity therapies, and social work are the dominant treatment modalities, nursing has an unparalleled opportunity to demonstrate its use-

[9] In a private communication, November, 1967. Slightly edited by the author. See also Esther Lucile Brown, *Newer Dimensions of Patient Care* (3 vols.; New York: Russell Sage Foundation, 1961, 1962, and 1964).

[10] Interim and Final Reports, *Visiting Nurse Study* (New York: Associated Hospital Service of New York, 1954–1958).

fulness in geriatric nursing. [See also Morris, Chap. 2 in this volume.] The Loeb Center for Nursing and Rehabilitation of Montefiore Hospital in New York is now engaged in such a demonstration under the administration of Lydia Hall, R.N.[11] The rapid growth of retirement communities for older persons also affords nursing an opportunity, which it has scarcely begun to realize, for assisting with planning that is designed to minimize accidents and health hazards and to provide requisite facilities for personal care (nursing care units) and for infirmary service. [See also Morris and Madge, Chaps. 2 and 8 in this volume.]

A third probable trend is the increasing use of nurses in hospital outpatient departments and in health clinics to hold "nursing conferences" for geriatric patients whose chronic condition has supposedly been stabilized but who need general encouragement and psychological support in the activities of daily living, as well as guidance in the use of prescribed medications or other treatment. Because of the acute shortage of practicing physicians interested in chronic conditions, it is my assumption that the greater use of the nurse in the continued treatment of geriatric patients may become as common as her use in the continued care of well babies and small children.

Finally, the opening of neighborhood or community family health centers in poverty areas of the large cities, where no such facilities have previously existed, requires the presence of public health and clinical nurses not only to carry out customary nursing functions but to train and supervise a corps of health aides. These aides serve both as nursing assistants and as channels of communication between members of minority or other unserved groups and the professionals responsible for delivering effective health care.[12]

TRENDS IN NURSING EDUCATION

This expansion of nursing services and specialities has brought into question the traditional organization of nursing schools that serves the needs of a particular health facility or hospital, rather than educates nurses flexible enough to meet diverse and changing community needs. Only in the last decades has there been a shift toward nursing care based on knowledge gathered through systematic research and a

---

[11] See Lydia Hall, "A Center for Nursing," *Nursing Outlook*, 11 (1963), 56; Lydia Hall and Alfano Genrose," Myocardial Infarction—Incapacitation or Rehabilitation?" *American Journal of Nursing*, 64 (1964), 20; and J. Bernardin, "Loeb Center as the Staff Nurse Sees It," *American Journal of Nursing*, 64 (1964), 85.

[12] A new literature is growing on the use of the community health aide. Foremost among the reports are those of Ellen Mansell and Bernice Loughlin, "The Navajo Health Visitor," *Practical Nursing*, 8 (1958), 13–15; and, more recently, that of Ione Carey, "Training and Use of Home Health Aides," *American Journal of Nursing*, 66 (1966), 1771.

rational search for insights from the accumulated data of the social sciences.[13]

Eleanor Lambertsen, in stressing education as an instrument of social change, comments on the need for such a shift:

The development of the system of education for nursing and the organization of the profession along its present lines took place under conditions vastly different from those of today. Changing economic, health and social conditions have built up new and diverse areas of work for the nurse without parallel discard of responsibility for other areas. Advances in medical science and technology have created an obsolescence of some nursing skills faster than ways of retraining practicing nurses have been devised or basic nursing curricula adjusted. The lag between the completion of research and the utilization of findings in the general practice of nursing should be appreciably reduced. This can be done by focusing today's graduate study for nurses preparing for teaching, supervision and administrative positions upon recent and current research which tomorrow they will be in a position to implement in the nursing services they administer or in the teaching of other nurses.[14]

Ellen Fahy echoes Doctor Lambertsen in her insistence that "professional nursing education should be a combination of preparation for the realities of the present and the unknowns of the future" but warns that such education "should assist students in confronting the realities of the bureaucratic structure of health agencies and should prepare them to capitalize on the hopes inherent in the situation."[15]

THE DEMAND FOR PERSONNEL

Expansion of the nursing profession has paralleled an enormously increased demand for nursing services. Although never in the history of this nation have so many registered nurses been actively at work as at present (over 621,000 were employed at the time of the 1962 census of nurses), population growth and upgraded definitions of adequate health care have combined to maintain the well-known and widely-discussed "chronic shortage of nurses." Thus any discussion of nursing programs for the aged must deal with questions of recruit-

[13] See Esther Lucile Brown, *A Thousand Think Together: Report of Three Regional Conferences* (New York: The National Nursing Council, 1948); and Brown, *Nursing for the Future* (New York: Russell Sage Foundation, 1948). See also Frances Cooke Macgregor, *Social Science in Nursing* (New York: Russell Sage Foundation, 1960).

[14] Eleanor C. Lambertsen, *Education for Nursing Leadership* (Philadelphia: J. B. Lippincott Company, 1958), 50.

[15] Fahy, *op. cit.*, 43.

ment and allocation of scarce human resources within the context of the total demand for nursing services.

One potential source for recruitment to nursing may exist in the very geriatric population that nursing aims to serve. For example, a cooperative grant from the Public Health Service and the American Nurses' Foundation has developed a plan to stimulate the states to establish pilot programs for the retraining of older, inactive nurses, in order to encourage the able and willing to return to nursing. *Facts About Nursing*, the statistical summary published annually by the American Nurses' Association, reported that, of the nearly 273,000 professional nurses who were registered but not employed in 1962, more than 130,000 were 60 or over, and another 85,000 were in the 50 to 59 age group. What proportion of these nurses—already sufficiently motivated to keep their registrations current—might be retrained and usefully returned to full- or part-time employment remains to be seen. Such a retraining program, if successful, might act as a stimulus to development of training programs in nursing for older women (and men) with no prior education or experience in nursing.[16]

PROFESSIONAL ASSOCIATIONS

A review of recent developments in health-related professional organizations reflects a growing importance attached to chronicity and aging, notably by the United States Public Health Service, the National League for Nursing, the American Public Health Association, and the American Nurses' Association. A promising step in insuring better nursing care to the aged at home was taken recently when the American Public Health Association and the National League for Nursing agreed to co-sponsor an accreditation program for public health nursing services which offer nursing to people outside of hospitals and nursing homes. Since the advent of Medicaid, certification of home health agencies in states electing to offer this program has also raised the minimum standard for home nursing care.

Current changes in the structure and function of the American Nurses' Association (ANA) are intended to facilitate performance in the area of clinical practice, and nursing care of the geriatric patient has received greater emphasis since this revision took place. A full-time program coordinator has been employed. Clinical sessions on the preventive, curative, and rehabilitative nursing care of older persons

---

[16] If the feminine pronoun is used for nurse in this essay, it is not because the profession lacks first-rate men practitioners, but because the ratio of women to men in professional nursing was, at the last count, 106 to 1. More male nurses are needed in every area of nursing, and especially in the care of older patients.

have been held at two recent regional conferences, and the papers are slated for publication in book form. A conference on the nursing care of the geriatric patient, sponsored jointly by the American Nurses' Association and the British Royal College of Nursing, was held in 1968. The American Nurses' Foundation, a nonprofit research organization associated with the ANA has selected as its primary research topic the problems and care of the long-term chronically ill. An updated list of articles on the nursing of geriatric patients will be issued by the ANA–NLN publications service.

The nursing literature on geriatrics

Nursing professes its philosophy and content not only through its practice and through the curricula of its basic, graduate, and continuing education programs, but also through the problems selected for study and research. A brief review of the relevant nursing literature over the past dozen years reveals the nature of the profession's concern with aging and suggests needs that are not currently being met and steps that might be taken to maximize nursing's contribution to care of the aged.[17]

One's first impression from such a review could well be that the nursing care of older people must be very extensive indeed, since the list contains nearly seven hundred articles bearing titles which indicate a concern with older patients. An impressionistic sample of these titles illustrates the range:

"Boredom in the Aged"

"Foot Care for the Elderly Patient"

"Fear of Aging"

"The Hospital Needs of the Aged"

[17] The nursing literature is indexed in a retrospective, classified, and annotated bibliographical *Nursing Studies Index* (Philadelphia: J. B. Lippincott Company, Vol. I, 1900–1929, in press; Vol. II, 1930–1949, in press; Vol. III, 1950–1956, published in 1967; Vol. IV, 1957–1959, published in 1963). Also available from 1960 onward is *The Cumulative Index to the Nursing Literature* (Glendale, Calif.: Seventh Day Adventist Hospital Association); and a new *International Nursing Index*, the first volume of which is now on the library shelves. See also cumulative indexes to the *American Journal of Nursing*, to *Nursing Outlook*, and to *Nursing Research*. A variety of other nursing journals are also indexed annually, while such library tools as the *Index Medicus* and *Medlars* pick up some, but not all, of the writing on nursing. The U.S. Public Health Service has prepared a 131-page bibliography on geriatric nursing, *Nursing Care of the Aged—An Annotated Bibliography for Nurses*, PHS Pub. No. 1603 (Washington, D.C.: Government Printing Office, 1967).

"Suggestions for Care of Elderly Eye Surgery Patients Who Experience Reduced Sensory Input"

"Medication Errors Made by Aged Patients"

"Self-Care Achievement of Institutionalized Senile Patients"

"The Impact of Federal Legislation (Title XIX) on Home Health Services"

"Better Things for Senior Citizens"

"Boarding Out Older People"

"Campus Living for the Aged"

"Diversion for Elderly Patients"

"When You Care for the Very Old"

"Elderly Citizens as Novice Nurses"

"Foster Grandparents for Deprived Children"

"The Role of the Geriatric Nurse in Health Maintenance"

"The Effect of Nursing Intervention on Senility"

"Geriatric Nursing in the Basic Curriculum"

"Epidemiological Studies of Home Safety for the Elderly"

"The Five Major Disabilities of Old Age"

"Alienation in the Aged: Implications for Psychiatric Geriatric Nursing"

Clearly, approaches to nursing problems of the elderly are manifold. Incontinence in the aged, for example, is tackled from neurological, psychological, psychiatric, and epidemiologic angles, as are various aspects of feeding problems, skin care, and infection control. Numerous articles outline "nursing responsibilities to the aged." Authors emphasize the importance of maintaining patients' self-respect and of nurses' understanding what it means to be old. Learning and obstacles to learning are described. Geriatric rehabilitation, especially the value of "teamwork," is espoused on various levels of potential for return to independent function. A dozen or more approaches are documented that have helped the mentally confused older person. Geriatric day hospitals, and the effects of personalized nursing care on psychotic geriatric patients, are reported in great detail. There are accounts of workshops for the elderly and workshops for registered and practical nurses in the care and rehabilitation of the elderly. There is even a report of a workshop sponsored, planned, and in part conducted by the elderly for the benefit of nurses and licensed physiotherapists on "the art of movement," or the maintenance and improvement of motion and balance in the elderly.

Continuity of nursing care, from the hospital to the home, is a major theme in this literature. The registered nurse may be aided in caring for the posthospital elderly patient by licensed practical nurses and by a whole new category of nonprofessional workers known as "home health aides," through organized home care programs, visiting nurse services, and governmental public health nursing agencies. Nursing care of the older person at home has an enormous literature of its own, indicating concern for emotional problems, cultural differences, accident prevention, errors in self-medication, eating and sleeping problems, difficulties in "ambulating, elevating and travel," the safeguarding of patients with sensory blackout, the psychological needs of aged patients, and "why old people fall."

The literature also contains guidelines on such topics as:

"Choosing a Nursing Home"

"Preparing a Patient for Transfer to a Nursing Home"

"Helping the Old Person Adjust to a Nursing Home"

"Nursing the Old Person Creatively in a Nursing Home"

"Establishing a Therapeutic Community of Patient, Staff and Family Within the Nursing Home"

"Preparing the Older Person to Leave the Nursing Home with Eager Anticipation for the Return to His Own, or a Foster, Home."

Finally, a host of material on Medicare has reached the nursing journals in recent years, including guides to the services given, criteria for eligibility, and information relevant to counseling older persons to take advantage of the benefits of current health legislation. Prior to 1966, articles gave ample evidence of economic obstacles to adequate health care of the older person, documenting graphically the need for new legislation.

A dominant note that pervades this flood of writing for nurses is one of zealous cheer: "The elderly can be happy"; "the task can be done better than it is being done"; "we did it successfully here." One reads of the profession's endless enthusiasm, useful recipes garnered from long clinical experience, a deep concern, and the will to improve. Only occasionally does the nursing literature view services to the aged with skepticism, as in such titles as, "For the Geriatric Patient, Home Away From Home Is a Myth" or "Rehabilitation: Fact or Figure of Speech?"

In quality, the geriatric nursing literature ranges from reports of controlled experiments, to loosely designed descriptive studies based on empirical clinical practice, to "how to do it" advice volunteered by almost anyone. On the whole, too much of the literature suffers because it is based on limited experience with a few patients from selected population groups or under atypical conditions, and then generalized—by writer, editor, or reader—to appear as if these limited insights could be applied widely through stepped-up effort alone. Moreover, when application of such loose generalization is tried and found wanting, the nurse practitioner all too often excuses herself from further effort by merely asserting, "It didn't work with my patients, they are different" without asking the necessary further question as to why it failed to work and how these particular patients are different.

INFLUENCE OF SOCIAL SCIENCE

Despite uneven quality, the nursing literature of recent years shows a promising trend in increasing reliance upon both the methods and the content of the social sciences. The introduction to Frances Macgregor's *Social Science in Nursing* documents the growing awareness by health practitioners and educators of the role which social science and social scientists might play in solving problems of health and illness.[18] Thus the student of nursing who traditionally sought insights exclusively from the natural sciences, and who later expanded her awareness to psychiatric research, today accepts help from a wider range of disciplines including sociology, psychology, and anthropology. Examples of this trend are found in numerous titles and publishers' descriptions of books advertised in professional nursing journals, such as: *Patient Studies in Medical Surgical Nursing* ("the author skillfully interweaves . . . the hospital milieu, . . . interpersonal relationships, psychosocial aspects, and the family."); *Social Interaction and Patient Care* ("serves as a link between the social sciences and clinical nursing practice"); *People in Hospitals* ("discusses some of the human problems and points of tension in hospitals; . . . poses a wide array of problems offering the social scientists a well-documented spectrum of problems worth further investigation").

Indeed, the growing impact of the social sciences upon nursing can be seen in the footnotes and bibliography of nursing articles and texts, as well as in the content of the material presented. Taking as example a single issue of the *American Journal of Nursing*, that of January, 1967, one finds a number of articles relevant to geriatric nursing, each with a bibliography including one or more social science

[18] Macgregor, *Social Science in Nursing*.

readings. One such bibliography contains a number of citations relating to ways in which an individual's mode of living, his habits, diet, and his ethnic, social, and religious inheritance determine the way he behaves as a patient.[19] Another article, reporting the effect of stress upon the nurse's thinking and judgment, cites references almost evenly divided between those related to clinical experience and those related to the social sciences.[20] Similarly, an account by a student of nursing on the care she gave to an older person (a man of Mexican origin with a residual hemiplegia and aphasia) utilizes both traditional and social scientific references in the search for clues to understanding of the patient's needs.[21] The author quotes from a classic reference on rehabilitation medicine, an equally classic essay on rehabilitation nursing, and Clarke's *Health in the Mexican-American Culture*.[22] (Another student might have chosen to make use of Lyle Saunders' *Cultural Difference and Medical Care*, which is also widely used today in schools of nursing.[23]) In describing the problem of communicating with this Mexican-American patient who was unable to speak, the student, Carol Jennings, writes:

> Since I knew nothing of Mr. F's past, I looked to his culture for a clue . . . [the Mexican-American views] illness as a state of physical and emotional discomfort, costly [in] time and money . . . and possibly debilitating or even fatal in consequences. . . . He believes that people will lose respect for him because he is no longer a whole man. . . . Life, as the Mexican-American sees it, is full of pains and trauma. Hunger, grief, cold, fear, pain . . . are all a part of life and should be borne with dignity and courage. . . . A man who admits to illness is not *macho* (tough and rugged). Mr. F was very *macho* . . .

Finally, in this same issue, a collaborative paper by a nurse and a psychologist—written with a light touch but quite serious in its aims —describes the transformation wrought on a ward of thirty-four confused and deteriorated old men by the introduction as innovations of "beer and t.l.c." (tender, loving care).[24] This study, with tables indi-

[19] Frances C. Macgregor, "Uncooperative Patients: Some Cultural Implications," *American Journal of Nursing*, 67 (1967), 88–91.

[20] Virginia Cleland, "Effects of Stress on Thinking," *American Journal of Nursing*, 67 (1967), 108–111.

[21] Carol Jennings, "The Stroke Patient—His Rehabilitation," *American Journal of Nursing*, 67 (1967), 118 ff.

[22] Margaret Clarke, *Health in the Mexican-American Culture* (Berkeley: University of California Press, 1959).

[23] Lyle Saunders, *Cultural Difference and Medical Care* (New York: Russell Sage Foundation, 1948).

[24] Anne Volpe and Robert Kastenbaum, "Beer and T.L.C.," *American Journal of Nursing*, 67 (1967), 100–103.

cating the decline in the need for tranquilizers when these were replaced by conviviality and an open atmosphere favoring patients' responses "as adults," confirms the value of systematic investigation.

These particular articles have been described in some detail, not because they differ from the usual content of today's nursing journals but because they illustrate, within the covers of a single issue, the broadened perspectives of nursing—perspectives not confined merely to the sophisticated leadership but extending to all of the approximately two hundred thousand subscribers of the *American Journal of Nursing.*

Routinization and depersonalization of patient care

As must be apparent from even the cursory description of the literature included in this essay, one crucial responsibility of nursing is that of maintaining the self-respect and individuality of old people under institutional care. As individuals age, the likelihood increases that they will become patients in a hospital for chronic illness, a geriatric hospital, or a nursing home. [*See Vol. 1, Chap. 6.B.7, pp. 141–142.*] Even in short-stay hospitals, older persons are hospitalized more often, and remain longer, on the average, than younger persons. [*See Vol. 1, Chap. 9.2.i, pp. 217–218.*] Such people are not only ill—perhaps dying—but tend also to be largely isolated from family, friends, and familiar surroundings.

Nevertheless, as social scientist Frances Macgregor indicates, a paramount problem is the danger of progressive depersonalization of patients, and concomitantly of nurses as well.[25] According to Dagmar Brodt:

Nurses must realize that individualized patient care runs counter to the habits of mankind and counter to the way the human being operates. Human beings, when bombarded with multiple complex stimuli, quickly convert usual tasks to a routine so that they can focus more attention on the new and unfamiliar. This routine transference phenomenon militates against the nurse's concentrating on the individualization of patient care. In the extreme, this phenomenon is responsible for the routinization which conceives of the individual patient as "number 203A in the East Wing." The nurse who is aware of the dangers of routinizing human beings will try to guard against it, but circumstances being what they are in

[25] Frances C. Macgregor, "Nursing in Transition: Challenge for the Future" (Paper read at the Fifth Expert Committee on Nursing, World Health Organization, Geneva, 1966; later published, with revisions, in the *Journal of the American Medical Association,* 198 [1966], 1196–1197).

a busy hospital, she may not always be able to resist the efficiency of routines.[26]

Perhaps the difficulty of providing individualized patient care is nowhere more apparent than in chronic illness hospitals and nursing homes, where routinization easily becomes a means of coping with a patient population characterized by immobilization, disengagement, hopelessness, and helplessness. A perceptive study by Rose Coser, noting the lack of prestige associated with a hospital that "only" cares for patients who will not get better, shows that one consequence of the abandonment of the "culturally approved goal of curing the sick" is a tendency for the nursing staff to engage in ritualistic or retreatist behavior; while ". . . the organization evolves a social structure that contributes to converting ritualistic and retreatist behavior into a socially established pattern."[27] This study, based on observations in a 650-bed hospital, distinguishes between custodial or terminal units where the nursing focus is on housekeeping rather than on patient-centered activity, and rehabilitation units where, because the goal is restoration of patients to the community, nursing concern focuses on the human implications of care.

One must recognize the enormous pressures on hospital staffs today as nursing tasks expand, in order to understand how easy it is to succumb to the efficiency of impersonal routine. A recent check of the disposable syringes requisitioned at a single general hospital revealed that 5,320 syringes for injecting medications into patients were used in a single week! Furthermore, the increase in medications that must be understood and administered by the nurse, the high mobility of the patient population from bed to other areas of the hospital, and the necessary utilization of machines, gadgets, and monitoring devices all encourage the nurse to exploit the efficiency of routines. Role diffusion, confusion, lack of preparation for uncertainty and change, and the attenuation of the nurse's time and energy combine to inhibit the exercise of the individualized nursing care that social scientists, speaking theoretically, have recommended.

Care of the elderly at home and in the community

Despite the importance of the nurse at the bedside of the hospital patient, the majority of the chronically ill live in the community rather than in an institution. Assessing the nursing needs of this segment

[26] Dagmar Brodt, "Obstacles to Individualized Patient Care," *Nursing Outlook*, 14 (1966), 35–37.
[27] Rose L. Coser, "Alienation and the Social Structure," in Eliot Freidson (ed.), *The Hospital in Modern Society* (New York: Free Press, 1963).

of the older population and administering to them constitute a great challenge to the resources and inventiveness of public health nurses. [*Cf. Vol. 1, Chap. 9.2.g, pp. 214–215, See also Chap. 14.1, pp. 317–323 on use of health services and old peoples' views of health.*]

The needs of older people reflect the needs of human beings everywhere——to have someone to love, somewhere to live, something to do, and to avoid, when possible, discomfort and suffering. These needs can be frustrated by cultural rejection, self-rejection, and isolation——by feeling "used up," as the means of asserting self diminish. Thus the nurse's responsibility is to help the older patient hold onto the future, however circumscribed. The old man who has no reserves is apathetic; he "dies" before his death. Every nurse has seen this repeatedly. The resourceful patient, however, meets death without being "used up" first. The sensitive and observant nurse knows that every human being fights for courage on occasion, and she will support her patient in what must often be an unequal struggle. With most old people, there is a daily need for courage because they are fearful of so many impending catastrophes. We see a great deal of courage in the aged who still are fighting.

Raymond Fosdick, describing the difficult transition that the elderly survivors of his generation are called upon to make, says:

> This generation is, in a sense, a bridge or a corridor between a past that is long outmoded: pre-telephone, pre-airplane, pre-automobile, pre-radio and T.V., and a future of continual revolutionary change. They have lived through an almost unique period of transformation, unique because it represented the first *sudden* acceleration of pace. . . . Their early roots go back into the Victorian period, but they were projected without preparation or time for adjustment into the kaleidoscopic alterations of the 20th Century.[28]

Those survivors of this generation who are chronically ill typically display the precursors of dependency; and the nurse must deal with symptoms that Otto Von Mering describes as the simple wearing out of physical equipment, the desocializing process which follows withdrawal, and those emotional problems which, though well-compensated for throughout the productive years, now frighten both the patient and his family under the pressure of illness, relative immobility, and unwanted leisure.[29] Two careful studies of a case load of

[28] Raymond B. Fosdick, *Chronicle of a Generation* (New York: Harper & Row, Publishers, 1958), 287.
[29] Otto Von Mering, from a paper presented at a nursing workshop on the needs of elderly patients, University of Pittsburgh, School of Nursing, 1959.

older patients under care of the Visiting Nurse Service of New York—one by Jane Holliday, a nurse, the other by the psychiatrist Alvin Goldfarb—note as some of the adjuncts of aging and chronicity a degree of loss of self-confidence, loss of self-reliance, loss of place within the family and society, and distortion of self-image.[30] [*See Vol. 1, Chap. 13, pp. 289–313, however, for various positive aspects of the older person's self-conception.*]

Yet Harold Wolff's description of the "fighting machine" still holds, and life cannot be turned off simply because illness or a 65th birthday has occurred.[31] Indeed there is much evidence that, while aging or cardiovascular changes may disturb the older person's homeostatic mechanisms, he is still able to learn new concepts and new skills. He does not, however, acquire these with speed. [*See Vol. 1, Chap. 10, pp. 221–239; Chap. 11, pp. 241–272.*] When pressed to move faster, the older person may become confused and the attempt end in failure. Thus, it is essential that rehabilitative care be properly paced to hold the interest of patients whose attention span is shortened and who may be upset by multiple nursing activities closely spaced. The nursing profession has a major responsibility for the restorative care of individuals with such conditions of chronicity, a responsibility requiring immense further effort. We may be faced with the tough assignment of breaking all teaching-learning down into small components, literally "programing it," to build new learning upon old knowledge in small, cumulative steps. We might, for example, begin with a program to prevent confusion in orientating an older patient to new surroundings, or a program to give an older patient instructions, even in a busy clinic, for beginning the use of a new medicine.

CARE OF THE CHRONICALLY ILL IN COMMUNITY SETTINGS BEYOND THE HOSPITAL

Perhaps no area of the care of older persons has a richer nursing literature than the care of the elderly homebound. Visiting Nurse Associations have pioneered instructive services to the sick of all ages, and today more than half the visits of nearly every large associa-

---

[30] Jane Holliday, *Public Health Nursing for the Sick at Home: A Descriptive Study* (New York: Visiting Nurse Service of New York, 1965); Alvin I. Goldfarb, *Study of Psychological Needs of Aged Patients at Home* (New York: Visiting Nurse Service of New York, 1965); and Goldfarb, "Responsibilities to Our Aged," *American Journal of Nursing*, 64 (1964), 78.

[31] Harold G. Wolff, "What Hope Can Do for Man," *Saturday Review*, 40 (1957), 42–45.

tion are to persons over 65.[32] Studies of older homebound patients are designed to help the visiting nurse assess with greater sensitivity the spectrum of problems that must be faced by her and by the "significant caring person," if any, within the home. [*See Vol. 1, Chap. 23.B.2.c, p. 553; Chap. 24.5.a, p. 573.*] Such a person is usually a relative, often a friend or neighbor and, increasingly in the past few years, a home health aide—one of a new category of community nursing agency staff. In addition, several recent researches have explored the consequences of public health nursing intervention for the patient. A long-range study by Ford, Katz, and Adams, for example, has demonstrated that patient performance in activities of daily living can be rated on a scale of progress (in bathing, dressing, toilet care, transferring from bed to chair, continence, and feeding).[33] If such techniques can be developed and widely used, the efficiency of home nursing care could be greatly enhanced.

Not all of the chronically ill are either completely homebound or in institutions. [*See Vol. 1, Chap. 25.1.c, pp. 580–583.*] Although the exact figures are unknown, large numbers of older people with chronic afflictions are ambulatory and able to travel to doctor or clinic for medical care. In an effort to learn more about the nursing needs of this category of old people, the writer, in association with Barbara Henley and Leonard Zeitz, conducted a study among a random sample of elderly patients with two or more diagnosed chronic illnesses who visited in a three-month period the New York Hospital–Cornell Medical Center's General Medical Clinic.[34]

The study suggested several ways in which more adequate nursing care might be provided to the elderly ambulatory patient. A more systematic approach to history-taking, for example, would bring to attention many patient needs and conditions that go unnoticed by medical personnel who do not have ambulatory patients under con-

[32] The terms *visiting nurse* and *public health nurse* have been used interchangeably in this essay although not all public health nurses visit in the home and not all visiting nurses are fully prepared in public health. See *Functions and Qualifications in the Practice for Public Health Nursing* (New York: American Nurses' Association, 1964); and Dorothy Wilson, *Combining Public Health Nursing Agencies: A Case Study in Philadelphia* (New York: National League for Nursing, 1967).

[33] Amasa Ford, Sydney Katz, and Mary Adams are the investigators of "Continued Care by Nurses and Doctors," an experiment underway at Case Western Reserve University, Cleveland. Mary Adams, Thomas Downs, and Hazel M. Deuble have reported on one aspect of the study, "Nurse Referral Outcome for Post-Hospitalized Chronically Ill Patients," *American Journal of Public Health*, 58 (1968), 101–106. A descriptive monograph on the nursing variable is in preparation.

[34] Doris Schwartz, Barbara Henley, and Leonard Zeitz, *The Elderly Ambulatory Patient: Nursing and Psychosocial Needs* (New York: The Macmillan Company, 1964).

tinuing surveillance. Clinic nurses are often too busy or lack standard guidelines for thorough assessment of the nursing needs of each patient. Moreover, a high rate of staff turnover limits the ability of any one nurse to familiarize herself with the situation of given patients.

Patients in our sample were beset by a wide variety of problems. Although labeled ambulatory, for example, some were in fact not. Most patients experienced difficulty in getting about because of ambulatory, respiratory, mental, visual, or hearing decrements. Inability to travel freely in turn affected the patients' ability to secure an adequate diet, limited leisure-time activities outside the home, and generally circumscribed their lives. A great many errors in self-medication were made, in part through misunderstanding of the purpose or importance of the medication or through inability to read directions for dosage. [*See Vol. 1, Chap. 14.1.d, pp. 320–321.*] Some patients were too sick to get prescriptions filled and lacked a helping person to attend to this for them. Another major area of difficulty was diet: Some persons for whom special diets had been prescribed were unaware of these restrictions; others were unable to adhere to special diets because of difficulties in shopping for and preparing prescribed foods; and still others, not restricted in their diet, had nutritionally inadequate eating patterns for want of interest or energy to do otherwise. [*See Vol. 1, Chap. 14.1.d, pp. 320–321.*]

With the help of vocationally trained aides, visiting nurses could do much to ameliorate the situation of elderly ambulatory patients, especially those living alone or in rooming houses, for whom help is not readily available. Instructions in the use of medication at home *after* prescriptions have been filled would prevent many medication errors. The patient should also be cautioned in the use of proprietary or home remedies contraindicated by his illness. To assure adequate diets, "meals on wheels," or neighborhood meal centers located at churches and school buildings which are well distributed throughout the community, and various new "instant" meals could be of considerable assistance. Much could be done, too, to help reduce home accident hazards for old people. [*See Lasagna and Madge, Chaps. 3 and 8 in this volume.*]

One important function of the visiting nurse is to identify and refer problems that lie within the competence of other professions and agencies. The need for counseling or for financial aid, for example, is often apparent to her. The visiting nurse must therefore acquaint herself with those resources in the community of potential benefit to her elderly patients, and should be able to initiate action in behalf of patients known to her who are about to be hospitalized, as well as to receive and to act upon referrals which originate in the hospitals.

NURSING OPPORTUNITIES FOR COMMUNITY EDUCATION

Not only should the nurse be sensitive to a need for referral for social case work or other services, but her appropriate interpretation of these services to the older patients who would benefit from referral would be a major contribution to the well-being of such patients. More generally, nurses oriented to community needs (as all graduates of collegiate nursing programs ought to be) can play an important role in the preventive aspects of geriatric mental health by teaching and encouraging patients who are still in the productive years, together with their families, to develop interests beyond their work and home. She should be able to acquaint them with the developing opportunities for older people at civic, church, and other centers, with preretirement planning courses, with foster grandparents service, and with the many recreational, educational, and service programs for older people.

Just as the nurse in industry works with people who will someday be retired, the nurse assigned to a senior citizens' club or a geriatric day care center has an opportunity to educate clients to the "normal" changes that accompany aging. While contemporary society is fast paced, organic changes often force the older person to slow down. When illness adds additional "slowing" pressure, the individual may react by disengaging from the seemingly uneven struggle.

In addition to such educational functions, public health nurses can encourage the development of creative programs for old people, thereby participating in "second stage prevention" through a special concern with this higher risk group. [*Cf. Susser, Chap. 5 in this volume.*] Nursing involvement may thus enhance appraisal and implementation of recreational and health maintaining community services.

The dying patient

The care of the dying patient has only recently been subjected to a social-psychological approach in the nursing literature. [*See Lasagna, Chap. 3 in this volume; and Vol. 1, Chap. 14.6, pp. 332–337 for older people's attitudes toward death.*] A widely reprinted early article entitled, "As Life Ebbs: The Art of Giving Understanding and Tranquility to the Dying Patient," relies almost exclusively on physical nursing care and gentleness, failing to perceive those aspects of nurse and patient behavior which may be functions of the dying person's interaction with significant persons around him.[35] Indeed, nearly all of the relatively few articles published on death or dying in the first sixty years of the *American Journal of Nursing* centered on technical practices to be followed during the final stages of life, and on procedures in disposing of the body after death. Nursing, no less than the wider society of which it is a part, gave scant attention to the social and psychological aspects of death. The first comprehensive examination of the nurse's role vis-à-vis the dying patient is the 1967 volume by Jeanne Quint, based upon rigorous empirical observation, and discussing such topics as "conversations with dying patients" and "encounters with death." Miss Quint discusses fully the implications of her findings for teaching, for the nursing curriculum, and for the personal problems of nurse identity.[36]

Along similar lines, Leo Simmons and Dorothea Jaeger, who have interviewed a large number of nurse practitioners and contacted "nursing leadership" through a mail questionnaire, focus part of their analysis on the attitudes toward the nursing care of elderly patients who are dying or not expected to recover.[37] Although the final report is still in process, permission has been obtained from the investigators to reproduce here my own responses as one member of the sample population, together with the study questions that provoked them. The questions and answers, lengthy as they are, are offered for purposes of illustration only, as examples of some of the

[35] Virginia Kasley, "As Life Ebbs," *American Journal of Nursing*, 48 (1948), 170–173. Only recently has the nursing literature demonstrated a shift in emphasis, evidenced by an increase in articles devoted to the psychological aspects of care of the dying. This trend began with Catherine M. Norris, "The Nurse and the Dying Patient," *American Journal of Nursing*, 55 (1955), 1214–1217; continuing the trend was the piece by Cicely Saunders, "The Last Stages of Life," *American Journal of Nursing*, 65 (1965), 70–75. Subsequent widely read articles in this tradition include Marilyn Folck and Phyllis Nie, "Nursing Students Learn to Face Death," *Nursing Outlook*, 7 (1959), 510–513; Berniece Wagner, "Teaching Students to Work with the Dying," *American Journal of Nursing*, 64 (1964), 129–131; and Jeannette Folta, "The Perception of Death," *Nursing Research*, 14 (1965), 232—a piece that looks at nurses' attitudes toward death in the context of their ability to function effectively with patients who are facing death.

[36] Jeanne C. Quint, *The Nurse and the Dying Patient* (New York: The Macmillan Company, 1967). See also Barney Glaser and Anselm Strauss, *Awareness of Dying* (Chicago: Aldine Publishing Company, 1965).

[37] Leo Simmons and Dorothea Jaeger, manuscript in preparation. Selected material, slightly edited, presented here by permission of the authors. The wider investigation, carried out at Yale University School of Nursing, examines many facets of aging that are relevant to nursing, such as the difference between technological (or occupational) retirement and psychological retirement, and the contrasting types of needs in aged and infirm persons.

salient concerns of nursing in relation to the dying patient. Many such answers to many such questions will be required, of course, if we are to respect the uniqueness, as well as the similarities, of particular patients and particular nurses in the face of death.

QUESTIONS AND ANSWERS: THE EXPERIENCE OF A NURSE

The questions and answers thus follow. If some of the answers seem to be overgeneralized, I can only say that, in my own experience, there have been times when this seemed a sound thing to do.

1. *How may one say that nursing care differs for an aged ill person who is expected soon to die in contrast to one who is expected to recover?*

For both groups of patients, those expected to recover and those expected soon to die, a similar basic premise can obtain—no living person should be left bereft of hope. The human organism is remarkably durable, and even when the patient's expectation is of approaching death, and his philosophy (religious or otherwise) is one of considerable acceptance of this fact, the attitude is often one of "Not today, Death. Come back a little later." No one who has watched a terminally ill patient continue to live day after day with a certain amount of effectiveness, long after expert prediction of imminent death, can doubt that a degree of conflict can exist between a philosophical readiness to die and a very practical unreadiness to "let go."

I have seen this happen most often among patients who died at home under the auspices of formal or informal home care programs (that is, care by helping family members, the visiting nurse, and a concerned physician). I believe (although the hypothesis has not been tested) that a higher proportion of patients cared for in this way, as compared with roughly matched patients without such care, would die continent, mentally alert, involved to the end in the world about them, with less restlessness and more freedom from pain on somewhat smaller doses of drugs. (Two modifications to this statement: First, it is extraordinarily difficult to "match" elderly, chronically ill persons so as to make sure that extraneous factors are not confounding the experimental results. Second, situations similar to those I have seen at home have been observed also in a very special kind of hospital setting, as reported by Dr. Cicely Saunders.[38] Thus it is perhaps not home care versus hospital care that counts, but the fact that the person who dies at home is more likely in our society to be surrounded by supportive helping persons, as is the person who dies in the special kind of hospital which Dr. Saunders describes.) For I believe it is not death which patients fear, but dying,

---

[38] Saunders, *op. cit.*, 70.

and especially dying with the feeling of not mattering to someone else. Thus the most supportive nursing care that can be offered is the feeling that the patient is cherished—that he matters. This is not usually accomplished merely through words.

The sharpest contrast in care between those who will soon die and those expected to recover is that, for the former, the nurse's goal is to permit the patient to accept, with dignity and spirit, increasing dependence as he needs it—to permit him, in Virginia Henderson's words, "to die as he would want to if he had the will and strength."[39] For the very sick old person with a potential for recovery, by contrast, the tiniest effort toward reaching out to regain some measure of independence is encouraged and sometimes lightly forced. For example, in caring for an old person with a stroke who needs to be encouraged toward greater effort, the ideal nurse might hold the sleeve of his pajama jacket an inch further away each day to encourage a fuller range of motion, until he realized himself that he was performing more independently than he believed possible. I have sat such a helpless patient in a chair, taped a magnet to his paralyzed hand, and played a game of checkers with him with bottle caps. I did this not because I believed he had the potential at that moment to move his hand with control, but because the dramatic effect of the "checkers" jumping through the air into his hand startled him out of apathy, replaced depression with amusement, and kindled the active cooperation of the patient which is the most important single step toward recovery from any kind of hopelessness and apathy.

2. *How may one say that nursing care differs for an aged critically ill person who is conscious and mentally alert in contrast to one who is semi- or unconscious or under heavy sedation?*

For the conscious and mentally alert sick old person, the nurse always gives anticipatory guidance to help him understand the next step in a plan of nursing care. For example: "I would like to turn you on your side, Mrs. Cassidy, and put a rectal tube in, to try to help get rid of those gas pains. It will feel a lot like having your temperature taken. May I?" I think the "may I" is important before undertaking any intrusive procedure with a conscious patient. It implies that the patient controls the situation and, although he seldom uses the control, I have often had a patient speak with appreciation of the sense "that if I said 'No,' you wouldn't do it." In any event, it helps to keep the nurse aware of what otherwise may be a patient's mounting passive resentment.

With a semi-conscious or heavily sedated patient, I would use a similar approach but with a different expectation. The approach would serve as a kind of screening test to make sure that my perception of the patient's state of unawareness is correct. It is not always. On one occasion, the "caring person," in reporting off duty to me, said of a highly

[39] Henderson, *op. cit.*

belligerent elderly man that he had been confused, unaware, and restless for twelve hours, had repeatedly attempted to climb out of bed, and so on and on. I knew that this report would have been true of him on several past occasions; yet, as I looked at this old man whose eyes were closed, I had the feeling that this time he was "playing possum." Although my feeling was a mere guess, I watched him a moment and then said in a casual tone "Mr. H———, I've been told that you're confused and unaware. I don't believe it. I will bet that right this minute you are just about as aware as I am." And I nearly collapsed with astonishment when Mr. H——— opened his eyes, in which there was a real spark of interest and a hint of amusement, and said in a scholarly voice, "And what, may I ask, do you propose to offer as evidence for that astonishing theory?"

For the truly unconscious patient, the nurse must "become" the person's mind and his nervous system, must anticipate bodily needs including positioning and skin care as though she felt for this patient with herself, much as a mother does for a newborn or a helplessly retarded child. Empathy is possible with the unconscious as well as with the active patient.

3. *How far into the terminal phase of life may a nurse justifiably urge natural and/or artificial life-sustaining measures or promote self-care and rehabilitative procedures?*

Certain natural or even life-sustaining measures are urged or used as long as life continues; these are the measures which promote comfort or prevent needless suffering or deterioration (such as adequate hydration including intravenous feeding essential to the comfort of the conscious dying patient, or the prevention of massive bedsores in the long unconscious patient. Distinguishing such procedures from the so-called "heroic therapy" available only in the medical center, I believe in general that those measures which one would want to see applied if the patient were dying at home or in a nursing home ought to be continued; while in general those "heroic measures" which are applied only when the patient— by a quirk of fate—happens to be dying in a specially-equipped, research-minded institution ought not to be continued. [*Cf. Lasagna, Chap. 3 in this volume.*]

This is, however, what Mrs. Roosevelt used to call a "very iffy question." It is easy to know what the doctor "should" do, or how family members "should respond," when one is not in their shoes. With one family, needless suffering can be prevented by the decision not to institute heroic measures. Yet, another family can derive great comfort from the last-minute use of supplies from the emergency box, thus feeling reassured that "everything possible was done for him."

In most instances it would seem better, when an elderly patient is hopelessly ill, not to begin heroic measures. Once begun, there is almost no morality to the continual decisions that inevitably follow—whether to continue or withhold. Far better that *a plan in advance of the fact be made,* in which doctor and family (and the patient himself, if he is aware and knowledgeable) participate in answering the question, "What, all things considered, should be done?" This question cuts deep into the finest contribution a professional can make to any situation, the use of trained judgment. For the goal of care is not the prevention of death but the prevention of *untimely* death and needless suffering.

Similar criteria should operate in decisions regarding nursing measures to promote self-care and rehabilitative procedures. If, by promoting small instances of self-care, one increases or sustains the dignity of the patient, such measures are worth continuing to the end. To put a washcloth into a patient's hand, even while having to guide that hand, is sometimes an important measure of good nursing care.

Different judgments are required in the case of rehabilitative procedures which falsely connote recovery. We once admitted a paraplegic patient, terminally ill with cancer, to an orthopedic rehabilitation unit because he—and we—thought there was merit in his regaining, for the period of time remaining to him, some ability to stand. Although at first he was highly motivated toward this goal, he quickly became a depressed, "uncooperative" patient, refusing to use the potential that he had. When I questioned him, he said angrily, "All of them here are geared to a normal lifetime—except me." And this was true. He was being rehabilitated in a setting of high hope among others made paraplegic through polio or accidents. Their illness was done with; they were moving toward wellness, while he was moving steadily toward death. Accordingly, we returned him to home care and exercised him in that setting. And under these circumstances, he learned to stand again, and with pride.

4. *What may a nurse do when an aged dying patient pleads "not to suffer" through his or her last days on earth?*

Say—and mean—"We are with you, we will help you in every way we can, with our most judicious use of all we know." Most persons *who remain involved with life* die well. It's harder when persons become disengaged from those around them, and from the outside world. Therefore, help them in every way to remain engaged! It is useful for the nurse to imagine that her patient is quoting the old saw to her, "What you do speaks so loud that I cannot hear what you say." There is much truth in this saying. At the same time, I think most dying patients need also to hear verbal reassurance, at least once, for many cannot believe at first that any help exists. If a relationship of trust is established between patient and nurse, verbal reassurance may then often be kept to a minimum. Every dying person—like every woman in labor—needs some one person to provide closeness. Again it is the principle of "the need to matter to someone." Ideally this is provided by a family member. When no family member is available to provide it, the nurse can serve as a useful substitute. More often, she may need to "coach" a suitable family member through anticipatory guidance.

5. *Under what conditions, if any, may a nurse resort to "kidding" or "joshing" aged ill patients or treat them "like children?"*

Humor is a useful human defense; and a kidding relationship may be useful under those special circumstances where observation of a particular patient leads the nurse to recognize that for him humor is a defense, initiated by him, and found by him to be of value. I have had a joshing relationship with a dying incontinent patient in which mutual kidding (about my need for work and his anxiety to see me well employed) helped both of us through innumerable bed changes which, without the straw of humor to clutch at, would have been a source of great dismay to him and an almost impossible basis for a neutral or reassuring attitude on my part. Here there is no single rule; it's a question of sensitivity and, once again, of deciding only after all things have been considered. But certainly no nurse has the right to inflict *her* humor on a sensitive patient. Here the leadership must be provided by the patient, whereas the nurse's leadership role should lie only in the provision of a good-natured environment.

If by treating patients "like children" is meant talking down to them, this is never justified. As Kathleen Newton notes, older people seldom regard themselves as old.[49] [*See Vol. I, Chap. 13.10.*] To be addressed by the nursing staff as "Grandma," for example, whether thoughtlessly, or even affectionately, indicates that the nurses are losing sight of the patient's individuality. Similarly, to use an old person's first name is usually an invasion of personal privacy, reducing his already fragile hold on status and independence. Yet, on rare occasions, when an elderly, dying patient or one isolated by debilitating illness has survived all who knew him by his first name, he may lament: "There is not a single person alive to call me John." Then, because the *patient* feels the need, I have seen this privilege *bestowed* on a young nurse, with what was obviously a therapeutic benefit to the patient and the relationship.

Under some conditions, also, providing bodily contact to a frightened dying patient, as one would to a frightened child, can offer a supporting kind of communication. I think of a woman dying of lung cancer, who coughed until she had not the strength to cough again. The only way I knew to provide some comfort in such a coughing spell, which drugs were ineffective to contain, was to sit next to her on the edge of her bed and "splint" her chest with my arms around her as one "splints" with one's hands the chest of a child with whooping cough. With tears in her eyes she spoke, not of the reduction in pain provided by the splinting, but

---

[40] Kathleen Newton, *Geriatric Nursing* (4th ed.; St. Louis: The C. V. Mosby Co., 1966). This book, first published in 1950, was the first text on this subject written by a nurse for student and graduate nurses, and has done much to alert nurses to the special needs of the elderly chronically ill.

of the fact that no one had put an arm around her for many years, a sensation she had never hoped to feel again.

6. *How may certain facts about or attitudes toward death tend to help nurses and aged patients to cope with this event? Under what conditions should a nurse discuss, or not discuss, the prospects of death with an aged ill person?*

I refer you to the best discussion of this I've ever read, by Dr. Allen Gregg.[41] In general, it is sound to be sensitively aware, but to let the patient take the lead. The important thing for the nurse is not to run away if the patient talks about death, but to try to assess the level on which the patient is discussing it. As a visiting nurse, I have had patients show me the clothes they wished to be buried in and had them discuss funeral plans, and still felt that they were no more concerned with death as an immediate stress problem than the individual who makes a will or buys a life insurance policy. And I have had other patients not speak of death at all who were, I felt, asking for an opening to speak. When this happened, I did not bring up the subject, but provided for quiet unhurried moments so that the patient could do so if he wished. Some did and some never did; but I think they all knew that the unfilled time was there to use as they wanted.

7. *Suggest and appraise possible ways of coping with the following situations:*

(a) *When there is a breakdown of conventional proprieties on the part of an aged ill person*

If the person is rational, provide a reminder, as one would remind a child, without any special show of feeling. If the person is irrational or entirely senile, provide sufficient protection through screening or segregating to protect him from the gaze, hostility, or amusement of casual visitors or other persons without understanding of the problem. If unprepared aides or students are involved in care, it is a nursing responsibility to discuss the problem with them so that the dignity of both patient and attendant can be protected. With the irrational or senile patient, the family also needs to be helped toward understanding and to see that the staff view the behavior as part of the sickness.

(b) *When an aged ill person hallucinates, has visions, or other illusory experiences, such as hearing voices, seeing absent or deceased persons, etc.*

---

[41] Allen Gregg, "Responsibility Teaches," *Rocky Mountain Medical Journal*, 44 (1947), 812–816. Since 1965, when this paragraph was written for the investigation by Simmons and Jaeger, I have also read the works cited above by Catherine M. Norris, Jeanne C. Quint, and Jeannette Folta, all of which add substantive content to any nurse's consideration of this question.

Too "iffy" a question for a simple reply. In the case of an agitated, senile person who climbed out of bed to hunt a relative dead these twenty years, energy was self-limiting. By gently walking with her the length of the ward and looking for Mother with her, I led her to use up physical energy which might otherwise have been spent in climbing over the bedrails; by the time we had opened various closet doors and walked the equivalent of a block, she was ready to sleep without sedation. In other cases, sedation may be the only answer to protecting the sleep of other patients. "What—all things considered—should be done?"

Quite another and terribly difficult nursing problem (and one where my personal knowledge is sparse) is that of reassuring the elderly person who hallucinates intermittently, knows that he does this, but is unable to recognize an episode when it occurs (as in the example of the patient with Parkinson's disease who is reacting to an overdose of medication). I have sometimes—but only sometimes—been able to move such a person away from an illusory experience by talking softly to him about a topic he is intensely interested in, literally disengaging him from an unwanted experience by engaging him in a more desirable one. This has worked most successfully with a patient who (1) trusts me, (2) has strong interests of his own, or (3) can have his interest caught by the repetition of something very familiar, such as a simple poem or a Biblical psalm. At times, such a patient will end up by replying to a direct question suddenly fired at him, in which case I would then continue in normal conversation as though the episode had not occurred, reviewing it with him on another occasion when he is under less stress.

(c) *When the patient shows mistrust and/or aggression toward those caring for him or her*

Again, this is a matter of judgment. When hostility is overt, it is sometimes useful simply to say "You're pretty mad at me today, aren't you? Perhaps if you could help me understand why, I could try to help." With another patient, this could be all wrong.

Renée Fox, in *Experiment Perilous,* found that terminally ill *young* adults use such defenses to cope with fear and frustration as physical activity, humor, and religion (or, in the absence of formal religion, a nonspecific "faith").[42] For the elderly who are terminally ill, by contrast, physical activity is likely to be at a relatively low ebb, and it is the rare patient who uses humor, although it does occur. For the patient well enough to participate in diversional therapy—even for very brief periods—such action is useful in diminishing aggression, as are all measures aimed to keep the patient involved with the world around him. And for the patient with faith, a nurse who provides understanding and opportunity to nourish this faith may help to avoid mistrust and aggression.

An important reason for mistrust and aggression given by many older

[42] Renée Fox, *Experiment Perilous* (New York: Free Press, 1959).

persons is the reasonable complaint ₋nat nobody listens to them. In this they are usually quite right. Thus, the nurse who does listen and extend herself toward patients is less likely to be the victim of aggression. Since older patients often have hearing loss—the dying older patient may be particularly hard to talk with—I have sometimes found that putting a stethoscope in a patient's ears and talking directly into the bell will "get through" to a patient who seems to be out of reach. This device applies also to many older persons who, though not terminally ill, are beyond the range of normal speech tones. It is a useful thing to know, especially for night duty.

(d) *When the aged ill patient appears to take advantage of nearness of death for gaining special and/or forbidden favors*

I'd evaluate this pretty carefully, although I know of no good reason why the elderly dying diabetic needs to be denied a banana simply because bananas are not normally part of his diet. There are times when "rules" require more liberal interpretation for the dying patient and/or the dying patient's family. The question for consideration is, it seems to me, "To what purpose are we attempting to cope with this bid for special favor?" If the purpose, as with a preschool child, is to prevent spoiling him in a destructive fashion that will create unnecessary suffering, then we must be kind but firm. But if the effect is to prevent the patient from exercising some control over a life situation in which he is rapidly losing his normal opportunities for control anyway, becoming a totally passive participant, our "coping" can sometimes border on the sadistic.

The need for change seems to be a basic human need, and there are few ways left to the elderly dying patient to exercise this need. Pure cussedness, as one of the last ways that he relinquishes, is sometimes an incredibly good defense.

8. *Suggest and appraise possible ways of keeping in contact or communication with dying aged persons:*

(a) *By means of the senses (sight, hearing, touch, smell, taste, hunger, thirst)*

Some of these—body contact, the anticipation of physical needs, the reading or repetition of content known to be familiar to the dying patient —have already been discussed. I have held the hand of a dying patient or, more effectively, have put her hand in the hand of a family member. I have taught even an unskilled elderly spouse to do simple nursing services for his wife in order to diminish awkwardness and increase their close contact. A dab of favorite cologne in wash water, the use of an old sweater or bed jacket the texture of which is familiar or comforting, the placing of a rosary in the hand of a patient for whom it had meaning— these and a hundred other tiny ways can be used to say, "I am your friend. I am here. You matter."

(b) *Manipulation of environmental factors (light, sound, familiar settings, etc.)*

Florence Nightingale said it well over a century ago in her *Notes on Nursing*.[43] What we need to do nowadays is to apply what we know. One point may be added: Where grandchildren or great-grandchildren are treasured, their voices or accounts of them by others are often helpful. The beginnings of life and the end of life go surprisingly well together, providing a sense of continuity.

(c) *Ministrations such as religious symbols, rituals, keepsakes, etc.*

Long after any chance of "wearing my pink slippers" is past, "keeping my pink slippers right there on the chair beside my bed" may be reassuring. So may the question, "Would you like to put on your glasses?" or "Would you like to have me brush your teeth so that they'll be here if you want to put them in?" Choice, even in the smallest ways, keeps the patient knowing he matters.

Religious rites ccmfort many patients, as does a visit from the hospital clergyman. Communion may infuriate an occasional patient when *imposed;* but the observant nurse knows for which patient the religious symbol and ritual are supporting, for which they present only a possible help, and for which they are definitely prcductive of mistrust. The meaning of the sacraments to the patient often has little to do with what is written on his record under "religious preference." I have had an elderly patient tell me proudly that he is an atheist; yet say warmly, after conversation, "God bless you!"

9. *What are some ways in which a nurse may deal with stresses experienced by fellow patients when death is taking one of them?*

Where there is an "in-group" of patients, they sometimes deal best with the matter among themselves, with the nurse quietly there extending a kind of nonverbal empathy. If they need to talk, they will as long as she is available. If a patient dies at night while fellow patients sleep through (or if the dying patient is removed to another room while they are asleep), it is simple justice for the nurse to be there when they awaken to interpret what has happened, rather than force them to make this adjustment unassisted. Sometimes when the event of death must be surrounded by unusual traffic or sounds, it may be best to remove the surviving roommate to another setting rather than the dying patient. The important point is not to let another patient face the shock of meeting a roommate's death alone; or in the event that this occurs unexpectedly, always to give him opportunity to talk about it afterward.

[43] Florence Nightingale, *Notes on Nursing* (facsimile of the 1860 edn.; New York: Appleton-Century-Crofts, 1946).

10. *How may a nurse make constructive use of the following situations:*

(a) *When relatives or close friends are present during a person's dying days or hours;*

(b) *when doctor, lawyer, religious adviser, or social worker is present;*

(c) *or when the presence of one or the other of those persons seems indicated?*

One conducts oneself with warmth and genuine concern for the welfare of the family as well as for the patient, recognizing that at times the family members themselves temporarily become patients. Family members often appear to feel less regret, frustration, or guilt when death occurs if they have actually participated in the care of the patient. To be sure, the relief is only a relative matter, and any elderly person who cares deeply for his dying spouse almost always seems to feel guilty merely for surviving.

It often helps family members to be assured, during the restlessness immediately preceding death, that this restlessness is far harder on the watchers than on the patient; and that, according to the best evidence we have, death usually occurs in a setting of semi-consciousness that is apparently free of anxiety, with the actual moment of death preceded by total unconsciousness. The nurse needs to know that the cultural background of the family may be an important determinant of their behavior in facing death. The ministrations of the patient's faith are often comforting to the family members. So too are a few moments of quiet talk, or just quiet sitting, before departing after a patient dies.

11. *What would be the potential effects of granting greater freedom to the professional nurse for independent action and practice in the care of aged terminally ill patients? Would you recommend this, and if so, under what circumstances?*

In private duty, in nursing homes, and in home care situations where visiting nurses are involved, the nurse already has great freedom for independent action since the doctor is unlikely to be present. I believe that, in general hospitals also, the practice of assigning leadership in patient care to the nurse might well be followed under appropriate circumstances, thus avoiding many of the "heroic measures" currently employed at the death of a person who is elderly and without potential for recovery. I find the possibility for such patients to be turned over to nursing leadership well before death to be at least as reasonable as the turning over of normal hospital deliveries to the trained nurse-midwife. Thus, at least three categories of general hospital patients might profit from becoming "nurses' patients": premature babies and normal newborns; normal obstetrical patients; elderly dying patients and certain categories of younger patients dying of chronic illness. Such a plan assumes two basic qualifications: (a) that the nurses have special preparation for their work and *knowingly accept the responsibility for care;* (b) that physicians are available as consultants when their special skills are needed. I would assume also that the taking on of primary responsibility by a nurse would imply the existence of designated "nursing beds" within the general hospital; and that each of the three types of patient would reach such a bed on referral from a physician at the appropriate time, as after completion of a careful prenatal examination, after completion of a careful examination of the newborn baby, cr when it became clear that further medical intervention was not in the interests of the dying patient.

In the latter instance, dying patients might be transferred to the hospital's satellite nursing home, but they ought still to have medical consultation available. When a doctor is *needed*, no nurse can replace him. When a nurse is *needed*, as she is when the dying patient requires excellent nursing care, the patient can benefit by being in a special nursing unit that is staffed, equipped, and paced to provide a dignified end to life. Or he may benefit even more—when appropriate—by being on a first-rate home care program, with visiting nurse and home aide help as needed. When the public health nurse does take over increased responsibility in the home, however, this transfer of responsibility must be carefully interpreted to the family by the physician; otherwise, the apparent desertion of the patient by the doctor leaves a vacuum which no nurse can fill. And, when patient and family are conscious and aware, desertion always does cccur, at least symbolically, if a doctor "pulls out" and a nurse "takes over" without adequate explanation and planning. Yet, when family and patient understand the purpose, I have seen this transfer of primary responsibility work very well indeed.

Emerging needs

Despite the growing interest in improving the quality of nursing care for the aged and the dying patient, much remains to be done. One high priority need is to identify the core of knowledge specific to nursing assessment and care of older persons, from whatever disciplines this essential content comes. The *Inventory* (Volume One in the present series) is a first necessary step in this direction. Having identified this knowledge, there is also a need to disseminate it to the full range of nurse practitioners through clinical conferences and programs of continuing education. To be sure, a variety of guides for nursing assessment are available, some specifically geared to the older person, others suitable for any nursing situation.[44] One guide, now in use by

[44] Schwartz, Henley, and Zeitz, *op. cit.*, interview guide, Appendix C.

students at the Cornell University—New York Hospital School of Nursing, seems well suited to any setting (acute general hospital, nursing home, public health nursing agency, or clinic) and to patients in any age group.[45] All such guides, however, need wider use and continued testing.

Perhaps of greater importance than the assessment of nursing needs, as narrowly defined, is the identification of those patient needs which require nursing attention or which the nurse could help to satisfy through coordination with, or referral to, other services. An interdisciplinary approach to the care of the aged patient, which rests on the thinking of an entire health team, deserves far more attention than it has yet received. [*See also Morris and Lasagna, Chaps. 2 and 3 in this volume.*] To make any program of health care work, physicians, nurses, physical and occupational therapists, and social workers must plan together, taking into account what the patient and his family think is possible and hope to achieve. This approach can eventuate only by listening to the patient, and to one another. At present, each discipline separately investigates a problem in the light of a separate core of knowledge, although the day-to-day implications and interrelationship of facts require coordinated analysis. The need is to work together, in order to implement and execute an overall plan of care. Such joint action is the price of quality. In this sense, we have moved away from speaking of the quality of nursing care, and are talking now about the quality of patient care—the planning and taking of all the steps that "tip the scales in the patient's favor."[46]

Consequently, studies are needed of the effectiveness of new interdisciplinary health teams. A problem of all attempted demonstrations of effectiveness is that they tend to interest and attract the eager "activist." While it may seem encouraging to hear that in a particular instance a nurse has made a "fine contribution" to a health team, what is done well in a simple demonstration all too often turns out to be less effective when replicated widely. Careful studies are needed, too, of the essential content of clinical care of the aged, studies that would test hypotheses, for example, as to effective methods of dealing with sensory deprivation, incontinence, fear of abandonment, difficulties in adjusting to new environments or to care by strangers, and other common problems of chronic illness and old age. [*Cf. Vol. 1, Chap. 25, pp. 577–596.*]

In addition to such needed developments in the assessment of

[45] Virginia Sanders and Carol Franck, *Guide for the Preparation of a Nursing Assessment* (unpublished).
[46] George James; informal communication.

nursing and patient needs, the field of clinical nursing could profit by innovation and bold experimentation along lines set out by Simms, Peplau, and Little.[47] Laura Simms, for example, observes that "nursing leaders more or less agree that the clinical nursing specialist is a nurse with advanced knowledge and competence capable of exercising a high degree of discriminating judgment in planning, executing and evaluating nursing care based upon assessed needs of patients having one or more common clinical manifestations. . . ." To date, reports of such nurse clinicians, though encouraging, are few in number. The potential for developing clinical nursing expertise for the care of the aged, of the sort described by Ilva Benjamin, is relatively untapped.[48]

Finally, any discussion of aging and the field of nursing ought to include more careful examination of the system of nursing education than the scope of this paper permits. To be sure, we have called attention to certain problems, and recommended a number of specific changes. More generally, we want to recommend that all basic professional curricula should include materials on growth and development throughout the full life span. Clinical practice in the care of the elderly in sickness and in health (that is, in all five stages of health care, with special focus on the needs of the dying patient) ought to be as thoughtfully planned and as carefully focused as the nursing care of, say, the child or the young adult.

Although students of nursing see large numbers of elderly patients who may have chronic illness, most often this experience takes place in the general hospital where the presenting need is for care of an acute or of a suddenly worsened chronic condition. The older person is often cared for at home, through the medium of the community nursing agency; but here too he is likely to be seen during an acute illness or during rehabilitation. Far less often is any nursing care devoted to the older person in the community center, the preventive health conference, the retirement home, or the retirement counseling program in industry.

Thus more emphasis is needed on the care of incipient ailments and manageable chronic conditions *before* they reach crisis proportions. The growing body of social science knowledge that has stimulated this essay cannot help but make an invaluable contribution to these new paths in nursing education.

[47] Laura Simms, "The Clinical Nursing Specialist," *Journal of the American Medical Association*, 196 (1966), 207 ff.; Peplau, *op. cit.*; and Dolores Little, "Emerging Role of Nursing is That of Specialist," *Hospital Topics*, 43 (1965), 121 ff.
[48] Ilva Benjamin, "The Role of the Geriatric Nurse in Health Maintenance," *Geriatrics*, 22 (1967), 58–62.

5

Aging and the field of public health

MERVYN SUSSER

In assessing the opportunity for the public health field to improve the length and quality of life among older people, Doctor Susser affirms the need to recognize and specify the impact of the social environment on the state of health of individuals and populations, and on the very definitions and measurements employed. Variations observed among and within societies both in age-related mortality and in major disabling diseases indicate that many illnesses associated with old age do not reflect age alone; these variations also reflect the character of the social system, the individual's position within it, and changes in the environment over time. Moreover, the onset of permanent dependence among older persons may derive from the adverse effects of such social conditions as retirement, isolation, or widowhood. Thus, unlike the prevailing tendency of existing health and welfare services to aid old people only after disablement has occurred, a public health approach, in its concern for the health status of a whole population, must aim at prevention—both

*through improvements in the environment of younger people be-
fore they ever encounter the ills of senescence, and through
screening out for special care those among the elderly who may
be particularly subject to these risks.*

*Advisers for this chapter were George Rosen, Yale University
School of Medicine; and Frederick D. Zeman, The Jewish Home
and Hospital for Aged, New York, New York.*

ON THE RELEVANCE OF VOLUME ONE

*The chapter by Doctor Susser on public health, following those
by Doctor Lasagna and Professor Schwartz, deals with the relationship between aging and health generally and thus draws
upon much the same materials from Volume One. The public
health official, however, in contrast to those physicians who concentrate upon diagnosis and treatment of individuals known or
presumed to be ill, focuses on total populations or communities,
examining the distribution and causes of disorder, impairment,
and disease. He seeks to determine how intervention may bring
about or maintain optimal health conditions. Here the full range
of social science knowledge has applicability; and Doctor Susser,
emphasizing scientific understanding more than practical programs and plans, points to numerous and varied connections between the problems confronting his profession and the relevant
chapters of Volume One.*

This chapter will pick its way through various topics where interpretation of the research findings set out in Volume One seems germane
to the purposes of public health. It will aim to be a companion in the use
of the compiled findings, rather than a rounded account of aging and
the field of public health. These findings lend themselves well to the traditional public health ideal of prevention. Emphasis will therefore be
given to the problems of identifying environmental factors that influence either the aging process or the effects of old age. Since factors
extrinsic to the individual organism, once identified, may yield to intervention, this chapter also explores the possibilities of socio-medical
intervention, first in the aging process itself, and second in the effects
of old age. The discussion aims to be general in its conclusions, and
does not include within its scope public health programs that have
been or could be executed but are particular to local circumstances.

Public health as a field

At the outset, the field of public health itself calls for definition, because our concepts of the field determine what is relevant to discuss. Public health has evolved and changed as society has changed. The objectives of previous years are regularly rewritten, and the tasks of public health in relation to aging and to other fields stated afresh.

THE MEANING OF PUBLIC HEALTH

Public health is a term with several meanings. First of all, it is an institutional *practice*. From the earliest times communities have had to cope with health problems that arise from group living, and they have created social institutions to do so. With the acquisition of knowledge and technical capacities, the institutions became specialized agencies. In one sense, therefore, public health is a social institution, and now comprises a linked system of national and local organizations designed to maintain and improve the state of health of populations and communities.

The state of health of a defined population or community gives the term public health its second meaning of *the* public health, describing in this sense the prevalence of health and disease. The organizations of public health intervene in communities in order to improve the public health. They try to prevent disease, to encourage the early detection of disease and avert its progress, and to restore people already disabled by disease to normal social roles.

To carry out these tasks, public health agencies must discover the causes and the consequences of the prevailing state of health of the society. Public health has thus always had a third meaning, namely, a subject of academic and *scientific study*.

Any such study of the health needs and problems of old people might well begin with an examination of society, for a society's state of health is a facet of its social and economic conditions, a reflection of its myriad structural and functional relations. If all those social phenomena that could generate health needs were to be identified for further study, however, the domain of public health would encompass the full array of social problems; at the extreme one might simply equate the problems of living with the problems of health.

To give focus to the field, and to provide it with the working definitions that lead to action, a narrower frame of reference must be found. This frame of reference takes the existing state of health of the population as its starting point. As its acknowledged field for research and action, it seeks out only those aspects of society that can be shown to impinge on health and to give rise to health needs.

DETERMINING HEALTH NEEDS

Needs versus demands "Health needs" is a glib phrase, difficult both to define and to measure. The insistent question that faces the health administrator, in his capacity as provider of services, is one not of underlying needs but of expressed demands.[1] Whether he leads or follows, he takes his cues from demands made known by the community through its use of services, its allocation of funds, and its articulation of beliefs and values. Thus demand for health care arises from those behaviors regarding sickness that are avowedly legitimate within a society.

The needs that confront the health administrator in his broader capacity of planner, however, transcend the pressures of overt demand. Need for health care arises from the impact of the social and economic milieu on the biological functioning of the population it contains. Unlike demand, need is neither dependent on recognition by the affected person nor the appropriate agency, nor on the willingness of such persons and agencies to take action once need is recognized.

Because of such discrepancies between need and demand, public health labors under a social strain. With few exceptions, health needs are greatest among those whose demands for health care are least. On most counts and in most investigations, the aged, the poor, and the least educated are found to suffer more ill health than the young, the wealthy, and the educated, and yet to make relatively less use of health services. [*See Vol. 1, Chap. 9.2.i, pp. 217–218; Chap. 14.1, pp. 317–323.*] Even though old people use services more than younger people do, this use is not in proportion to their ills. For example, two psychiatric surveys of communities have found a rising proportion of mental disorder with age without a proportionate rise in rates of care. [*See Vol. 1, Chap. 16.A.3, pp. 375–385.*] Thus, in trying to meet recognized needs irrespective of demands, public health agencies must often press other institutions and agencies for redress in favor of those at the least advantage in society.

Problems of measurement Because need is not fully mani-

---

[1] In the fairly precise sense of the economist, demand is a description of willingness or ability to pay for services. Often he measures this indirectly by expenditure or utilization of services, which is the outcome of a balance between supply and demand. In the sense used here, demand includes expenditure and utilization, but it also includes the broader sense of "want" or "desire."

fested in demands, public health requires objective measures of need. A large literature deals with the questions of value and definition raised by the concept of health needs. Some of these difficulties are avoided by a pragmatic approach that specifies arbitrarily the criteria by which needs are to be measured. For example, if a sense of well-being, good dentition, good nutrition, or recreation are taken to be the relevant dimensions of need for old people, standards can be established against which to measure these dimensions.

Such pragmatism does not resolve all the difficulties of measurement, since priorities among the chosen dimensions of need must still be settled, particular needs selected as worthy of study, and the results of study interpreted. Priorities among needs are generally set by demand or, more precisely, by the values and other forces underlying demand. Decisions as to which needs should be measured and used as standards for action depend on the purposes and values of the individual planner or researcher. Conservative planners will measure needs in relation to the aims of existing services, reformers in relation to the hiatus in services, while radicals will aim to create new services with new goals. Yet, however conservative certain practitioners may be, a degree of reformism and radicalism is implicit in the ideological orientation of public health toward needs. Thus the body politic of public health did not demur from the World Health Organization's omnibus definition of health as a state of complete physical, mental, and social well-being and not merely the absence of disease or infirmity.[2]

Even when criteria are agreed upon for defining and measuring need, however, there is still room for wide variation in interpretation. Interpretations of the findings of studies of old people are pervaded by dichotomies: Should emphasis be given to health or disorder? well-being or discomfort? contentment or deprivation? The idea that old age is a "phase of replacement" in society and a phase of social displacement for the individual is countered by the idea of the voluntary and contented "disengagement" of old people from previous social roles. The idea of aging as a deteriorative biological process is countered by the idea that aging is a continuing adaptation to new social roles as the life cycle unfolds, even to the final passage into death.

Moreover, any given interpretation may reflect the particular professional training, functions, or reference groups of the interpreter. The sociological perspective, for example, includes whole societies and whole classes of people within societies, and sociologists may be more

[2] World Health Organization, *Basic Documents* (Geneva: WHO, 1964), 1–18.

impressed by the 85 per cent of old people with chronic conditions who maintain their major activities than by the 15 per cent who do not. Hospital physicians, by contrast, are confronted with the sick among old people. Their chief concern is with the quick and efficacious care of individual patients, and they are likely to think of the problems of aging in terms of the high rates of pathology among elderly patients, the multiplicity of coexisting disorders, and the conflict between chronicity of old people's disabilities and the pressure for turnover in hospital beds. The physician's emphasis on pathology and his vested interest in sickness was satirized by George Bernard Shaw in *The Doctor's Dilemma*. In a more charitable version, Scheff notes that medical training, by making the missed diagnosis a cardinal sin, teaches the doctor to presume disorder in his patient until proved otherwise.[3]

EPIDEMIOLOGY

Still another perspective is offered by epidemiology, a discipline which provides the operating data and strategic analyses for the practice of public health. Like the sociologist, the epidemiologist culls his data on disease from broad populations, and he too typically takes note of the large body of old people who maintain independent roles. But unlike the sociologist, the epidemiologist focuses special attention upon the 15 per cent or more of old people who are entirely disabled from their major activities at any one time, and upon those likely soon to undergo disabling experiences—for example, upon that half of the people reaching age 75 without a chronic disorder who may expect such affliction by the age of 80.

The epidemiological consideration of health needs unavoidably begins with an understanding of disorders, since measures of health have not been developed to the point where they can be used with the same discrimination as measures of disorder. Moreover, the focus on disorder, impairment, and disability has especial utility in the study of old people. Even though the disabled comprise much the smaller part of the elderly population at any one time, the proportion of disabled is large compared with younger age groups. In other words, the "relative risk" of disability (an epidemiological estimate used to identify vulnerable classes of persons as well as the hazards of exposure to particular experiences) is high at the older ages. Allowing for limits imposed on the duration of illness by the imminence of death. there is

[3] T. J. Scheff, "Preferred Errors in Diagnosis," *Medical Care*, 2 (1964), 166–172.

an enormous accretion of disability with aging. [*See Vol. 1, Chap. 9.2, pp. 204–218.*]

Measures of health needs in individuals   For individuals, health needs stem from existing or predicted disorders of function of the body. Since such disorders can be conceived in several ways, several different if overlapping criteria of ill health are in common use. These criteria include the subjective sense of well-being and happiness; discomforting symptoms or complaints elicited by medical history or questionnaire; diseases regarded as clinically meaningful entities in terms of cause, course, and prognosis; impairments of bodily structure and function resulting in particular disabilities; adoption of the social role of sickness which, by barring a person from normal social roles, produces a generalized disability; and finally death, the definitive end point.

Each of these criteria yields a different estimate of disorder and of need. Each reflects a part of reality and has validity in its appropriate context; none reflects the whole reality. Inquiries after feelings of happiness, for example, may seem to yield flimsy evidence of the condition of a group of people. Yet among the old, the morale reflected in these reported feelings has an important influence on the individual's behavior and his self-definition as either sick or well. Diseases and their symptoms can be borne with fortitude; although chronic disorders afflict most older people, few of the afflicted either complain or sink into dependence. [*See Vol. 1, Chap. 15.2, pp. 345–348.*] Despite the presence of chronic disorders in four out of five people older than 65, only two out of five allow their major activities to be limited, and fewer than one out of five are disabled completely. [*See Ex. 9 · 17 in Vol. 1, p. 214.*]

Thus disease must be differentiated from sickness. Disease is a pathological process that affects the physiological and psychological state of the individual organism and is confined to it. Sickness is a pathological process that affects the state of the individual's relations with others through his assumption of a special social role. Both are important criteria in measuring the health of old people. The criterion of disease is important as an indicator of threat to the integrity of the organism and to adequate social performance. The criterion of sickness is important as an indicator of actual social performance, independence, and the quality of life.

The fact that sickness and disease are not one and the same can give rise to social strains. The assumption of the sick role exempts an individual from his normal social obligations, hence the traditional hostility of physicians to hysterics or others who acquire this exemption without being able to produce legitimizing pathology. The assumption of the sick role also carries the obligation to seek recovery, hence the resentment toward the hypochondriac who appears to resist recovery.

Older people are reported to be more likely than younger to see advantages in being sick [*see Vol. 1, Chap. 14.1, pp. 317–323*]; yet the old, the poor, and the uneducated are especially unlikely to adopt the sick role even when it is fitting. Herein lies a cause for public health concern. For example, in Scotland, death rates from prostatic hyperplasia are comparatively low in the highest social classes. However, the prevalence of symptoms of prostatic disease among old men in the community, as well as fatality rates from prostatectomies, show little variation by social class.[4] Thus the social-class gradient in death rates is the probable consequence of nonrecognition of the disorder among the lower social classes. Working-class men, more often than men of higher classes, do not come into care until the emergency of acute retention of urine supervenes, even though the National Health Service is freely available to all. In the United States, to take another example, studies of Spanish-American War veterans in their 80's show that a much larger proportion reported symptoms than made use of the free facilities for medical care available to them.[5] In the United States generally, more than six out of ten persons whose health was rated poor by physicians gave themselves a favorable health rating [*see Ex. 13 · 4 in Vol. 1, p. 293*], and similar results were found in a British survey.[6]

Such maintenance of normal social roles in the face of disease can be regarded as socially and psychologically to the good. The depressing effects on morale of actual ill health may be outweighed by the individual's conviction that he is in good health. On the other hand, the failure of old people to seek care is in conflict with objective medical needs, and can well frustrate efforts to arrest the progress of incipient disorders or to cure established ones. [*See Vol. 1, Chap. 13.3, pp. 292–294.*]

Measures of health needs in populations   For populations or communities, in contradistinction to individuals, basic statements of needs are made in terms of incidence and prevalence. *Incidence* de-

[4] I. M. Richardson, "Prostatic Cancer and Social Class," *British Journal of Preventive and Social Medicine*, 19 (1965), 140–142.

[5] H. E. Freeman, A. H. Richardson, J. F. Cummins, and H. W. Schnaper, "Use of Medical Resources by Spancos: 1. Extent and Sources of Medical Care in a Very Old Population," *American Journal of Public Health*, 56 (1966), 1530–1539.

[6] W. Hobson and J. Pemberton, *The Health of the Elderly at Home* (London: Butterworth & Co. Ltd., 1955).

scribes the frequency with which disorders arise in a population during a defined period of time. By contrast, *prevalence* describes the amount of disorder existing in a population at a particular time regardless of time of onset.

The search for causes is best pursued by incidence studies. *Incidence* relates disorders to circumstances at the time of onset, and can obviate some of the crucial uncertainties about the time sequence of events inherent in much observational research. Most incidence rates, however, unless derived indirectly from repeated prevalence studies, must use data from service agencies, and these data may be unrepresentative of the population as a whole. Such biases make incidence a measure of demand on services rather than of need.

For uniformly severe or fatal conditions, particularly those where the interval between onset and death is short, incidence rates of hospital admission and death can provide useful criteria of need. These rates may be fairly representative of the total population in countries with adequate coverage by health services and universal registrations of deaths. Yet even in these circumstances, deaths may escape observation and proper tabulation. One-half to two-thirds of coronary deaths occur outside hospitals; and among the old, many patients die quietly at home. Their certificates of death are notoriously unreliable and difficult to interpret. Recorded diagnoses are often inaccurate and confused by the coexistence of multiple diseases in a single individual. Although more than one cause of death can be entered on death certificates and coded, ordinarily only one underlying cause is tabulated and analyzed.

In estimating the occurrence of chronic disorders having insidious onset or low fatality rates, such as rheumatoid and osteoarthritis, peptic ulcer, diabetes, and psychiatric disturbances, incidence measured by demand on health services can be misleading. For this reason, demand may not be helpful in the early detection of such disorders. Since chronic disorders occur frequently among old people [*see Vol. 1, Chap. 9.2.a, p.* 205], early detection of those conditions amenable to treatment could be an important preventive technique; yet we have emphasized that among the old especially, the demands on services underrepresent need. Poverty, limited education, and social isolation occur together with old age to exacerbate this discrepancy between demand and need. The determinants of low demand are to be found in the perceptions and beliefs among old people that lead to fatalism, negative views of health and medical services, and pride in independence; in the social causes of these modes of perception and belief; and in the unsubtle treatment (if not outright rejection) old people meet from relevant agencies. [*See Vol. 1, Chaps. 14.1 and 14.2, pp. 319–325.*]

In contrast to incidence rates, the *prevalence rates* that describe the amount of disorder existing in a population at a point in time, afford a useful measure of the current load of disorder to be provided for. The prevalence of a disorder compounds two elements however: (1) duration and (2) frequency of occurrence, or incidence. As a result, the degree to which acute as compared with chronic illness will occur in a prevalence study can vary enormously, even when incidence rates are similar.[7] Whereas peptic ulcer, psychoneurosis, or other conditions of relatively long duration are likely to be found in any given set of prevalence statistics, serious but short-lived epidemics may not be detected at all. Influenza, bronchitis, deaths due to smog, and even heart disease may all take on an acute epidemic character, particularly in winter months and among old people. By age categories, then, as Figures 1a and 1b show, the sharp rise in prevalence of chronic disabling illness contrasts with the decline in acute disabling illness; from age 40, chronic illness has a greater prevalence than acute. Incidence rates, uninfluenced by the duration of illness, present a different picture, with acute disabling illnesses exceeding the chronic except in the age groups over 75.

The state of old age

Against this background of the intricacies of programing and research encountered by public health, we turn to examine the nature of aging as both a personal and a social phenomenon. From an epidemiological point of view, chronological age is a complex variable, an attribute of the population as well as the individual, involving numerous difficulties of definition and of interpretation. [*Cf. Vol. 1, Chap. 1, pp. 1–11.*]

AGE AS AN ATTRIBUTE OF POPULATIONS

As an attribute of populations, age is so complicated as to have stimulated the rise of the independent science of demography. The discrete individuals in a population are brought by the social environment into some sort of ordered relation with each other, to form social categories and groups. Such a population is young or old according to the distribution of age groups within it, and its age composition constitutes a specific attribute at a given point in time. In the longitudinal

---

[7] See, for example, B. MacMahon, T. F. Pugh, and J. Ipsen, *Epidemiologic Methods* (Boston: Little, Brown and Company, 1960), Chap. 5.

FIGURE 1 *Prevalence of chronic versus acute conditions, by age*

(a) **Average annual prevalence of disabling cases per 1,000 population, 1938 to 1943**

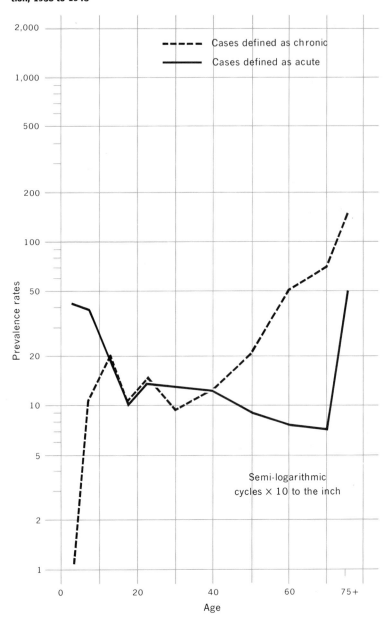

Source: S. D. Collins *et al.,* "Age Incidence of Specific Causes of Illness Found in Monthly Canvasses of Families," *Public Health Reports,* 66 (1961), 1227–1245 (adapted); based on sample of Eastern Health District of Baltimore.

FIGURE 1 *Incidence of chronic versus acute conditions, by age*

(b) Average annual incidence of episodes of disabling illness per 1,000 population, 1938 to 1943

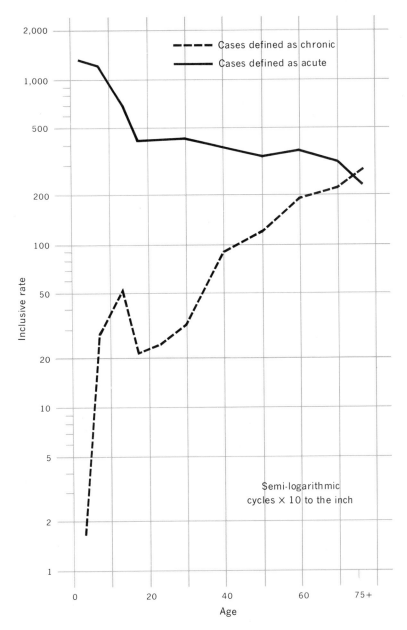

Source: S. D. Collins *et al.*, "Age Incidence of Specific Causes of Illness Found in Monthly Canvasses of Families," *Public Health Reports*, 66 (1961), 1227–1245 (adapted); based on sample of Eastern Health District of Baltimore.

Aging and the field of public health **125**

dimension of time, the age of a population is an outcome of the interplay of historical forces. It is a statement of the dynamic balance of fertility and mortality experienced through time, an experience unique to each of the constituent generations.

AGE AS AN ATTRIBUTE OF INDIVIDUALS

As an attribute of individuals, age has at least three dimensions: It is a description specific to the state of the individual at a particular point in time; it is a statement of the duration of an individual's exposure to life experience; and it is a mark of membership in a particular historical generation (or cohort). In the first dimension, number of years is the banal but important measure of whether a person is currently young or old. By manipulation and study of the latter two dimensions of age, we try to infer the extraneous molding forces to which the individual has been subject during aging, and their effect on his given constitution or genotype.

Seen as an attribute of individuals at a point in time, any particular age is like a measure of prevalence; it describes an existing condition. It serves as an index at many levels at once. It is, for example, a social indicator of status in society. Over the life span age marks a stage of life, and each stage confers on the individual a set of social roles appropriate to that stage. Age is also an indicator of psychological development, with characteristic cognitive abilities, modes of perception, and psychodynamics. Finally age is a physiological indicator with a set of functional accompaniments, and these can help to describe and predict the physical state of the organism.

Such indicators are, of course, interrelated. Those physiological accompaniments of age that manifestly affect appearance or performance, like gray hair or a shuffling gait, also affect the individual's social status. Social status is bound up with physiological status. Since age, like sex, has social, psychological, and biological meaning, and no simple criteria exist that fully encompass these meanings, a public health task of epidemiology and social science is to disentangle these elements of the life stages, in order to reveal which can be modified and improved.

Social definitions of old age   The various social and individual criteria by which old age in particular is defined well illustrate the complexity of the age variable. Old age, socially defined, can be taken as that portion of the life span demarcated as old by the norms of a particular society. Among social groups being "old" is a relative matter, a particular and not an absolute and universal state. Kinship societies give regularity to life stages by *rites-de-passage.* Industrial societies have few *rites-de-passage*, but for the old, fixed ages for retirement and pensions from work organizations introduce regularities that mark the displacement of employees from their occupations, and their entry into a phase of social replacement. (Within an industrial society the manner of entry into this phase depends on occupation; self-employed and professional persons may elect their time, while persons with skills in demand may continue in related work.)

This social definition of old age thus rests on a more or less abrupt transition from one life stage to another, and the taking up of new sets of social roles as old ones are relinquished. In contemporary societies old age ordinarily involves a decrement in social status. [*See Vol. 1, Chaps. 13.11 and 13.12, pp. 306–311.*] The most productive and powerful social, occupational, and domestic roles are given up. The final phase of life, however, may yet become one of continuing development rather than one of abrogation. Society today is in the course of inventing roles for old people, roles that are socially productive and personally satisfying and intended for more than the favored few. The need for such roles has become pressing with the increase in the numbers of old people and the many years of later life that may be expended in socially unproductive and personally unsatisfying economic, family, and sex roles. [*See Morris, Chap. 2 in this volume.*]

Defining the individual as old   The performance of social roles depends ultimately upon the physical and mental integrity of the particular individual. In clinical terms, old age may be recognized by changes in skin, hair, physique, and physiological function. Psychological changes in attitudes, memory, speed of comprehension, and approaches to problem-solving appear to accompany the physical changes. [*See Vol. 1, Chap. 11, pp. 241–272; Chap. 14, pp. 315–339.*] In essence these changes are deteriorative in relation to the earlier years, and present knowledge offers only the prospect of organic decline in the last phases of life. Each complex of signs that underlies the social, psychological, or physical perspectives is interconnected with the others, but the signs vary in time of onset and may be out of phase with one another, as in earlier stages of growth and development. Thus the rate of aging is irregular; social roles and states of mind are not entirely limited by physical condition. On reaching the age of 80, E. M. Forster wrote that aging was an acute experience that he had got over at about the age of 35.

The array of physical, psychological, and social stigmata that accompany old age in contemporary society cannot with confidence be attributed to degeneration caused by the intrinsic process of aging alone. Insofar as other causes are active, preventive and remedial action becomes possible. In order to consider this possibility, a distinction must first be made between old age and aging.

The process of aging and primary prevention

Old age is a state or condition of a human being at a given time; aging is a process taking place through time. Thus a person in the state of old age embodies the outcome of a process of interaction between the environment and the individual constitution. A key question for preventive medicine and public health among the old is whether the connection between the state of old age and deteriorated health is ineluctable. To answer this question, one must look to the antecedent aging process and the factors that influence it. If such factors can be discovered and are amenable to change, there is hope for action to counter them. Only action focused upon the aging process can approach the ideal public health goal of *primary prevention,* that is, successful intervention before the onset of disorder.

AGING AND PHYSICAL DETERIORATION

The individual organism, the phenotype, is a survivor of a process through which the development of its genetic inheritance, the genotype, has been modified by the wear and tear and the acquisitions of experience. Some external injuries have immediate and observable effects on the organism, while others are incorporated in it to produce effects either continuing, or latent and deferred. For instance, infection by the tubercle bacillus produces at each age a constantly unfolding pathology. Pathogenesis begins with the "primary infection" dangerous to infants but otherwise seemingly benign until, after a variety of environmental assaults, it produces the acute cavitating pulmonary disease characteristic of young adults, and later culminates in the chronic fibrotic disease of older people. All these age-related effects are modified by the particular environmental experiences of the individual. Thus an organism has stored within it a memory, so to speak, both of its genetic inheritance, and of its past experience. When chronological age is used at any given time as an indicator of the outcome of this process of interaction between inheritance and experience, all three dimensions of age as an attribute of individuals are involved. The first dimension, it will be recalled, defines the point on the continuum of the life span that the process has reached, the second measures the duration of the individual's exposure to life, and the third marks his membership in a particular generation or cohort.

Populations can be thought of, then, as collections of individuals who survive this process of selection forged by the interaction of constitution and environment in time. Aging can be described in epidemiological terms by morbidity and mortality in the population, arising from deteriorative tissue change that increases through the life span with advancing age. The common method of analyzing the effect of duration of exposure to life is to examine the age-specific incidence or prevalence of relevant phenomena, that is, their frequency in successive age groups at a defined period in time. The shape of the curve plotted by age reveals whether a phenomenon is characteristic of old people (or of any particular age group) at that time, and whether the phenomenon tends to increase or decrease in frequency as a function of age.

In contemporary industrial societies, curves of mortality plotted by age have a characteristic shape. Once the death rates have fallen sharply from the high rates of infancy to reach their lowest point at puberty, they tend to rise exponentially, that is, the rate rises by the same proportion in each successive age group. [*See Vol. 1, Chap. 8, pp. 187–194.*] Similarly, in the meager data on chronic disabling sickness, a pattern appears that is also consistent with deterioration accompanying age. Both the frequency of disability and the number of disorders affecting each individual rise regularly with age.

The regularity of physical deterioration and death with aging does not finally establish an intrinsic quality of aging as the entire cause, nor does it mean that efforts to defer the decline are hopeless. Some room for question and maneuver can be found on three grounds: (1) the variation of aging patterns in different environments; (2) the responsiveness to the environment of some of the major causes increasing the probability of death in later life; and (3) the revisions suggested by cohort analysis in certain accepted interpretations of age-related phenomena.

ENVIRONMENTAL VARIATION

When different societies are compared, the longevity of their populations is far from constant and varies in close relationship to their social and economic modes of life. In the harshest environments the survivors of the hazards of the early years tend to die off at a high and even rate throughout the rest of life. Alex Comfort has pointed out that this model of mortality resembles the mortality experience of robins in the wild, or the random destruction of annealed glasses in a restaurant; at each successive age the survivors run the same high risk of death, in contrast with the age-related increases in risk that characterize senescent populations.[8] Contrast, for example, the survival curve for British India in 1921–1930, as shown in Figure 2, with the curves for other populations at other times. In these harsh conditions, after the high mortality in the first years of life, there is no modal or most common age at death. This characteristic feature of an aging population is lacking. Only with more favorable social and economic circumstances that reduce the causes of death in childhood and early life does the greater vulnerability of older age groups compared with the young emerge. The increasing probability of death as people grow older then becomes evident, and a modal age at death tends to appear.

The modal age at death in any society is thus an ecological phenomenon. The Biblical allocation of three score years and ten is evidence that man has long recognized *specific age*, meaning a life span characteristic of the species, and specific age may be presumed to approach a physiological limit in optimum environments. For contemporary industrial populations, the modal age at death (ignoring infants) is in the neighborhood of 75 years. For individuals now and in the past, life spans of 120 years have been authenticated. Although even in harsh environments some individuals attain such great ages, in favorable environments the number who do so is much increased, and the modal age around which their deaths occur may begin to approach the specific age.

Extension of average life expectancy seems in this light to be a reasonable possibility. However, during the past century (for which relevant data are available) the older age groups have had only a minor share in the considerable increase in survival in industrial societies, and projections predict little improvement. [*See Vol. 1, Chap. 2.3, pp. 24–35.*] Moreover, while the general increase in longevity over the past half century is not to be ignored, we have no direct evidence that describes in terms of health the quality of the years that have been added. We cannot be sure that there has been any improvement in the health of the greater number of survivors into old age in recent times as compared with the health of the fewer survivors of the past.

Despite this uncertainty, there is reason to think that in the United States research and application in public health might extend the average length of life and improve the quality of health. The long-term decline in recorded age-adjusted death rates in the United States seems to have halted in the last decade, and the death rates for all age groups still stand well above the levels attained by countries with the

[8] Alex Comfort, "The Biology of Ageing," *Lancet*, 2 (1956), 772–778.

FIGURE 2 *Survival under varied environmental conditions*
Estimated number of survivors, at 10-year age intervals, of 100,000 male births

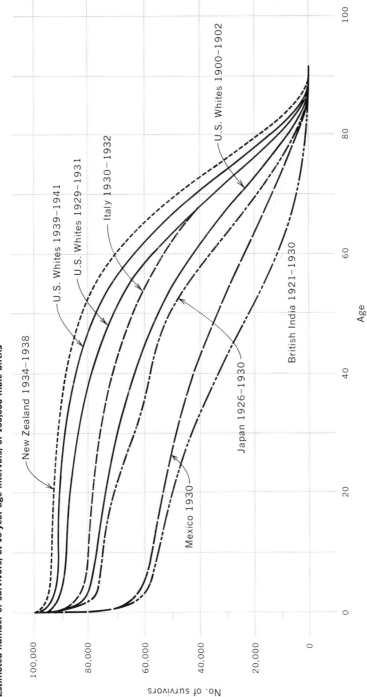

Source: Alex Comfort, "The Biology of Ageing," *Lancet*, 2 (1956), 772–778; from life-tables for selected countries, after Greville, 1946.

FIGURE 3 *Prevalence of disability among older men, by social class*
Percentage of men with disability (all grades)

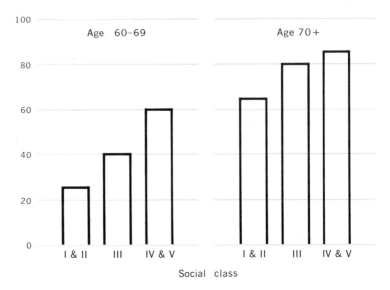

Source: F. Edwards, T. McKeown, and A. G. W. Whitfield, "Incidence of Disease and Disability in Elderly Men," *British Journal of Preventive and Social Medicine*, 13 (1959), 51 (adapted); based on 641 men in Birmingham, England.

lowest rates. [*Cf. Ex. 2 · 8, p. 25 and Ex. 9 · 7, p. 202 in Vol. 1.*] Even within a single society, disease, disability, and death do not fall equally upon all its strata, and their onset may be avoided, postponed, or advanced. The chances of an individual vary with socioeconomic status, his marital status, and other aspects of his position in the social system.

Disabling chronic disease is much commoner among lower income groups and the lower social classes than among the higher, as illustrated in Figure 3, for example. Most of the health disadvantages of American nonwhites as compared with whites may be attributable to similar socioeconomic factors. In interpreting these prevalence data, the possibility must be allowed that some of the difference between social classes may be the consequence rather than the cause of disability. For example, downward social mobility may follow chronic disability. It seems unlikely, however, that the downward social mobility of disabled persons could alone produce so large a difference between social classes.

Equally large divergences are found in rates of disorder by marital state.[9] [*See Vol. 1, Chap. 2.3.c, pp. 32–33.*] These divergences too can be attributed in part to the social and self-selection of people who enter or remain in the social statuses of marriage, bachelorhood, or divorce and who may have characteristic predispositions to disease, the use of health services, and death. On the available evidence, however, part of the variations in disease and death rates among people in differing marital states can be ascribed, like the variations among social classes, to the different environments to which they are exposed.

Such variations with environment, both in longevity and health in old age, argue that public health action could attain throughout society at least the rates that exist under optimum conditions at the present time.

VARIABILITY IN MAJOR CAUSES OF DEATH AND DISEASE

Particular causes of mortality and morbidity in later life also vary with the environment. The exponential rise with age of rates of death from all causes combined, found in most societies today, has parallels in the age distributions of various specific causes of death. Coronary heart disease, a major cause of death in industrial societies, displays such a mortality curve, as in the instances shown in Figures 4 and 5.

Nevertheless, although the contour of coronary heart disease death rates displays so regular an association with age, this regularity does not admit the easy generalization that the disease can be attributed solely to the degeneration of tissues with aging. The increase in the incidence of coronary heart disease during the last half-century has been so sharp that the disease now assumes epidemic proportions among middle-aged and elderly men. Little doubt remains that the increase is not a mere statistical artifact. Moreover, marked variations occur in the incidence of coronary disease and deaths, not only at different times in the same country, but also among different countries, and among people with different experiences even though they belong to the same ethnic groups. In England and Wales in 1931 the death rate per 100,000 from coronary disease for men aged 45 to 69 was 49, whereas in 1957 it had risen to 359. In Israel, comparable differences were found among two categories of immigrant Yemeni Jews, even when the variables of race, diagnosis, and availability of

[9] M. Kramer, "Some Implications of Trends in the Usage of Psychiatric Facilities for Community Mental Health Programs and Related Research" (Paper read at the Annual Meeting of the American College of Neuropsychopharmacology, San Juan, Puerto Rico, 1965); A. M. Adelstein, D. Downham, Z. A. Stein, and M. W. Susser, "Epidemiology of Mental Illness in an English City," *Social Psychiatry*, 3 (1968), 47–59.

FIGURE 4 *Deaths from arteriosclerosis and degen-*
erative heart disease, by age, United States (1956)
and South Africa (1954 to 1956)
Deaths per 100,000 (logarithmic scale)

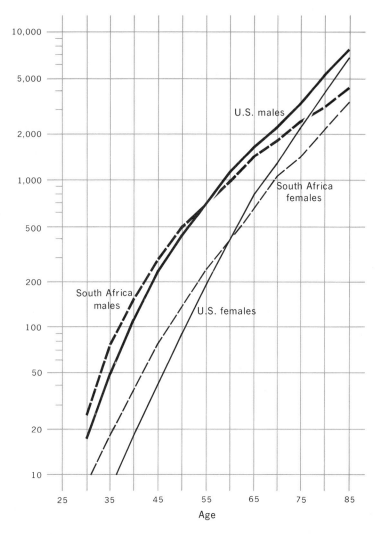

Source: A. M. Adelstein, "Some Aspects of Cardiovascular Mortality in South Africa,"
British Journal of Preventive and Social Medicine, 17 (1963), 29–40.

FIGURE 5 *Deaths from arteriosclerotic heart disease,[a]*
by age, sex, and ethnic group, South Africa
(1954 to 1958)
Deaths per 100,000 (logarithmic scale)

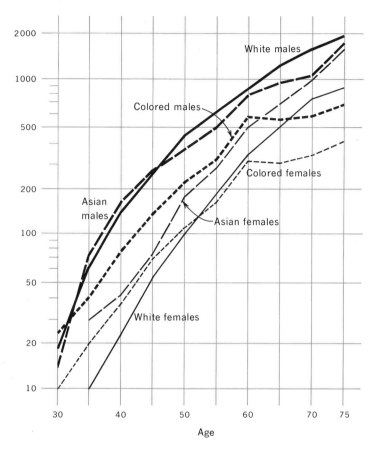

Note: Whites: *mean* 1954–1958. Coloreds and Asians: *mean* 1955–1957.
[a] Including coronary disease
Source: A. M. Adelstein, "Some Aspects of Cardiovascular Mortality in South Africa,"
British Journal of Preventive and Social Medicine, 17 (1963), 29–40.

medical services were constant.[10] For recent immigrants entering
Israel after 1948, the death rate in middle-aged men from degenerative heart disease (mainly coronary disease) was 49 per 100,000;
whereas for immigrants between the wars, who had been exposed to a
Western way of life for 20 years or more, the rate was as high as 330

[10] A. Kagan, "Atherosclerosis of the Coronary Arteries—Epidemiological Consideration," *Proceedings of the Royal Society of Medicine*, 53 (1960), 18–22.

per 100,000. Even if the lowest of these rates could be attributed entirely to the deterioration of aging, extraneous factors that are by implication preventable must cause the great excesses of coronary deaths that are made apparent by the higher rates.[11]

While the variable pathology of coronary disease afflicts men more than women and better displays its variability among them, variability in the rate of physiological development, which is in effect the obverse of the aging process, is better displayed among women. The available records of the past hundred years suggest that girls mature earlier than before, and that the age at the menarche has advanced by about four months each decade.[12] Recent studies suggest that women may also retain their reproductive functions longer than they used to; in Britain over the past century the menopause seems to have been deferred by some two to four years.[13]

The epidemiologic issues relating age to other specific and major causes of death and disease, like the cancers and cerebrovascular disease, are in principle the same as those set out in the preceding discussion. In general, closer examination of mortality and morbidity in terms of specific causes makes difficult the direct attribution to the aging process of any particular pathology. Multiple disorders afflict old people, yet few associations are found among such disorders, except where the links of pathogenesis follow one upon another, as in the sequence of hypertension and vascular disease of heart and brain.[14] Indeed, the essential characteristic of old age in the human being seems to be a *general* vulnerability to the forces of morbidity and mortality, for neither the state of old age nor the process of senescence has a single distinctive pathology. Nevertheless, some disorders are much more prominent causes of sickness and death in old age

---

[11] Indeed, several characteristics of the disease differ between younger and older men. Among the young, infarcts are more often large and caused by acute thromboses, whereas among the old the associations of the disease with high cholesterol levels, smoking, and lack of exercise are less clear-cut.

[12] J. M. Tanner, *Growth at Adolescence* (Oxford: Blackwell Scientific Publications Ltd., 1955).

[13] B. MacMahon and J. Worcester, "Age at Menopause," in *Age at Menopause, United States, 1960–1962*, PHS Pub. No. 1000, Series 11, No. 19 (Washington, D.C.: Government Printing Office, 1966), 1–9; M. Jeffereys and G. Cartwright, *The Age at the Menopause of British Women and the Prevalence of Related Symptoms* (mimeographed; Report of the work of a study group from the diploma in public health course, London School of Hygiene and Tropical Medicine and the Health Visitor Tutor Course, Royal College of Nursing, 1962–1963); D. J. Frommer, "Changing Age of the Menopause," *British Medical Journal*, 2 (1964), 349–351.

[14] L. A. Wilson, I. R. Lawson, and W. Brass, "Multiple Disorders in the Elderly," *Lancet*, 2 (1962), 841–843.

than others, and the best chance for the improvement of health in old age rests on prevention and control of these.

COHORT ANALYSIS

Whatever the hard core of deterioration caused by aging, understanding of the process has been obscured not only by scanty knowledge of environmental effects, but also by the weakness of some of the analytic procedures that have been applied to the available data. Typically, the studies we have been examining have tried to demonstrate variation with age and through time by *current analysis,* that is, by comparing the rates of disease or death in the several age groups viewed in cross-section at given points in time. This approach assumes that all the age groups have been exposed to similar conditions of life and differ only in duration of exposure. The assumption of similar conditions is often far from correct, however, because a central characteristic of our world is the increasing rapidity of social change so that every generation must experience an environment in some respects unique. Yet current or cross-section analysis fails to take this uniqueness into account. [*See Vol. 1, Chap. 1, pp. 1–11.*] *Cohort analysis* is an alternative that does take social change into account.[15] Here the analysis, in order to focus more nearly on the effects of aging, attempts to control for change through time, and the resulting differences in life experiences, by holding date of birth constant. Successive generations or cohorts are thereby compared age for age.[16] In

[15] More precisely, cohort analysis examines the joint effects of age and generation differences. On the one hand, it controls those effects of social change that distinguish one cohort from another, particularly differences in early experiences or exposures, in order to examine the effects of age; on the other hand, it controls the age variable in order to examine such cohort differences. This method can therefore be used to reveal effects of cohort differences in early life experiences that persist through time or that manifest themselves at later ages. By contrast, current analysis examines the joint effects of age and of environmental differences at successive points of time. On the one hand, it controls the current effects of environment by holding the date of observation constant, so as to focus on age; on the other hand, it controls age in order to examine these current effects. This method can therefore be used to reveal effects that are the immediate outcome of factors current at the time of observation, such as epidemics of acute infectious disease. Neither method of analysis can control both cohort effects and current environmental effects simultaneously, but each is appropriate for particular limited objectives.

[16] For practical reasons analysis of mortality by this method is a recent development in biomedical work, beginning some forty years ago: K. F. Andvord, "What Can We Learn by Studying Tuberculosis by Generations?" *Norsk. Mag. F. Laegevidensk,* 91 (1930), 642–660; W. O. Kermack, A. G. McKendrick, and P. L. McKinlay, "Death Rates in Great Britain and Sweden," *Lancet,* 226 (1934), 698–703; W. H. Frost, "The Age Selection of Mortality from Tuberculosis in Successive Decades," *American Journal of Hygiene,* Section A, 30 (1939), 91–96; V. H. Springett, "Comparative Study of Tuberculosis Mortality Rates," *Journal of Hygiene Cambridge,* 48 (1950), 361–395; and "An Interpretation of Statistical

order to carry out a cohort analysis, the events under examination are referred not to the year of occurrence (for instance, year of death in an analysis of mortality) but to the cohort designated by its point of entry into the relevant experience (for instance, year of birth, or year of entry into an institution).

With any condition that is affecting later generations (cohorts) either more or less than earlier ones, because of changes in cohort characteristics or in the life circumstances to which the cohorts were born, cohort analysis will reveal an association with age quite different from that shown by the more usual current or cross-section analysis. If, for example, a condition begins to rise in incidence among new cohorts of later birthdate, then the rise will be reflected in the cross-section curves, tending to create age peaks in the newly affected younger age groups, but without raising the rates among the old. Alternatively, if a condition begins to decline in incidence among new cohorts of later birthdate, then the decline will be reflected in the cross-section age curves by lowered rates among the young, but not necessarily among the old. The higher rates among these older age groups represent earlier cohorts that continue to manifest a residual incidence caused by their experience in earlier years, while the younger age groups representing later cohorts have escaped that experience and its effects on incidence. Thus cohort analysis of trends in the occurrence of disease is usually more discriminating than current or cross-section analysis in unraveling the variables of age and generation effect, and in sorting out the components of life-experience due to membership in particular cohorts from the components of intrinsic age changes. Where cohort analysis indicates a generation effect, by manifesting a changing pattern of some disease for successive generations, the field of investigation can often be narrowed because many factors (such as particular treatments or fashions in diagnosis which would presumably affect all age groups in the same way at the same time) may be seen to be incompatible with the generation effect. Cross-section analysis retains its greatest value in the study of factors with immediate effects.

Trends in Tuberculosis," *Lancet*, 262 (1952), 521–525, 575–579; R. A. M. Case, "Cohort Analysis of Mortality Rates as an Historical or Narrative Technique," *British Journal of Preventive and Social Medicine*, 10 (1956), 159–171; B. MacMahon, T. F. Pugh, and J. Ipsen, *op. cit*. Because of the length of the human life span, the life-experience of an adequate number of generations for comparison covers some hundred years, and forty or fifty years of data may be wanted to make a satisfying analysis. Data relating to the necessary time span have only recently accrued.

Increasing incidence   Death rates from lung cancer illustrate the case of a disease that is increasing and affecting cohorts of more recent birthdate with increasing frequency, as illustrated in Figure 6.[17] Although mortality from the disease is rising rapidly and the curve for every birth cohort shows deaths rising regularly with age (continuous lines in the figure), the curves for each date (broken lines in the figure) suggest that, after a peak around 70 years of age, the oldest age groups have relatively *lower* rates of lung cancer. Thus the cross-section data create the impression that the oldest individuals have become less susceptible, but this impression rests on the incorrect assumption that the age groups had equivalent experience.

Decreasing incidence   Death rates from tuberculosis in the United States illustrate the converse case of a declining disease that is affecting later cohorts with decreasing frequency. Figure 7a shows in the cross-section contours for successive dates the gradual disappearance of an age peak among young adults, together with a shift toward a pronounced peak in the residually affected older age groups. By contrast, the analysis by birth cohorts of Figure 7b shows a consistent age peak in the mid 20's.[18] The peak that emerges among older age groups in the cross-section analysis, which seemingly points to a newly acquired susceptibility among them, again appears as an artifact of the assumptions underlying the analysis by current age curves.[19]

Rise and fall in incidence   Death rates among males from peptic ulcer in England and Wales illustrate the age patterns of a disease that first waxed and has since begun to wane.[20] As this condition wanes, it too is now affecting later cohorts with decreasing frequency. At first sight, the trends of gastric and duodenal ulcer mortality are confusing in the extreme, as shown for male deaths in Figure 8. The trends appear to show a rise in death rates among the old during the

---

[17] U.S. Public Health Service, *Smoking and Health*, PHS Pub. No. 1103 (Washington, D.C.: Government Printing Office, 1964), 138.

[18] Wade Hampton Frost, a founding father of epidemiology in the United States, demonstrated this result in a paper published posthumously in 1939: W. H. Frost, *op. cit.*

[19] The residue of tuberculosis among old people, however, constitutes an important focus of infection that demands attention in public health practice. The same is true of typhoid; residual foci persist in old women with gall bladder infections who carry the disease and handle food.

[20] Mervyn W. Susser and Zena Stein, "Civilization and Peptic Ulcer," *Lancet*, 1 (1962), 115–119. From the point of view of public health, it can be said for peptic ulcer, as for coronary heart disease, that the environmental factors that cause such large fluctuations of the disease outweigh the significance of its intrinsic age-associations despite their regularity.

FIGURE 6 *Death rates for cancer of the lung and bronchus, by age, white males, United States, 1914 to 1961 (rate per 100,000 white males)*

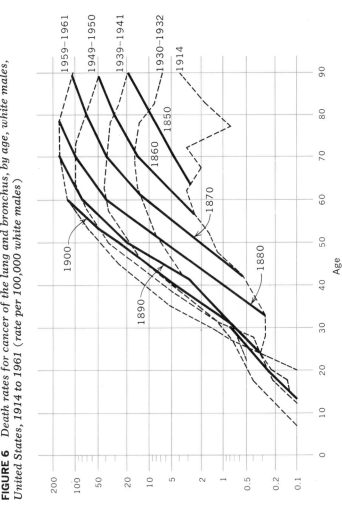

[a] Designated by central year of birth

[b] Designated by date of death (date contours)

Sources: B. MacMahon, T. F. Pugh, and J. Ipsen, *Epidemiologic Methods* (Boston: Little, Brown and Co., 1960), 94; U.S. Public Health Service, "Smoking and Health," PHS Pub. No. 1103 (Washington: Government Printing Office, 1964), 138; R. A. M. Case, "Cohort Analysis of Mortality Rates as an Historical or Narrative Technique," *British Journal of Preventive and Social Medicine*, 10 (1956), 159–171.

FIGURE 7 *Death rates for tuberculosis, by age,*
United States, 1900 to 1960 (per 100,000 population)

(a) Cross-section curves for selected dates of death, 1900 to
1960 (date contours)

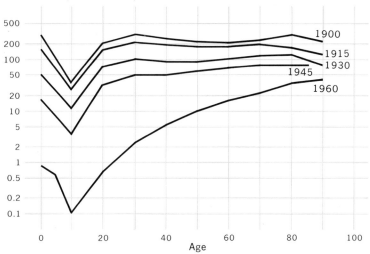

(b) Cohort curves for years of birth, 1860 to 1950[a]

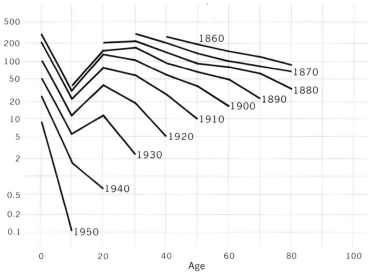

[a] The line associated with each year indicates death rates by age group for persons
born in that year.
Source: T. C. Doege, "Tuberculosis Mortality in the United States, 1900 to 1960,"
Journal of the American Medical Association, 192 (1965), 1045–1048.

FIGURE 8 *Death rates for peptic ulcer, cross-section curves for each age group,[a] males, England and Wales, 1900 to 1959 (death rates per 1,000,000 living males)*

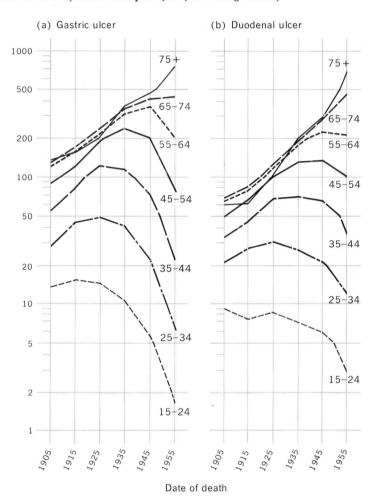

(a) Gastric ulcer (b) Duodenal ulcer

Date of death

[a] These age contours represent average of death rates for successive 10-year periods; each period is designated by central year of death.
Source: Mervyn Susser and Zena Stein, "Civilization and Peptic Ulcer," *Lancet,* 1 (1962), 115–119 (adapted).

past fifty years, but a fall among the young. Although biological phenomena are notorious for their irregularity as compared with the lesser vagaries of the physical world, the variability exhibited in these data is too great to make even biological sense. The data begin to make sense only when it is recognized that the diverging fan shape of these cross-section age curves for gastric and duodenal ulcer is characteristic of a condition that has both risen and fallen in frequency during the period of study.

When these same data are converted to cohort graphs, as in Figure 9, the regularity of the age association of the disease becomes evident. In order to avoid overlapping contours in these graphs, it is necessary to plot mortality for each age separately. Each birth cohort can be seen vertically, by reading upward from one age-contour to the next, while the differences among successive cohorts can be seen by reading horizontally along each age contour. With impressive regularity and regardless of age, the death rates rise for each of the cohorts born from the mid-nineteenth century until the last decade of that century; for all the more recent cohorts, rates decline. Thus the apparent divergence in the rates of peptic ulcer in different age groups through time is again an artifact of statistical and graphic representation.

Stable incidence   Suicide rates among white males in the United States illustrate the case of a cause of death that, though associated with age, has shown relative stability through time with little change in frequency between birth cohorts. [*See Vol. 1, Chap. 16.B.1, pp. 392–399.*] In such a case, a cohort analysis is no more informative than a cross-section analysis; both will reflect the absence of secular change. In the short run, suicide rates are sensitive to current social forces, and thus illustrate the special utility of current or cross-section analysis for phenomena affected by conditions associated with the time of observation (rather than with the time of birth). It can be readily seen from the cross-section age curves in Figure 10, for example, that regardless of age men showed a rise in the incidence of suicide after 1929 at the depth of the Depression, and a fall with the engagement of World War II.[21]

POTENTIAL FOR PRIMARY PREVENTION

At this juncture the implications of the preceding discussion can conveniently be drawn together. The afflictions of old age are produced by a combination, in unknown weights, of biological and environmental factors. In biological terms, senescence is a corollary of the processes of growth, organic differentiation, and development that arise in the course of evolution. The evolutionary forces affecting the fitness for survival of a species and its patterns of growth and development act

---

[21] B. MacMahon, S. Johnson, and T. F. Pugh, "Relation of Suicide Rates to Social Conditions," *Public Health Reports*, 78 (1963), 285–293.

FIGURE 9(a) *Death rates for peptic ulcer by age, cohort curves,[a] males, England and Wales (death rates per 1,000,000 living males)*

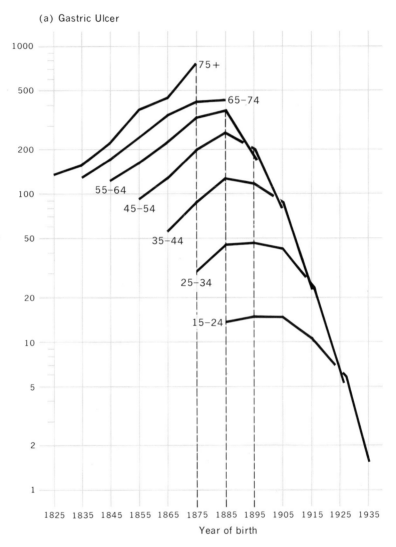

(a) Gastric Ulcer

[a] These age contours, arranged vertically in cohorts, represent averages of death rates for 10-year periods; each period is designated by central year of birth.
Source: Mervyn Susser and Zena Stein, "Civilization and Peptic Ulcer," *Lancet,* 1 (1962), 115–119 (adapted).

FIGURE 9(b)   *Death rates for peptic ulcer, by age,
cohort curves,ᵃ males, England and Wales (death
rates per 1,000,000 living males)*

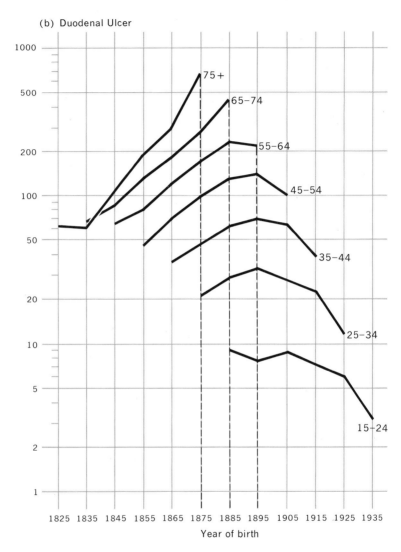

(b) Duodenal Ulcer

ᵃ These age contours, arranged vertically in cohorts, represent averages of death
rates for ten-year periods; each period is designated by central year of birth.
Source: Mervyn Susser and Zena Stein, "Civilization and Peptic Ulcer," *Lancet,* 1
(1962), 115–119 (adapted).

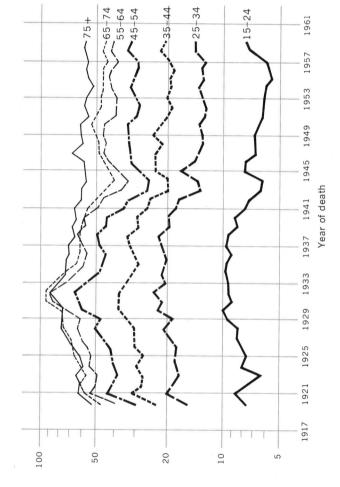

FIGURE 10 *Suicide death rates by age, cross-section curves, for each age group (age contours), United States, 1921 to 1964 (rates per 100,000 white males)*

Source: B. MacMahon, S. Johnson, and T. F. Pugh, "Relation of Suicide Rates to Social Conditions," *Public Health Reports,* 78 (1963), 285–293.

in the reproductive phase of the life cycle. The postreproductive phase, which is becoming increasingly important in our society, has not been subject to these evolutionary forces, since it could not have affected directly the survival of progeny and natural selection.[22] In other words, the postreproductive phase is an evolutionary backwater in which there is no known mechanism that can eliminate traits inimical to survival. Consequently, deterioration with aging in human individuals can be seen as the outcome of organic differentiation and development deferred to the postreproductive phase, or else as the outcome of an accumulation of injurious genetic characteristics whose effects are deferred to this phase.

In this light it appears that, when every alternative avenue for isolating and controlling environmental factors has been explored, a certain undetermined minimum of disorders will have to be ascribed to the biological aging process. The minimum has certainly not been reached, and the first hope of public health is still to prevent the onset of afflictions of old age. The known variations with environment in the incidence of major killing and disabling diseases are great enough to make the hope of such primary prevention a reasonable one to entertain for the future. Prevention of particular diseases may not add a great deal to the mean life expectancy of old people, however, because other pathologies may substitute for those that are avoided. Nonetheless, such prevention can surely add to the life expectancy and the quality of life for social groups now at a disadvantage. The way will thereby be cleared for research into deceleration of the aging process itself.

Social dependence and secondary prevention

Where primary prevention aimed at preventing the onset of disorder is not possible, public health looks to the methods of secondary prevention. These methods aim at the early detection of a disorder, with the object of early and effective intervention to stem its progress and alleviate its effects. Incipient social dependence arising out of deteriorating health presents a suitable target for secondary prevention. The appropriateness of these terms is affected by the frame of reference. For a profession like social work, the emphasis is on role behavior rather than on health, and to prevent the onset of dependence is primary prevention in relation to role.

The state of social dependence or its imminence in an old person

---

[22] P. B. Medawar, *An Unsolved Problem in Biology* (London: H. K. Lewis, 1952).

is a central problem in public health, for dependence is a source of economic, social, and mental strain to the affected person and to all on whom he depends. No one at any age can ever be independent of society, but the social dependence of old age has distinguishing features. These features are akin to those of the role of chronic sick persons at any age. Thus dependence in the elderly is likely to progress unless death intervenes; dependent old persons are often permanently exempt from normal social responsibilities; and it is recognized that they need help and must be cared for. Society accepts a legal obligation to provide for them, and many children feel a moral obligation to do so. [See Vol. 1, Chap. 23.B.2, pp. 550–554.]

For the purpose of this discussion, social dependence is defined as a condition of varying degree in which the individual is physically or mentally unable to perform social roles and individual functions that will insure for him the means of subsistence. The incidence and the effects of social dependence vary with the type of dependence as well as with the social setting. Inability to continue as a wage-earner may cause financial dependence. In the home, bodily incapacity may cause domestic dependence and, according to the severity of the disability, require assistance from others for such basic activities as dressing, bathing, feeding, and evacuation. In the extreme, the individual may sink into dependence on medical services for the continued physiological function of his cardiovascular, respiratory, or renal system. Information about the distribution of these various forms of dependence is scarce, and the public health reviewer or planner must often make do with crude and undiscriminating criteria of dependence.

The public health practitioner strives for secondary prevention of dependence by searching out disabilities, or incipient disabilities, and stemming their progress. To accomplish this in the face of the large and growing numbers of old people at risk, he must seek an economy of means. He must command effective treatment and know when and in what circumstances it may be useful to intervene. For this purpose he must identify the groups that are at highest risk, discover the events and time periods that commonly precede the decline into dependence, and recognize the circumstances that are dangerous to independence and those that favor it. Not only sickness and disability but also retirement, social isolation, and bereavement are circumstances in old age that can be critical for continued function. These circumstances might serve to mark out persons who require help in retaining independence and avoiding the further crisis of admission to institutional care. Each of these social circumstances will therefore be examined briefly.

Physical and mental incapacity due to disease is the overriding cause of social dependence. Disabilities reach a peak in the late 70's, and so too do the failures in social function that follow. [*See Vol. 1, Chap. 9, pp. 195–220; Chap. 10, pp. 221–229; Chap. 11, pp. 241–272.*] Some measure of the prevalence of social dependence due to organic causes is given, for example, by one survey of old men over 70 in Birmingham, England.[23] If the reliability and validity of the clinical judgments of the general practitioners who assessed these old men can be taken on trust, domestic help was necessary for 25 per cent aged 70 to 74 years, nursing that called on technical skills for 5 per cent, and nursing that involved care of the person for about 2 per cent. For men aged 80 to 84 years, the need for each service was at least twice as great. [*See Vol. 1, Chap. 9.2.i, pp. 217–218.*]

In general, the main medical problems are much accentuated beyond the mid-70's. Practitioners and hospitals devote proportionately more time to the care of old people than of the young, and the prevalence of "disability"[24] that restricts activity increases markedly with age. The capacity for movement is a useful yardstick of health, but restrictions of movement arise from a number of causes common to old age. After the age of 75 an increasing proportion of old people suffer restricted physical mobility, and after 80 many are confined to their homes. The causes of the decline in physical mobility include potentially lethal failures of heart, lungs, and brain. Nonlethal causes also assume importance in the 70's, including diminution in the sensorium, in muscle power and in joint movement, a tendency to falls, and the mundane disorders of urinary incontinence and of painful feet. In survivors over 80, mental disturbance, blindness and deafness, and incontinence of bladder and bowel all show a sharp rise in frequency, and octogenarians run a particular risk from falls, for these readily cause injuries or fractures of their frail bones.[25] Particular

[23] F. Edwards, T. McKeown, and A. G. W. Whitfield, "Incidence of Disease and Disability in Elderly Men," *British Journal of Preventive and Social Medicine,* 13 (1959), 51–58.

[24] Precision in the use of terms relating to disease and its consequences is not maintained in the medical literature. The disability of sickness, with incapacity for social roles, is a more general and inclusive measure of health than are particular disabilities. A particular disability in turn may be a more inclusive measure than impairments of the structure and function of particular tissues, or than the specific diseases (diagnoses) that cause the impairments. On the other hand, a specific disease may give rise to many particular disabilities as well as the general disability of sickness. Hence questions about operational definitions must constantly be asked in assessing the literature.

[25] J. H. Sheldon, "On the Natural History of Falls in Old Age," *British Medical Journal,* 2 (1960), 1685–1690.

disabilities are mediated by the local environment. For example, the fear of negotiating traffic often confines the aged to their homes, and they may be further restricted by steep stairs within their homes.

In old age the burden of illness is often more of a threat to the individual than death, especially for women. Sickness and particular disabilities are consistently more frequent in women than in men, although the death rates of men are higher than those of women. In the United Kingdom, for each man who has survived into the 80's there are approximately two women, and three women for each man who has survived into the 90's. [*For the United States, see Ex.* 2 · 4 *in Vol. 1, p. 19.*] The old women, who survive in greater numbers and are more often sick, therefore present a large health problem. The disparities in morbidity between men and women in old age probably reflect their experience of life as well as constitutional differences. The environmental hazards to which men and women are exposed are unequal, by virtue of sex differences in familial, occupational, and recreational activities. In addition, the differing demands of the social roles ascribed to men and women set different thresholds for complaints, as well as for the sick role exemptions permitted to each sex. Although men carry in their working phase a heavier load of severe and fatal illness than women, women in paid work make more complaints of minor illnesses, are more often absent from work, and receive more medical care than men.[26]

The potential for intervention Illnesses assume greater importance in old age because then they are often chronic or disabling. Failures of physiological function, diminished resistance to disease, and pathological changes tend to be cumulative and enduring, and readily initiate a cycle of decline into chronicity. Such risks of deterioration emphasize the need for intervention whenever it can be effective. Relief of the organic basis for perceived ill health can be expected to improve both health and morale, because there is an interplay between morale and disease; self-awareness of ill health in old people is associated with low morale and feeling old.

Many of the physical and mental disorders that underlie the disabilities of old people are amenable to treatment, and some are even reversible. Vision can be corrected and false teeth fitted. Prostates that cause problems of urinary continence can be removed, feet

---

[26] A. Cartwright and M. Jeffereys, "Married Women Who Work: Their Own and Their Children's Health," *British Journal of Preventive and Social Medicine*, 12 (1958), 159–171.

can be cared for, depressive psychosis relieved, and the outcome of stroke ameliorated.[27]

In the United States Title XVIII of the Social Security Amendments Act of 1965 (Medicare) is belated recognition of the confrontation of health services with the burden of disease and the slender resources of old people. The Medicare Act provides financial support for old people, in the manner of health insurance schemes but paid for out of social security funds.

The Act will not be sufficient in itself, however, to promote thorough case-finding and the early detection of disease. Services much more comprehensive and far-reaching than the regular services available through Medicare often fail to bring poor and isolated old people into medical care. To obtain participation, special efforts at communication and education in health matters must be made, for old people are less oriented toward prevention than the young. [*See Vol. 1, Chap. 14.1, pp. 317–323.*] Effort could be directed to groups among those approaching old age, as well as among the old, who are likely to lack the information, the perceptions, and the motivations that would enable them to make effective use of health care.

The service agencies themselves can help remove the barriers to participation created by their own administrative organization, social structure, and organizational culture. A number of working models exist for health education programs, and for clinics that screen old people through periodic health examinations and other forms of referral. These models should be evaluated and developed with a view to their being made generally available.[28]

Although certain aspects of secondary prevention in relation to dependence have been stressed here, other opportunities for preventive action should not be ignored. The location and construction of homes can help in the primary prevention of accidental injury and the deteriorative cycle that may follow. Education about food, and facilitation of its supply and preparation, can help to prevent malnutrition and deficiency disorders. Care in prescribing drugs can prevent poisonings. In the case of disabilities amenable to physical treatment, rehabilitation programs are essential to help prize the disabled person from the sick role, and to complete his social and psychological restoration to more normal roles.

[27] G. F. Adams, "Prospects for Patients with Strokes with Special Reference to the Hypertensive Hemiplegic," *British Medical Journal*, 2 (1965), 253–259.
[28] I. Starin and N. Kuo, "The Queensbridge Health Maintenance Service for the Elderly, 1961–1965," *Public Health Reports*, 81 (1966), 75–82.

Physical criteria alone are not sufficient to assess the health needs of old people in a community. The social circumstances in which the enfeeblement of age overtakes individuals, and the support available to them from kin and others, determines not only their need for social services, but also, in part, their need for medical care. Their circumstances affect their reactions to the advent of sickness, retirement, isolation, and bereavement; and these events in turn affect the capacity of old people for social independence and survival, and the social support available to them.

Retirement from work is an important landmark in the individual's progress through life, an overt sign that he has entered the phase of social replacement: For most individuals in our society, retirement is a first step toward social dependence. Full social responsibility is no longer enforced when the obligation to work ceases. The imminence of dependence is recognized by the community, and the governments of industrial societies provide pensions to alleviate the financial side of dependence among the old. [*Cf. Sheppard and Kreps, Chaps. 6 and 7 in this volume.*] Qualifying ages for pensions are set by government, while other large-scale organizations typically impose retirement at a defined age, which has the effect of keeping open the channels of promotion for the young. These circumstances have much reduced the proportion of old men who continue in employment. Those older men who are able to continue in their usual occupations tend to be self-employed or working in smaller and more flexible organizations, and in the higher occupational classes. [*See Vol. 1, Chaps. 3.A and 3.B, pp. 40–63.*]

General attitudes toward retirement are becoming more favorable and accepting, and an increasing number of men who retire (about two out of every three wage and salary workers) say they retire by their own decision. [*See Vol. 1, Chap. 18.C.2, pp. 447–451.*] A rising minority say that they prefer leisure to work, and most who continue in work give the chief reason as financial.

But among those who do retire, the chief reason given for not continuing is failing health. [*See Ex. 18 · 24 in Vol. 1, p. 448.*] Certainly men who continue in work are healthier than those who retire. Thus the causes of retirement are a legitimate public health question. It is not a simple question, and the nature of appropriate action requires discriminating study. Although men most often say they would continue to work for financial reasons, working into old age is commonest in occupations with high earnings where financial deprivation can only be relative and not absolute. Men in these occupations not only enjoy far better health than the poorly paid, but also the satisfactions they gain from work and their commitment to it are likely to be greater. There is, then, no single cause of retirement but a configuration of factors.

The effect of retirement, like its causes, is also a significant public health question. [See Vol. 1, Chap. 18.C.4, pp. 453–459.] Because ill health can cause retirement, to show that health can in turn be affected by retirement requires longitudinal studies that control for the state of health before retirement. A few available studies of sample populations show little effect *on the average*, using measures of death rates or illness. [See Vol. 1, Chap. 18.C.4.b, p. 454.] But case studies have shown, at least for certain individuals, that the sudden discontinuity in a major role brought about by retirement can lead to social maladjustment and acute emotional disturbance.[29]

So far, large-scale surveys have done little to give any full account of the transition into retirement, or to provide adequate tests of the dramatic descriptions provided by case studies. To be sure, retired men seem less well-adjusted to life than those at work. At the same time, the retired are selected from those who are comparatively less healthy, worse off, and of lower social status, and this selection may account for their poorer adjustment. Thus, the most dissatisfied among the retired are those who are poor and in bad health. Longitudinal study has indicated, however, that a shift in affect does tend to occur among retired people, though the shift is toward a state of mild dissatisfaction rather than dejection or despair. [*Vol. 1, Chap. 18.C.4.f, p. 458.*] Feelings of deprivation are most common when there was reluctance to retire and retirement had serious financial consequences. The fall in income with retirement is usually severe, often about one half, and those who earn least are bound to suffer most. Poverty has effects on health that are obvious and more serious to the integrity of the organism than mere dissatisfaction, as any *complete* sample of a population will reveal. The existence of these effects is a public health problem.

In sum, retirement comes as a blow to some, as a release to others. Responses are affected by anticipatory attitudes, and by material and social consequences, and thus depend upon the individual's position in society. Although retirement does not of itself seem to reduce the level of participation in available social roles, it reduces by one the number of roles available. [See Vol. 1, Chap. 18.C.4.e, pp.

[29] J. S. Tyhurst, "The Role of Transition States—Including Disasters—in Mental Illness," Symposium on Preventive and Social Psychiatry, Walter Reed Army Institute of Research, Washington, D.C., 1957, 149–169.

457–458.] The men most likely to continue in work are those who can exercise the choice to do so, are healthy, and gain satisfaction from work. An aim of public health, then, should be to help maintain people in better health so that they can exercise this choice. For those who do retire, the transition marks their entry into a social category for whom the risks of sickness and death are higher than for others, whether or not the transition itself heightens such risks. By retirement, men declare themselves an appropriate target for some form of health screening procedure. Screening can be tied in with the health programs run by trade unions and similar organizations for their retired members, thereby reducing the difficulty of reaching the entire population at risk.

ISOLATION

Social isolation has been indicted by ecological studies as a possible cause of schizophrenia, of certain mental disorders of the aged, of suicide and attempted suicide. It is a condition well suited to test the stability of an individual's values and norms of behavior, since these are no longer sustained by interaction and the continued reinforcement of what others expect.

The physical, psychological, and social elements of isolation overlap but are distinct. Old people living alone in physical isolation may not be socially isolated; many have close relatives nearby. Moreover they may be healthier than their age-peers who live with others. Among people over 80 in the northern English city of Stockport, for example, those who lived alone were evidently the independent survivors; the dependent sick lived with kin or in institutions. The independent old people often lived in meager circumstances, however, and failed to husband their resources or to maintain an adequate diet.[30]

Psychological isolation also, although it occurs more frequently with physical or social isolation, may not always coincide with them. Many socially isolated persons do not complain of loneliness, but pursue with equanimity the limited social intercourse to which they are accustomed. Conversely some, especially those who have suffered recent bereavement, feel lonely even though they share homes with others. Loneliness brings with it feelings of loss of affection and uselessness, and is associated with low levels of activity. [See Vol. 1, Chap. 15.6.a, pp. 353–354; Chap. 17.3, pp. 415–416.]

Social isolation may be the involuntary consequence of a set of related conditions. It affects chiefly the old, and chiefly women among

[30] C. F. Brockington and S. M. Lempert, *The Social Needs of the Over-80's* (Manchester: Manchester University Press, 1966).

the old, because they survive in greater numbers than men and out-live their spouses. Restricted physical mobility and the loss of spouse and peers further diminish social contact, while those who never married will have neither spouse nor children. Retirement enforces withdrawal from a major set of social relations. In certain instances, social isolation can be a voluntary withdrawal from interaction and participation in reciprocal roles; this may be the characteristic life-style of a minority.

The association of physical and social isolation with feelings of loneliness, low levels of activity, inadequate nutrition, and poor living conditions brings a vulnerable group into focus for public health at-tention. At the same time the very isolation of these people makes them relatively inaccessible to services. They are infrequent users of health and caretaking agencies,[31] except at that late stage when ad-mission to an institution is the only recourse. [*See Vol. 1, Chap. 14.1.e, pp. 321–323; Chap. 25.1, pp. 579–583.*] Effective health care for this social category of isolates requires a special effort, not only to mobilize resources but to reach them.

BEREAVEMENT

The feature that most often distinguishes those who feel lonely from others in a like situation is a recent bereavement or separation. [*See Vol. 1, Chap. 23.A.3, pp. 540–541.*] The death of a spouse in the previous five or ten years is characteristically accompanied by symp-toms of loneliness, though less so as time goes on.[32] Feelings of loneliness can express the emotional reaction to bereavement.

Bereavement at any age is likely to be a major crisis in the life of the individual; but partners who have survived together into old age have achieved a habitual distribution of roles and duties in their domestic relations and in their social relations with others outside the home, and their personal relations move in deep and customary grooves. In these circumstances, widowhood results in a drastic change, even if the dead partner had been languishing, and the sur-viving spouse is faced with the necessity of readjusting to new situa-tions at an age when transitions are not easily made.

Research into the effects of widowhood has shown that widowhood is associated with high death rates. It has proved difficult, however, to establish that the loss of a spouse actually causes the accelerated

---

[31] *Ibid.*

[32] Peter Townsend, *The Family Life of Old People* (London: Routledge and Kegan-Paul, 1957); B. Kutner, "Modes of Treating the Chronically Ill," *Gerontologist*, 4 (1964), 44–48.

death of the surviving partner.[33] Spouses share more personal and cultural attributes with each other than with the population at large, and they also share a common domestic environment. Thus the forces that cause the untimely death of one marital partner may act equally upon the survivor. The difficulties in interpreting the mortality data are compounded by technical difficulties that reside in the different sources of the numerators and denominators.[34] Moreover, the populations assigned to each marital state are not of comparable ages.

Morbidity as well as mortality rates appear high among the widowed. High rates of mental illness, for instance, have several times been reported. [See Vol. 1, Chap. 16.A.4.c, pp. 391–392.] As with other aspects of disease, when mental disorder is studied in hospital patients, social and psychological correlates may be found because such factors influence hospital admission rather than the disease itself. Bereavement is such a factor, for it may throw a surviving but already dependent person onto the charge of supportive agencies, while other equally ill persons are maintained by their spouses in their own homes. In one incidence study, the likelihood of a spurious association of this kind was reduced by including all mental illness coming into psychiatric care from an entire community, and first entry into psychiatric care was indeed found to be related to recent transition into widowhood.[35] A similar relationship has been found with suicide.[36] Although these results support those case studies that have described emotional reactions of bereavement,[37] they have not established the risk as peculiar to old age; indeed, it seems not improbable that the most severe consequences may occur among younger persons.

Whatever the psychological effects of bereavement on the aged may be, the social effects mark a step toward displacement from previous roles and toward the eventual possibility of social dependence and institutional care. Widowhood, like retirement, can serve as a

---

[33] A. S. Kraus and A. Lillienfield, "Some Epidemiologic Aspects of the High Mortality Rate in the Young Widowed Group," *Journal of Chronic Disease*, 12 (1959), 207–217.

[34] M. Young and B. Benjamin, "The Mortality of Widowers," *Lancet*, 2 (1963), 454–456; J. Berkson, "Mortality and Marital Status," *American Journal of Public Health*, 52 (1962), 1318–1328.

[35] Mervyn W. Susser, *Community Psychiatry: Epidemiologic and Social Themes* (New York: Random House, Inc., 1968); Zena Stein and Mervyn W. Susser, "Widowhood and Mental Illness," *British Journal of Preventive and Social Medicine*, 23 (1969).

[36] B. MacMahon and T. F. Pugh, "Suicide in the Widowed," *American Journal of Epidemiology*, 81 (1965), 23–31.

[37] E. Lindemann, "Symptomatology and Management of Acute Grief," *American Journal of Psychiatry*, 101 (1944), 141–148; P. Marris, *Widows and Their Families* (London: Routledge and Kegan Paul, 1958).

marker for routine public health screening. A simple procedure to identify vulnerable persons makes use of the official certificates attesting the death of a spouse.

SOCIAL SUPPORT AND INSTITUTIONS

A frequent end point of the process leading to dependence is admission to an institution. [*See Vol. 1, Chap. 25, pp. 577–596.*] This point is reached when the burden of caring for an old person outweighs social support. One inference that can be drawn from the marital state of old people admitted to institutions is that they are likely to have a minimum of available family support. In geriatric and mental hospitals and nursing homes there is an excess of single men, single women, and widowers, in that order. In Bethnal Green in London even the married who had no children, or whose children were dispersed, entered institutions more often than others. In other words, old people with available support from kin make the least claim on institutions, and those isolated from kin the heaviest.

The preference that people in our society show for an independent household, which does not decrease with age, is manifested by the elderly in living arrangements of various forms. Many independent old people live entirely alone, and their ranks are continually recruited from the widowed. The widowed without available children sometimes renew contact with siblings, and thus find a surrogate for the spouse. In one English study of old people in a working-class community, almost half the unmarried formed couples with siblings or others,[38] though in the United States this is a less typical arrangement. Some elderly people themselves share households with aged parents.

The continuing independence of these households is related to the physical capacity and the social and economic resources of their members. Old people who possess financial reserves can afford to pay for services that preserve their independence, whether or not a supportive social network is available to them. For the many old people in poverty, however, relationships with family and friends inside or outside the household take on major significance. It is doubtful that any existing public system of agencies and pensions fully meets the needs of old people whose powers are declining but who continue to live in independent households. In these circumstances, kin relations play a large part in independence. Several studies show the contribution relatives make in preventing old people from falling a charge on the community. [*See Vol. 1, Chap. 23.B.2, pp. 550–554.*]

[38] Townsend, *The Family Life of Old People.*

The cycle of family development is evidently an important determinant of the forms that interdependence takes among family members. In contemporary industrial societies, extension of the postreproductive phase, reflecting a combination of increased longevity and compression of the childbearing years, has had a great impact on the cycle of family development. A long phase of independence free of formal obligations to children has emerged, and although large numbers enter the "phase of replacement" as they give up productive social roles, many older couples can delay until advanced old age the stage where kin obligations are reversed and it is they who require support.

The support rendered by old people's social networks is a resource that public health agencies do well to recognize. The form of these networks is largely determined by the extent to which children and siblings have been socially and spatially mobile, and will tend to differ according to the older person's own occupations and social class. At one extreme, social networks are close-knit and contained, at another, loose-knit and dispersed; and each type is likely to have characteristic modes of reciprocity, exchange, and responsibility.[39]

Independent old people do not favor institutional life, although once they are inmates, they may become more accepting or resigned. Judging by many accounts of institutions, such negative attitudes are well-founded.[40] Although institutions vary a great deal in the kind of care and facilities they provide, they have in common a comprehensiveness that often envelops all the activities of the individual. The impact of their social structure and culture on the social behavior of residents is inevitably powerful and potentially damaging.[41]

Evaluation of the effects of institutions on the well-being of old people is a task that public health can undertake. Public health agencies often have the official assignment to inspect institutions so as to maintain standards of care. Scientific evaluations of care and living

[39] E. Bott, *Family and Social Network* (London: Tavistock Publications Ltd., 1957); Townsend, *The Family Life of Old People;* M. Young and P. Wilmott, *Family and Kinship in East London* (London: Routledge and Kegan Paul, 1957).

[40] Peter Townsend, *The Last Refuge: A Survey of Residential Institutions and Homes for the Aged in England and Wales* (London: Routledge and Kegan Paul, 1962).

[41] E. Goffman, "Characteristics of Total Institutions," Symposium of Preventive and Social Psychiatry, Walter Reed Army Institute of Research, Washington, D.C., 1957, 43–84; R. L. Coser, "Alienation and the Social Structure: Case Analysis of a Hospital," in E. Freidson (ed.), *The Hospital in Modern Society* (New York: Free Press, 1963), 231–265.

arrangements are beginning to be made;[42] codes for nursing homes and convalescent homes have been written;[43] and the Medicare legislation has made explicit the concern of Federal authorities. The standards established in the past have usually been limited to such matters as hygiene, crowding, and sanitation. This area of interest could be extended, with profit, to the quality of social relations and their effects.

Conclusion

This review has taken as its brief the interpretation of research findings in the context of the public health ideal of prevention. Consequently little has been said about the administrative work of public health agencies in the field of old age. Public health administration has grown in significance as the configurations of disease in the population have changed. With the effective control of acute and serious infectious disorders, the focus of public health has shifted to the growing numbers of persons with chronic diseases, many of them ambulant, who are in need of care. To meet the needs of these large numbers, impressive among the aged, new forms of administrative action are required of health agencies. [*Cf. Morris, Lasagna, and Schwartz, Chaps. 2, 3, and 4 in this volume.*] Thus public health agencies have assumed the function of developing facilities for the aged including housing, various forms of home, day, and residential care, and special clinics. They have invented programs for homemaking, home nursing, and rehabilitation, as well as a variety of educational and case-finding methods. They have conceived new caretaker roles, and have educated the persons who must fill them.

These programs, although they show what can be done, are far from being universal practice. Even in the best-served areas, administrations provide only some of these activities and cover only a modest proportion of the population at risk. In assessing the existing standards of public health services for old people, it is salutary to examine the conclusions of a detailed report from a country where health and welfare services have been given on the principle that they should be

[42] H. R. Kelman and J. Muller, "Role of the Hospital in the Care of the Ambulatory Chronically Ill and Disabled Patient after Discharge," *American Journal of Public Health,* 57 (1967), 107–117; R. P. Walkley, Wiley P. Mangum, Jr., S. R. Sherman, S. Dodds, and D. M. Wilner, *Retirement Housing in California* (Berkeley and San Francisco, Calif.: Diablo Press, 1966).

[43] R. E. Trussell, "The Quality of Medical Care as a Challenge to Public Health," *American Journal of Public Health,* 55 (1965), 173–182.

free, comprehensive, and available to all. In England, in the town of Stockport in Lancashire, a socio-medical survey was made of the total population over 80.[44] The completeness of the survey was checked in several ways, so that it does not suffer from the unrepresentativeness of many urban surveys. The authors write as follows:

In general it could be said that help was given at a point of relative or absolute breakdown. Thus it was most obviously available when family care had broken down and when the old person could no longer manage by himself. No amount of domiciliary services at this stage could be expected greatly to improve the situation. It was then a question of institutional care with every effort concentrated on making institutional life as home-like as possible. . . .

Prevention, in the sense of having as its primary object to avoid undue deterioration and ultimate breakdown, could hardly be said to have existed. The general practitioners were able to supply the names of only about a quarter of the total over-80 population and after making every allowance for the difficulties of their record keeping, it must be assumed that domiciliary medical care was not primarily preventive in character. The health visitors (public health nurses) visited 34,133 houses in 1956; but less than one-tenth were classed as visits to old people. Re-housing was being carried out in such a way that the old people and the younger generation were separated. The single and those living with single sons and alone, and those in Social Class IV and V, where social problems are most frequently encountered, did not receive any special consideration. No action was taken at danger periods, i.e., on leaving the hospital and on the death of the spouse. Social visiting was not directed to the real needs for sociability as revealed in the survey. The services themselves were inadequately used and often ill directed. The authorities responsible for providing services did not know of the existence of the people who were to benefit from them and had certainly not succeeded in getting the old people themselves to know what was available to them.

A general consequence of these failings, singly and together, appeared to be unnecessary admission to an institution on social grounds and failure to survive.

In most parts of the United States at the present time, there is little reason to think that the health and welfare services—often limited in scope and available only to those who by some derogatory official procedure can demonstrate that they are eligible—are doing better than those of Stockport from the point of view of public health. Much can be done for old people by a public health approach, and it is the responsibility of public health to see that it is done.

[44] Brockington and Lempert, *op. cit.*

6

Aging and manpower development

HAROLD L. SHEPPARD

This essay is addressed to the spectrum of persons engaged in the many phases of occupational counseling, and to those responsible for public policies affecting the labor force: (a) personnel directors and staff in commercial establishments, government and civic organizations, employment offices, and labor unions; (b) corporate managers and directors; (c) legislators and public officials, as they make decisions involving personnel policy; and (d) labor economists and industrial sociologists working in applied aspects of their disciplines.

Doctor Sheppard's discussion is organized in two main parts. In the first part, he attempts to go beyond or behind the statistics on the labor force participation of older workers, concluding, for example, that age discrimination by employers and employment services prevents many qualified older workers from finding jobs. Furthermore, older persons are often handicapped by lower achievement motivation and by failure to utilize effective job-seeking techniques. Despite existing barriers, Doctor Sheppard suggests that age-related differences between younger and

*older workers can be minimized by retraining programs devel-
oped specifically to deal with learning needs, attitudes, and motivations of older persons; by further prohibition of age-discrimination in employment; and by redesign of jobs to suit the
capacities of older workers.*

*In the second place, Doctor Sheppard reconsiders these sta-
tistical trends and alerts us to the many fallacies inherent in
the use of unrefined data. There are great differences, for example, between full-time and part-time employment, between
labor force participation rates and "work experience," between
"younger" and "older" workers in the 65-plus category, and so on.
Perhaps the most intriguing question raised concerns the effect
of education. As educational levels rise in the future, Doctor
Sheppard points out, the work behavior and labor force participation of older people are likely to show quite different patterns
which may present new and unexpected problems and opportunities.*

*Advisers for this chapter were Geneva Mathiasen, National
Council on the Aging, New York, New York; Walter J. McNamara, Personnel Assessment Programs, International Business
Machines Corporation; and Charles E. Odell, United States Employment Service, Department of Labor.*

ON THE RELEVANCE OF VOLUME ONE

*Of significance for both practice and policy are the wide range
of social science findings on work activity in the later years
which are summarized in Chapters 3 and 18 of Volume One. In
today's labor market, many older people are disadvantaged in
respect to health (see Chapter 9) or educational background,
and are comparatively unlikely to participate in retraining programs (discussed in Chapter 5); however, older individuals vary
greatly and there is little indication that their average ability to
perform in many types of jobs is any lower than that of younger
men. But despite the potential work performance of many older
persons and the fact that retirement is generally accompanied by
marked reductions in income (as described in Chapter 4), release from work obligations and the freedom for leisure pursuits
(see Chapter 22) appear to be widely acceptable to the American
public, raising the possibility that a new leisure ethic may replace, or at least coexist with, that of work.*

It may be ironic, if not paradoxical, that the emergence of a society that enables increasing proportions of its members to live more than 60 years is the same society in which a smaller proportion of those living to be "old" are defined as wanted or "needed" participants in the productive population—the labor force. The transition from an agricultural to an industrial-urban economy has been accompanied by a decreasing utilization of older persons, especially males. And even among older persons who are employed within today's basically industrial economy, a disproportionate number are found in the agricultural sector. [*See Vol. 1, Chap. 3.A.1, pp. 40–43; and 3.B.2, pp. 53–56.*]

INTENDED AUDIENCE

The purpose of this chapter is to orient training and personnel specialists, as well as interested laymen, to the occupational status and employment problems of older workers. Actually, there is at this time no clear-cut, neatly demarcated "audience" for such a chapter. In the first place, "industrial gerontology" is an infant specialty. Second, personnel managers and employment agency professionals (in public and private agencies) expert in the solution of older worker problems are extremely rare. Although we are now beginning to see the emergence of "older worker specialists" (or counselors) in the public employment service offices, these are few in number, and their training (often their experience) certainly has not been directed to the problems considered in this chapter. Equally important, there is no guarantee of the permanence of this specialty. Interest in the older worker at the governmental bureau level has waxed and waned, depending largely on the whims of individual administrators rather than upon the objective demand for such attention. Nevertheless, the passage, in late 1967, of legislation outlawing age discrimination in employment will certainly provide an impetus to the development of a permanent interest, a body of trained personnel, and a search for ways in which to facilitate the implementation of the law.

This chapter may therefore be said to be addressed to those in the field of personnel management in general and, in particular, to the gradually emerging cadre of older worker specialists and counselors in the United States Employment Service. In addition, it may interest scholars and educated laymen who have researched, thought, or expressed themselves about the capacities and the future of workers as they become old. Because so many personnel managers, employment agency officials, and opinion-making citizens are complacent or poorly informed, much of the essay is devoted merely to setting the record straight and to defining this record as a basis for a general recognition of a social problem. In short, practitioners in "industrial gerontology" are in need of a perspective that will guide their actions toward a positive set of policies and programs. A good deal of this chapter is thus an attempt to develop such a perspective. Although a few practical measures are suggested that can be adapted by professionals who directly or indirectly affect the work lives of older men and women, the major stress is on "why-do-it" and less on "how-to-do-it."

THE MATERIAL TO BE CONSIDERED

The task is to identify and develop the implications for manpower development of the impressive inventory of research findings that is in Volume One of *Aging and Society*. We have only begun to take small, hesitant first steps in defining the problem of the older worker. The next stage (beyond taking giant steps in this process of problem-definition) is to develop, on the company and community level, an ongoing program of special training techniques, job redesign, and realistic counseling, as part of a national effort to reduce and prevent the negative consequences to self and society of being an older worker in our dynamic economy.

Contrary to the usual treatment of the employment and training problems of older workers, which first presents historical trends and contemporary patterns of age differences based on national aggregate data, the first part of this chapter will attempt to go beyond the usual statistics. Much of the presentation initially may appear to be technical and/or scholarly, that is, of limited value to "practical" men and women. But the nature of the topic is such that a fresh look requires both an unsettling of stereotypes and a challenge to policy-making based solely on *averages* and *overall* trends. What is needed is a "functional" as well as a categorical approach to older workers.

Following a brief consideration of the range of external factors—hiring policies, shutdowns, mass lay-offs—that affect the status of older employees and job seekers, three topics will be brought into specific focus. First, a case study of the *job-seeking behavior* of older workers is reported in some detail, along with a consideration of the social-psychological and institutional factors that affect this behavior and its outcome. The next section, focusing on *training*, is designed to persuade practitioners of the feasibility as well as the desirability of expanding the participation of older workers in training programs. Such expansion requires, however, new departures in the creation of special training techniques designed to overcome any learning handicaps that older workers may have, either because of previous educational deficiencies or because of psychological tendencies acquired as a result of "environmental insults" over time. The final section of this part is devoted to a relatively new proposal for the solution of older worker problems, that is, *job redesign*. It is hoped that the brief description to be presented of the potentials of job redesign will stimulate greater interest on the part of industry, the unions, and government.

The second major part of this chapter is somewhat more analytical and statistical, suggesting the global foundations of what may well develop into a new field: applied industrial gerontology. The material deals with recent trends in labor force participation rates of older men and women; the importance of the distinction between such rates and data on actual work experience; the role of education in explaining age differences in occupation and employment; the increasing need for recognizing the heterogeneity of the over-65 labor force; the need to distinguish between (a) analyses of workers as they themselves grow older ("cohort analysis") and (b) comparisons between the statuses at any one point in time of workers in different age groups; the critical nature of the 45–54-year-old part of the work cycle; and the possibility that the increase in the general educational level of all Americans will in the future tend to blur age differences in occupational and employment status.

Beyond the statistics

The emergence of an "older worker problem" is the unintended consequence of more than a secular shift from agriculture to industrialism. It is also a cumulative result of recurrent cutbacks in employment and shutdowns, company relocations, and temporary illnesses occurring in the work lives of older workers, starting perhaps in their mid- and late-forties. The micro-economics of the older worker problem frequently originate with such experiences. Although such phenomena recur in good times and bad, we have few systematically collected data on mass lay-offs and similar events. One of the few such studies, carried out by the Department of Labor, indicates that between July, 1963, and June, 1965, 525 establishments reported mass lay-offs, affecting nearly 190,000 employees.[1] Frequently, such establishments (especially those going out of business or relocating) are in older and declining sectors of the economy and likely to employ a high

---

[1] See Robert E. Smith, "The Impact of Mass Layoffs," *Proceedings of 18th Annual Meeting of Industrial Relations Research Association, New York, 1965* (Madison, Wisc.: IRRA, 1966), 204–219.

percentage of older workers. After many years of steady employment in a given company or industry, the older worker thus unemployed must then join the ranks of other, younger job-seekers and undergo a greater number of obstacles to reemployment. Some of these obstacles are *individual*, attributes of the worker himself, including inadequacy in job-seeking skills and attitudes. Some of them are *institutional*, including the types of services rendered by employment service office personnel, and the hiring policies of potential employers.

Employer hiring policies have not changed much over the past few decades, despite the occasional "show case" example of an exceptional company here and there. The most recent systematic attempt to provide an overall picture, undertaken by the Department of Labor, is contained in the Secretary of Labor's report to Congress in June, 1965, entitled *The Older American Worker*. [*See Vol. 1, Chap. 3.B.4.c, pp. 62–63.*] The report documents an employer bias—whether rational or nonrational—against the hiring of older job-seekers. More than one-half of all private employers in states without age-discrimination legislation in 1965 admitted utilizing age limits in hiring practices. About one-half of all the job openings among such employers were barred to applicants over 55; one-quarter, to those over 45. As the report states, "An unmeasured but significant proportion of the age limitations presently in effect are arbitrary in the sense that they have been established without any determination of their actual relevance to job requirements, and are defended on grounds apparently different from their actual explanation." [*See Vol. 1, Chap. 18.B.1, pp. 426–434.*]

Unfortunately, the macro-statistics to be found in reports of the Department of Labor and the Census Bureau—indispensable as they are—do not tell the complete story of the older workers and their problems. What is needed to fill out the picture must be found in micro-economics and micro-sociology, that is, through systematic and detailed case studies which yield information on the behavioral and social-psychological level. Ideally, such studies should be longitudinal. The two government agencies named above do not seek such information on a scale comparable to the kinds of data they do report, although there is no methodological reason why they cannot.

THE VALUE OF SMALL, INTENSIVE STUDIES

Many smaller studies merely verify generalizations based on standardized Census and Labor Department data, for example, the lower rate of unemployment of older workers or their higher rate of long-term unemployment once unemployed. But such smaller studies may also help to answer further questions. What happens to older workers once they do become unemployed? What factors affect their subsequent employment status? If they do become reemployed, at what skill and wage levels? What is their job-seeking behavior? What is their experience with employment agencies and potential employers?

The role of education and skills The findings of several studies should put to rest the easy "conclusion" permeating much of the literature, namely, that age is not the "real" reason for the problems of older job-seekers—the "real" reason being that such persons happen also to be less educated, less skilled than younger job-seekers and that, as a logical result, employers will naturally choose the better-skilled, better-educated applicants (who just happen to be younger).

Some studies indicate that even among older manual workers with above-average education, chances of reemployment after having lost a regular job are no better than among those with less education. Wilcock and Franke found this to be true in the cities they studied in 1959.[2] In 1964, Sheppard and Belitsky found that among job-seekers aged 39 and older, skilled workers were no better off than lesser-skilled workers of the same age group.[3] In their report on the aftermath of the Packard Motor shutdown, Sheppard, Ferman, and Faber[4] found that the older the ex-Packard workers, the less likely they were to obtain reemployment in the same industry, auto manufacturing, although such men may be assumed to have *remained* qualified to fulfill the job requirements in that industry.

In a rather extensive study based on multiple classification analysis of the characteristics of over two thousand hard-core unemployed persons in Detroit in 1962, Howard Wachtel found that even when many other factors—education, sex, labor force attachment, etc.— were taken into account, age was *still* found to be significantly related to the unemployment status of the workers studied.[5] The analysis revealed education to be important, of course, but only slightly more so than age per se. Even when education was held constant, age remained a significant variable affecting the unemployment experience of the population analyzed. Out of a total list of eight factors, age was

[2] Richard C. Wilcock and Walter H. Franke, *Unwanted Workers* (New York: Free Press, 1963), 55–57.

[3] Harold L. Sheppard and A. Harvey Belitsky, *The Job Hunt* (Baltimore: Johns Hopkins Press, 1966), 19.

[4] Harold L. Sheppard, Louis Ferman, and Seymour Faber, *Too Old to Work, Too Young to Retire*, U.S. Senate Special Committee on Unemployment Problems (Washington, D.C.: Government Printing Office, 1960), 18–22.

[5] Howard Wachtel, "Hard-Core Unemployment in Detroit: Causes and Remedies," in *Proceedings of 18th Annual Meeting of Industrial Relations Research Association, New York, 1965* (Madison, Wisc.: IRRA, 1966), 233–241.

the fourth most important explanation for their employment problems.

The Job Hunt, by Sheppard and Belitsky, covered in great detail the job-seeking behavior of a sample of over five hundred workers in a local economy who had been unemployed at one time or another in a given period of approximately fifteen months prior to being interviewed. To begin with, they found not only that older workers (aged 39 and older) were less successful in finding new jobs but also that those who *were* reemployed (including skilled older workers) received wage rates below those earned on the old job. The *opposite* was true for younger workers who generally were earning *more* in their new jobs.[6]

Wage expectations   An additional suggested explanation for the greater reemployment problem of older workers has been that their wage demands may be higher than those of younger job-seekers, which might operate as a handicap when competing for available job vacancies. This hypothesis was tested in *The Job Hunt.*

Workers were first asked the question, "When you've been looking for a new job, do you have some hourly wage or weekly salary that you won't go below—that is, do you have in mind some *minimum* wage or salary?" If they answered yes, they were then asked to name the wage or salary figure.

There was no difference in proportions of younger and older workers stating they did have some minimum wage level below which they would not accept a job offer. Slightly more than 70 per cent of each age group reported they had some figure in mind. Moreover, reemployment success among older workers with some minimum wage in mind was identical to that for older workers who said they did not have any wage floor. At each level of wage expectation, however, older workers were reemployed to a lesser extent than younger workers.

THE JOB HUNT

Thus the employment problems of older job-seekers are not susceptive of easy explanations. In an effort to contribute to analysis of such complex problems, additional selected findings from *The Job Hunt* are reported at some length. This study is reported in some detail also because it draws attention to the obvious fact that people do not sud-

[6] Sheppard and Belitsky, *op. cit.* "Older" in this study was any worker aged 39 or over, the median age of the total sample interviewed. Even when analysis was restricted to those 39–50, the generalizations cited here held in nearly every case. Although the total number in the study was over 500, including females and all white-collar workers, many of the comparisons in this chapter are based on 309 male blue-collar workers, or a more limited number of 176 of the latter, after excluding those men eventually recalled by their former employers.

denly become "old." In the world of work an "older person" is frequently one who has barely passed his 40th birthday.

Much of the literature on unemployed workers, young and old alike, is concentrated exclusively on the role of external factors in the outcome of their search for reemployment. There is little consideration of the reciprocal nature of the interaction between employer demand or the level of economic activity, on the one hand, and the characteristics of the job-seeker (including skill, age, and job-seeking behavior), on the other. *The Job Hunt* was an attempt to determine the role of the latter set of factors, especially job-seeking behavior.

The findings from *The Job Hunt*, though exploratory and tentative in character, are cited here in order to supplement the massive aggregate statistics on older worker employment status emanating from official sources—statistics that take no consideration at all of the *behavioral* and *attitudinal* variables that may have a critical bearing on the meaning of such statistics. It is not that these statistics are impersonal and leave out the "human factor"—to invoke an old cliché—but rather that in themselves they provide a weak foundation on which to draw sound inferences, or through which to derive comprehensive explanations. And without sound inferences and comprehensive explanations, the costly result may be misguided policy-making, program design, and implementation.

When they became unemployed, older blue-collar workers waited, on the average, less than one week before they started their job hunt, and in this respect were no different from younger workers. The major exception was in the case of those workers who expected to be called back to their old jobs. In this group of workers, the older ones delayed the search for a new job longer than did younger workers. One-half of the young workers expecting a call-back began their job hunt before the end of one week after being laid off, in contrast to less than one-third of the older workers.

Once they did start looking, older workers used a smaller number of different job-seeking techniques than did younger, out of a total list of eight methods and sources of job-leads (such as using the Employment Service, direct company application, and checking newspaper ads). This does not adequately explain, however, the fact that fewer older workers found reemployment, since even among those men aged 39 and older who used at least six of the eight techniques, job-finding success was much lower than for younger workers.

Approaching employers for a new job   In the first month after being laid off, older workers visited a smaller number of companies, on the average, than did younger workers. This is partly explained by the fact that older workers, in comparison with younger, tended to restrict their job hunt to those companies which they believed in advance were looking for workers. One of the reasons given by older workers for avoiding some companies was their belief that they would not be hired because of their age. The contrasting "wide-ranging" pattern of job-seeking behavior consists of inquiring at company personnel offices or hiring gates *regardless* of any prior assumption about whether the company has any job vacancies. A critical point is that the "wide-ranging" pattern obviously should result in visits to a greater number of companies, and the greater the number of potential employers reached, the greater the probability of job-finding success. This is clearly the case among the older workers in *The Job Hunt*. Older workers using the more restrictive "prior awareness" approach checked with fewer companies, and they were therefore less successful in obtaining reemployment than those using the "wide-ranging" approach.

The psychology of older job-seekers　　Age per se is not necessarily an adequate explanation for the greater tendency of older workers to rely on the selective pattern of job-seeking. One dimension of "explanation" might be found in certain psychological characteristics that could be more typical of older than of younger workers. *The Job Hunt* attempted to explore this possibility, by testing the relevance of such measures as "achievement motivation" and "job-interview anxiety"[7] to patterns of job-seeking behavior among unemployed blue-collar workers.

It was found that achievement motivation affected job-seeking behavior of young and old alike, but such motivation was higher among younger job-seekers. Older workers, as well as younger, who did exhibit a high degree of achievement motivation checked with more companies to find a job, used the "wide-ranging" approach to selecting companies, or tried out more techniques of seeking a job—factors in turn related to subsequent reemployment. Thus age by itself was

---

[7] Achievement motivation, a concept based on a pioneering works of David McClelland and John Atkinson, refers to an individual's behavioral tendency to persist and excel in situations involving success or failure, a tendency measured by such techniques as the Thematic Apperception Test, instead of the usual agreement-disagreement with a number of verbal statements. For a brief description of this concept and its theoretical and practical use, see McClelland's "Achievement Motivation Can Be Developed," *Harvard Business Review*, 43 (1965), 6–14, 20–23, 178.

Job-interview anxiety refers to the fears workers may have when confronted with the prospect of being interviewed by an employer for possible employment. It was measured in *The Job Hunt* through use of an eight-item scale developed, from previous research on academic test anxiety, by Lawrence Littig, a psychologist.

TABLE 1 *Reemployment rate by subjective and chronological age*

Age	Per cent of workers finding new jobs
Subjective age	
"Young"	85
"Middle-aged"	61
"Late middle" or "old"	31
Chronological age	
Under 39	84
39 to 47	68
48 and over	54

Source: Harold L. Sheppard and A. Harvey Belitsky, *The Job Hunt* (Baltimore: Johns Hopkins Press, 1966).

not as important as the psychological factor of achievement motivation in determining how a worker reacted to his unemployment situation.

Another psychological measure, job-interview anxiety, yielded the finding that age was negatively correlated to degree of anxiety (the older the worker, the lower the anxiety), but that anxiety played a role in job-finding success *only* among older workers. Older workers, probably because of experience over the years in being interviewed for a job, exhibited less anxiety than younger men about the prospects and outcome of a job interview. But of those older workers who did have high job-interview anxiety, the percentage finding new jobs was lower than among older workers with low anxiety. Again, one explanation for the relationship between psychological dimension (in this case, anxiety) and reemployment success lies in the effect of such a dimension on job-seeking behavior. For example, older workers avoiding use of the "wide-ranging" approach to prospective employers had the greatest proportion of very high anxiety scores.

One more psychological aspect of *The Job Hunt* study—the role of *self-conception* regarding one's age—cannot be ignored in a discussion of age and employment. Workers in the study were asked, "How do you think of yourself as far as age goes? Do you think of yourself as young? Middle-aged? Late middle-aged? Or old?"

As might be expected, 92 per cent of the men under 39 called themselves "young," as contrasted to only 20 per cent of those 39 and over. The use of these subjective age-ratings proved to be a more sensitive "predictor" of job-finding success than actual chronological age, as Table 1 suggests. While the job-finding rates range from 84 to 54 among workers classified according to *chronological* age—a difference of 30 percentage points—the classification according to how

TABLE 2 *Reemployment rate and chronological versus subjective age*
Per cent of workers finding new jobs

	Chronological age	
Subjective age	Under 39	39+
"Young"	85	81
"Middle-aged" or older	63	55

Source: Harold L. Sheppard and A. Harvey Belitsky, *The Job Hunt* (Baltimore: Johns Hopkins Press, 1966), 238.

old the person viewed himself *subjectively* yields a wider range, from 85 to 31, a difference of 54 percentage points.

But the more significant finding is that job-finding success is related to subjective age, even when chronological age is controlled. Thus, as shown in Table 2, persons 39 years old or more who viewed themselves as "young" had reemployment rates virtually equal to under-39 workers also calling themselves "young," and these rates were much higher than under-39 workers not viewing themselves as "young." [Cf. *Vol. 1, Chap. 13.10, pp. 302–305.*]

The complexity of the job-seeking process and the role of institutions   These and other findings suggest that the phenomenon of job-seeking and the degree of its success is much more complex than commonly assumed. It involves not merely the level of employer demand for labor at any given time, but the nature and intensity of the individual worker's job-seeking behavior as well. In the case of older workers, it may involve more than the policies and attitudes of employers regarding the hiring of persons over a certain age. Employer discrimination is a reality, but variation in individual job-seeking behavior is also a reality affecting job-finding success.

In addition to the two variables of the worker's job-seeking behavior and employer demands and hiring policies, there is a third variable that warrants our attention, namely the practices of intermediate agencies and institutions with which the worker and the employer interact in the labor market. One such agency or institution is, of course, the public employment service.

In *The Job Hunt* study, workers were asked if they sought reemployment assistance through the local Employment Service and if so, what was the kind and degree of assistance obtained.

Comparing responses of older and younger workers, it was found that there was no age difference in the proportion checking with the Employment Service when looking for a new job. Although the vast majority of workers, regardless of age, used the local office of the

TABLE 3 *Reemployment rate and assistance from
state employment service*
Per cent of workers finding new jobs[a]

No. of types of assistance given	Young	Old
None	81	48
One	84	70
Two or more	96	75

[a] Based on very small samples of male blue-collar workers who use State Employment Service.

Source: Harold L. Sheppard and A. Harvey Belitsky, *The Job Hunt* (Baltimore: Johns Hopkins Press, 1966), 80.

State Employment Service, older workers received differential treatment. Compared to younger job-seekers, a smaller proportion were, for example, referred to employers for a job interview; given tests or counseled; or offered training in a new occupation. Out of five such possible types of assistance inquired about, fewer than one-half of the older workers received at least one type of assistance, in contrast to more than three-fifths of the younger job-seekers.

The significance of such *prima facie* evidence of age discrimination on the part of this important intermediate agency may be inferred from the fact that the degree of job-finding success was found to be related to the number of types of assistance given to the person checking with the Employment Service. As revealed by Table 3, the relationship between reemployment success and Employment Service assistance was strongest in the case of older workers. In other words, receiving one or more kinds of assistance, instead of none at all, is critically related to job-finding success among older workers. Fewer than one-half of the older workers receiving no help from the Employment Service were reemployed, as contrasted to 70 per cent or more of those receiving at least one kind of assistance. The corresponding contrast among younger workers is not as great, although in the same direction.

What was the relationship between the reemployment status of older workers and referral or nonreferral by the Employment Service to an employer for a job interview? And, if referred at all, are older workers as fortunate as younger referrals in finding new jobs? While no direct causal relationship may be claimed, two important findings are worth noting:

1. The proportion of older workers reemployed among those referred by the Employment Service was nearly twice the reemployed proportion of older workers *not* referred (81 per cent versus 43 per cent).

2. Taking into account skill-differences, referred *older* workers had a lower reemployment rate than referred *younger* workers.

The first finding points to the difference it makes whether the Employment Service personnel refer older workers to prospective employers. The second finding supports the suggestion that older workers—even when referred by the Employment Service—tend to be discriminated against by employers.

On balance, then, the Employment Service gave least attention to older job-seekers, which may, in turn, have had something to do with their ultimate job-finding success. When attention was provided to older workers, the chances of reemployment were considerably enhanced. Thus, although what a worker himself does to find a new job after becoming unemployed is a crucial factor in his job-finding success, the relevance of what other persons and organizations do for that worker cannot be ignored. The findings of *The Job Hunt* suggest the effect of both factors, individual and institutional; and further suggest that age alone is not necessarily an adequate explanation for the fact that older workers check with fewer companies and follow job-seeking patterns that differentiate them from younger job-seekers, with consequences for ultimate job-finding success.

RETRAINING OF OLDER WORKERS

One of the major emphases in this chapter is that age per se may be an inappropriate, misleading, and oversimple concept when used to explain many of the contrasts in the work status and job performance of different age groups.[8] This proposition becomes important in any discussion of policy and program issues.

If we take into consideration such factors as health, education, skill, job-seeking behavior, psychological attributes, and intermediate agencies that play a role in the employment experience of job-seekers, some of the differences between younger and older workers tend to be minimized. Given these sets of empirical findings, it is possible to take a variety of policy positions. The conventional position has been

---

[8] This observation is reminiscent of the decades-old issue concerning "race" as an analytical variable in the behavioral sciences, wherein a social scientist will posit an irrelevant concept and then proceed empirically to show that by careful, systematic consideration of *other* variables (such as region, age, type and degree of education and occupation), differences between "races" tend to cancel out. *But* despite such exercises in refutation, the social sciences—partly because of the popular mentality—persist in committing the same fallacy in research, analysis, and conclusion. Just as "racism" as a form of social "explanation" has not really been exorcised from our everyday culture, so it may be that "age-ism" stays with us in the employment field, and provides tragically unnecessary opportunities for some social scientists to show repeatedly the extent of its irrelevancy.

to accept as natural and inevitable those age differences in the above factors (for example, health and education) which have a bearing on employment. For example, for years it has been an accepted "fact" that *skill obsolescence* is a greater risk among older workers, and that once unemployed this handicap will naturally make them less attractive as new employees. Recently, however, the more positive viewpoint has developed that if unemployed workers, young and old alike, have skill deficiencies, *retraining* might improve their skills and hence their reemployability. As increased recognition of "structural" factors takes place, certain employment problems of older workers need no longer be accepted as inevitable and irremediable. [*See Vol. 1, Chap. 3.B.3.c, p. 59; Chap. 18.B.4, pp. 440–442.*]

Some recent experience The Manpower Development and Training Act of 1962 (and the training provisions of the 1961 Area Redevelopment Act) marked a sharp break from the previous policy position of government that retraining—with stipends—as a solution to an individual worker's problem of employment was not a public responsibility. Unfortunately, in the first four years of MDTA activities, older trainees (45 and older) have been underrepresented. Only 10 per cent of all trainees from 1962 to 1966 were 45 and over, although roughly 25 per cent of all unemployed persons were in this age group. The Department of Labor reportedly set a fiscal 1967 goal of 23 per cent, but the actual outcome was slightly below the previous years— 9 per cent.

Older workers thus are not being involved adequately in the most important program designed to alleviate unemployment through skill betterment. Explanations of this discrepancy must be sought in several directions. In addition to possible *discrimination* on the part of recruitment personnel (which was hinted at in the discussion of *The Job Hunt*), we cannot exclude *self-selection* on the part of older workers themselves, that is, the possibility that many older job-seekers or potential members of the labor force feel themselves not capable of "learning new tricks" or feel they would not be hired anyway because of their age.

But among those older workers who do become enrolled, what is there to say about their experiences? Recent tabulations carried out for the Senate Subcommittee on Employment, Manpower, and Poverty provide a number of findings, of interest to practitioners launching training and related programs who are concerned about their potential benefit to older trainees.

In the first place, the completion rate of older enrollees appears to be higher than for younger enrollees. That is, once recruited and

TABLE 4 *Content of* MDTA *training courses, by age of enrollee, 1965 (percentage distribution)*

Content	Age 45+	Age under 22	All ages
Technical and subprofessional	11	8	9
Clerical and sales	22	26	24
Service	20	15	15
Agriculture	11	2	4
Skilled	23	27	28
Semi-skilled	12	22	19

Source: U.S. Senate Subcommittee on Employment, Manpower and Poverty, *Examination of the War on Poverty:* Staff and Consultant Reports (Washington, D.C.: Government Printing Office, 1967), Vol. II, Table H–4, p. 308.

registered for MDTA courses, older men tend to complete such programs more often than younger trainees.

Second, once older workers complete their training, the odds for obtaining employment in occupations related to training content are nearly 6 out of 10, only slightly less than for all trainees.

Third, the type of training received by all older trainees (including noncompleters) is not identical with the training of other trainees, as indicated by the relevant comparisons in Table 4. Relationships indicated in the table are consistent with national data on the employed labor force. The relationship between agriculture and employment of older persons is revealed, for one out of every nine older trainees was registered in courses related to agricultural employment, in contrast to but one out of every 25 for the total group, and one out of every 50 youths. However, these contrasts may be primarily due to the fact that rural areas tend to have older populations. If we concentrate only on the nonagriculture types of training, we find that in comparison with the total group of trainees, older workers are clearly *over*represented in service-type occupational training, slightly so in technical and subprofessional job training, and equally represented in clerical and sales training—but underrepresented in blue-collar training. We can only speculate on these differences in the job-training distribution according to age. The fact that a lower proportion of older trainees has been enrolled in blue-collar production training may partly be due to patterns of age discrimination in hiring more characteristic of manufacturing industries than of other sectors of the economy.

Fourth, this speculation of industry differentials in age discrimination tends to be supported by the fact that, for each of the three years reported, among those older workers completing blue-collar training,

TABLE 5 *Training-related employment among*
completers of MDTA *courses for blue-collar workers*
Per cent employed in jobs related to training

Year	Skilled			Semi-skilled		
	Age 45+	Age under 22	All ages	Age 45+	Age under 22	All ages
1964	42	58	56	38	48	50
1965	40	56	56	42	50	52
1966	48	59	62	55	59	62

Source: U.S. Senate Subcommittee on Employment, Manpower, and Poverty, *Examination of the War on Poverty:* Staff and Consultant Reports (Washington, D.C.: Government Printing Office, 1967), Vol. II, Tables H–12 to H–13, pp. 311–313.

the proportions actually employed in such occupations, shown in Table 5, are below the average for all trainees, and for youths. Nevertheless, there is a suggestion in these data that, along with other blue-collar trainees of lower ages, the older persons' placement rate in training-related jobs has been rising from 1964 to 1966. The same trend was noticeable for service, clerical, and sales trainees.

Fifth, and perhaps most critical, is the employment status of the older trainees over a period of time. The cumulative record through April of 1966 shows that one year after completing their training, 81 per cent were employed; 13 per cent, unemployed; and 6 per cent had left the labor force. As indicated by Table 6, such proportions turn out to be almost the same as those for the youngest and the total group of MDTA completers.

Despite this record of relative success, and despite the admitted need for the retraining of older workers (especially those unemployed, but also those in industries and companies with high displacement risks), we cannot overemphasize the policy implications of the fact that "the current retraining revolution has largely passed them by."[9]

The benefits of training   The critical nature of this neglect of older workers is further highlighted when we consider the kinds of differences that training makes for such persons. According to Somers' analysis,[10] older workers under MDTA improved their employment experience, their posttraining job status (compared to other older workers who did not get retrained) and, despite their fewer years of formal education, their employment opportunities.

While the analysis by Somers of other data is preliminary and based

[9] Gerald G. Somers, "Evaluation of Work Experience and Training of Older Workers" (Report to the National Council on the Aging, 1967; mimeographed), 26.
[10] *Ibid.*, 31.

TABLE 6 *Employment status of* MDTA *trainees one year after completion of training (percentage distribution)*

Employment status	Age 45+	Age under 22	All ages
Employed	81	80	83
Unemployed	13	10	11
Out of labor force	6	10	6

Source: U.S. Senate Subcommittee on Employment, Manpower, and Poverty, *Examination of the War on Poverty:* Staff and Consultant Reports (Washington, D.C.: Government Printing Office, 1967), Vol. II, Table M, p. 333.

only on experiences within one state (West Virginia), one further set of findings is pertinent to the policy issues concerning the retraining and reemployability of older workers. First, *regardless* of age and education, the earnings of trainees were higher than those of non-trainees in the posttraining period. Second, "in all of the age categories, those who completed retraining were able to reduce their dependency on social welfare payments within 6 months of their completion date. . . . In the 45-and-over category, non-applicants (for training) experienced an increase in social payments at the same time as the trainees experienced a significant decline."[11]

Given the current preoccupation of government with "cost-benefit" analyses, such improvements illustrate, if not demonstrate, the concrete value of "salvaging" the personal and work lives of older men and women through broader and more effective programs of retraining.

Beyond recognizing advantages accruing to the company through the employment and training of older workers, practitioners should also be appreciative of another level of benefit, namely, that of the community and economy of which they and their companies and agencies are a part. Rarely do we confront the question (of wider relevance than the issue of older workers), what does it cost *not* to do something—in this case, not to train and/or employ workers over a given age? Training can make a difference, not only for the individual older worker involved, but also for other members of the same community and economy. Retrained older workers not only become more active consumers: they also become taxpayers, and their dependency on welfare programs is reduced. This improved status, furthermore, contributes to the morale base of a stable social order.

New methods for old workers The retraining of older workers

[11] *Ibid.,* 38–39.

may require some changes in traditional methods of training, in order to adjust the *institution* (in this case, education) to the individual. The point here is that many more older persons can learn new skills if teaching methods are designed to cope with whatever learning problems characterize the older trainee. In the past few years a spurt of activity in this particular area may be discerned, which contains potential for changes in the traditional outlook and practices of educators and employers. Officials in public and private organizations need to become informed of advanced special training methods for persons traditionally condemned as "untrainable." Only now are we beginning to consider the possibility that to a very large extent the fault may lie with the teachers and trainers—not with their pupils.

The most notable example of the new thinking is to be found in the research and conference programs stimulated by Solomon Barkin,[12] for the Organisation for Economic Co-Operation and Development's Social Affairs Division. R. M. Belbin's work is of special significance, and his *Training Methods for Older Workers*[13] deserves wide attention on the part of vocational educators, trade unions, employers, and government agencies. He is now actively engaged in redesigning training methods for specific occupations both in Europe and in the United States.

But few and far between are those efforts aimed at training older persons through special training techniques. Unfortunately, the overwhelming emphasis in learning theory and teaching practice for adults in this and other modern societies has been based on experience with youths, starting with nursery school infants. (The same has been said of counseling, too.) Because of this bias, it should be no surprise that attempts to train older workers through traditional teaching methods have been relatively unsuccessful.

Belbin's comments on typical laboratory experiments on learning and aging are worth repeating:

(i) Experimental studies of learning have often been based on highly artificial tasks, chosen to minimize the effect cf prior knowledge in the learning situation. It has been established, however, that older adults react unfavourably to being presented with tasks that appear to them strange and meaningless. Thus, some of the apparent decline in performance is known to be a function of reaction to the nature of the material.

---

[12] Currently on the faculty of the University of Massachusetts, Department of Economics.

[13] R. M. Belbin, *Training Methods for Older Workers* (Paris: Organisation for Economic Co-operation and Development, 1965).

(ii) Older persons are usually out of practice in learning. Measurements, therefore, refer largely to initial or immediate ability rather than to potential learning ability.

(iii) The majority of studies on human learning ability have been carried out without any attempt being made to adapt the method of training and instruction to the needs of the older subject.[14]

Belbin's studies support the results of a statistical analysis to be discussed in the second part of this chapter, that when such factors as education are held constant, age differences tend to diminish. Belbin describes, for example, the retraining of oil refinery production workers wherein "the differences in attainment between age groups were very nearly eliminated when comparison was confined to trainees having the same number of years of formal schooling."[15] The same was true in the case of inexperienced aircraft production workers who were trained through a succession of skills.[16] Neither in these nor in some other projects cited by Belbin were the older trainees given any special treatment or instruction. In contrast, a study of a Yorkshire steel firm concluded that

. . . older trainees tend to absorb what they see rather than what they hear, and it was decided accordingly that lecturing should be minimized and that initial training should consist of simulated exercises, working to a written brief with models of control panels, furnaces and so on. . . . The simulation training was considered highly successful and after a period of practical training on similar processes in other factories, the men were able to operate the new plant as soon as it came into commission.[17]

Lest the reader have a misconception about the ages involved in such case studies, it should be noted that many of the workers were in their 30's or 40's, and were considered at first as having "lower learning potentials" than men and women in their 20's.

Given appropriate conditions and methods of training, age differences in actual performance tend to be minimized. The value of Belbin's work is that he has sought, first of all, to account for the presumed lower learning potentials of older workers in terms of the particular teaching method used. The challenge is thus presented to our educational system. Second, he has been culling relevant vocational performance investigations in order to identify principles and

[14] *Ibid.*, 65.
[15] *Ibid.*, 36.
[16] *Ibid.*, 36–37.
[17] *Ibid.*, 39.

techniques crucial for the effective instruction of older persons. Third, he has attempted to apply these principles and techniques in experimental settings to test and demonstrate their value in comparison with traditional teaching approaches. Each new experiment calls for tailor-made instructions in keeping with the particular task to be taught and learned, and with the particular attributes of the trainees involved. Needless to say, it very often happens that the new techniques useful in enhancing the learning of older workers also produce beneficial results among younger workers. For example, in a British post office training project,[18] only 26 per cent of older trainees (aged 35 and over) trained in the traditional method passed the entry test, in contrast to 54 per cent taught under the new experimental method designed by Belbin. For trainees under 35 the corresponding percentages were 52 per cent and 75 per cent.

Belbin's analysis and experimentation has led him to formulate a number of general principles aimed at overcoming the problems of training older workers. They are as shown on page 182.[19]

In the United States, as part of the overall OECD effort to stimulate interest in the challenge of training older workers, Belbin has been designing and monitoring a number of courses on an experimental basis in New Haven, Connecticut, sponsored by the United States Department of Labor. The experiment was unique in that the trainees involved were essentially drawn from the hard-core unemployed male population, including nonwhites and rural migrants. The teaching of such skills as machine operation through Belbin's "discovery" method produced results among the older workers (aged 40 and older) superior to those among older workers taught through traditional instruction, in every type of comparison (such as accuracy of measurement, completion rates, and amount of time taken to carry out test assignments on the machine).

Finally, Belbin argues that in seeking to induce an older person to enter into new training or employment situations, the specialist must be alert to the possibility that anxiety and lack of self-confidence—rather than actual or potential "learning capacity" per se—may be the factor inhibiting acceptance of the new situation. Because of this, the successful practitioner cannot rely merely on mass, impersonal announcements of training and upgrading opportunities in the company or community. As Belbin has stated, "The mere provision of facilities is not sufficient to attract older adults to learn."[20] It is at

[18] *Ibid.*, 59–60.
[19] *Ibid.*, 61–62.
[20] *Ibid.*, 26.

Procedures for Overcoming Difficulties

Difficulties Increase with Age	Suggestions as to How the Training Programme Could Be Suitably Adapted
1. When tasks involve the need for memorizing	(a) Avoid the need for conscious memorization. This may often be accomplished by making use of cues which guide the trainee. But the timing and placing of these cues is critical. (b) Use a method which involves learning a task as a whole rather than a method which breaks down a task into discrete parts. If a task has to be learned in parts, these parts should be learned in cumulative stages. (c) Ensure consolidation of learning before passing on to the next task or the next part of the same task.
2. When there is "interference" from other activities or from other learning	(a) Restrict the range of activities covered in the course. (b) Employ longer learning sessions than is customary for younger trainees. (c) Vary the method of learning rather than the content of the course.
3. When there is need to "unlearn" something for which the older learner has a predilection	(a) Ensure correct learning. (b) Employ automatic feedback system to convince the older learner of his errors.
4. When there is need to translate information from one medium to another	(a) Avoid the use of visual aids which necessitate a change of logic or a change in the place of presentation. (b) If simulators or training devices are to be used, then they must be designed to enable learning to be directly related to practice.
5. When tasks are "paced"	(a) Allow the older learner to proceed at his own pace. (b) Allow him to structure his own programme within certain defined limits. (c) Aim at his beating his own targets rather than those of others.
6. As tasks become more complex	(a) Allow for learning by easy stages of increasing complexity.
7. When the trainee lacks confidence	(a) Use written instructions. (b) Avoid the use of production material too soon in the course. (c) Provide larger induction periods.
8. When learning becomes mentally passive	(a) Use an open situation which admits discovery learning. (b) Employ meaningful material and tasks which are sufficiently challenging to an adult.

this juncture that direct contact—of the sort presumably provided by qualified older worker counselors—becomes indispensable.

To summarize, the employment problems of older workers can be substantially alleviated by establishing a number of prerequisites: if presumed skill obsolescence can be compensated through retraining; if new training methods are developed to meet learning needs; if intermediate agencies such as employment service offices develop capabilities and policies designed for the older job-seekers, and if legislation effectively prohibiting age discrimination in employment is enacted.

ADAPTING THE JOB TO THE OLDER WORKER: JOB REDESIGN

Very little recognition, however, has been given to the potentials of *job redesign*, although the OECD has carried out pioneering studies in this sphere of innovation.[21] More recently, the United States Department of Labor has published ten case studies in a 1967 report, *Job Redesign for Older Workers*. This report indicates that few of the one thousand largest American industrial corporations have redesigned jobs specifically for older workers. Instead, they have adopted such practices as reassigning older workers to less strenuous jobs; setting aside specific types of jobs for them; and resorting to "early retirement plans to handle aging workers' declining capacity." On the other hand, when jobs have been redesigned the results have almost invariably been favorable. Three points from this report are of special interest: (1) the process of job redesign has typically been carried out through the informal actions of plant supervisors rather than through formal programs, (2) the process has involved very small money costs for new equipment, and (3) "scarcely any loss in output due to work interruption" has been reported. Clearly, this new approach to the work problems of older people has great promise.

The statistics reconsidered

The preceding material has been on a relatively practical and descriptive level, and its purpose has been chiefly to inform administrators and practitioners of the value and the possibility of special programs for older workers. Planning and implementation of such programs will often require, however, a "macroscopic" consideration of

---

[21] See Stephen Griew, *Job Redesign: The Application of Biological Data on Aging to the Design of Equipment and the Organization of Work* (Paris: OECD, 1964); and the final report by OECD, *Job Redesign and Occupational Training for Older Workers* (Paris: OECD, 1965).

the nature of the older work force and of the potential labor force represented by the older population. We now turn, therefore, to a reconsideration of the statistical trends and their implications. [*See Vol. 1, Chap. 3.A.1.c, pp. 42–43; and 3.B.2.b, pp. 53–54.*]

As we have already noted, the American labor force has become decreasingly composed of older persons. Among males, this is true of those 55–64, as well as those 65 and older. In 1950, males 55–64 years old constituted 12.8 per cent of the total labor force; in 1965, 11.3 per cent—and projections for 1975 indicate a further decline to 10.5 per cent.

THE TRENDS IN REVIEW

Although most of the literature on the "older worker" has typically focused on those 65 and older, the discussion above suggests that we will need to give greater attention than previously to trends for workers under 65. For example, there has been a gradual decline since 1950 in the labor force participation rate of men between the ages of 55 and 64, and individual employment problems related to aging begin to emerge even earlier.

The age group of critical interest regarding trends in labor force participation, however, is the traditional 65 and older category, and for this group the projected trends from 1950 to 1975 show the following:

1. As a per cent of the total labor force, there will be a decline from 4.7 in 1950 to 3.5 in 1975, and, among men only, from 3.8 to 2.2.

2. In 1950 about 46 out of every 100 older men were either working or seeking work. By 1965, this proportion had dropped sharply to 27, and by 1975 it is expected to decline to 23. In other words, in a quarter of a century, we can expect a reduction of the labor force participation rate for elderly men (65 and older) by exactly one-half.

3. Contrary to male trends, elderly female representation in the total labor force rose from less than 1 per cent in 1950 to 1.2 per cent in 1965, and is expected to incease slightly to 1.3 per cent in 1975. Because of the greater participation of women generally in the labor force, the proportion of the female labor force representing older women is expected to decline slightly from 3.7 per cent in 1965 to 3.6 per cent in 1975. However, in 1950 the rate was only 3.1 per cent.

4. Despite general trends of increased labor force participation among females, the participation rate for those 65 and older has remained relatively constant and will probably continue at slightly less than 10 per cent.

TABLE 7 *Labor force participation rates, 1950 to 1980 for males born in 1916–1925*

Age	Rate
Actual	
25–34 (in 1950)	96.2
35–44 (in 1960)	97.7
Projected	
45–54 (in 1970)	95.0
55–64 (in 1980)	83.6

Source: *Manpower Report of the President* (Washington: Government Printing Office, 1967), Tables A–2, A–4, and E–4.

It is not merely that the labor force participation *rate* of elderly men has declined over the past decades, and will continue to do so, but the *numbers* of workers age 65 and older have also decreased. In 1950, slightly fewer than 2.5 million elderly men were in the labor force. By 1965 the number was down to 2.1 million, and the projections for 1975 indicate approximately 2 million.

Aging versus intergenerational comparisons Such trends are useful in suggesting generational comparisons in labor force experience, but they cannot be used with any great certainty to tell us what happens to workers as they grow older. The elderly workers of the year 1950 are not the same elderly workers of the year 1965 or 1975. [*Cf. Vol. 1, Chap. 1, pp. 7–11.*] Unfortunately, we do not have any longitudinal manpower studies concentrating on the employment experiences of a cohort of individuals as they age.

Nevertheless, some inferences may be drawn from a cohort analysis of aggregate data published by the Department of Labor which contain, for example, (1) the labor force status of a given age group in one year and also (2) the status of an age group ten years older a decade later. These data suggest very strongly that as workers grow older, starting perhaps in their mid-40's, they undergo a number of significant employment experiences. For example, if we take only those males born during 1916–1925, and examine their labor force participation rate in 1950 (when they were 25–34 years old) and then check the 1960 rate of the group ten years older, as well as the projected rates for 1970 and 1980 for the 45–54 and 55–64 age groups respectively, we find the trend shown in Table 7. For men 25–34 years old in 1950, 96 per cent were in the labor force at that time. Ten years later, 98 per cent of these men still alive were in the labor force, but by 1980, it is expected that only 84 per cent of the "survivors" will be in the labor force.

This expectation appears to be verified by past reality: in 1956, 966 out of every 1,000 men 45–54 years old were in the labor force, but in 1966, out of every 1,000 men who were ten years older (55–64) only 845 were still labor force participants. Indeed, the actual experience from 1956 to 1966 makes one suspect that the projected rate in 1980 of 83.6 for men 55–64 might well turn out to be an overestimate.[22]

Full-time, year-round employment   But no single index of labor force participation tells the complete story. For example, the degree to which such participation is based on full-time, year-round employment as opposed to part-time work makes a good deal of difference in assessing the situation of older workers. Today, no more than two-thirds of all nonfarm workers 65 and older—no more than one million men—are working year-round on a full-time basis. Slightly more than one-half—about 450,000—of the total group of nonfarm elderly female workers are on such a schedule. [*See Vol. 1, Chap. 3.A.3.a and b, pp. 46–47.*]

"Labor force participation rate" versus "work experience"   A caveat must also be entered concerning the statistics from several of the manpower and employment reports used in this chapter. Such reports frequently do not distinguish between *jobs* and workers, and when they cite a given figure to indicate the size of the labor force for any year or any age group, the reference may well be to jobs and not to workers.[23] There is quite a difference. For example, in 1964, the manpower tables of the Department of Labor report an employed labor force of approximately 70 million; but in the same year there were actually 85 million men and women who worked either full- or part-time! The 70 million figure in reality refers to the *average* number of *jobs* filled at any one time in 1964.

For our purposes the significance of the discrepancy between *jobs filled* and *people working* is that the data on labor force participation among elderly workers understate the number of such persons who have actually worked in a given year by more than 40 per cent. For example, the 1964 data report approximately 3 million persons 65

[22] Actual experience of older females shows the same trend: in 1956, 553 out of every 1,000 women 45–54 years old were in the labor force, but by 1966, only 491 among women ten years older. Thus, while it is correct to say that each decade witnesses a higher participation rate of older females, *it is not correct to conclude that over time, as women grow older their rates increase.*

[23] The only major examination of this critical distinction is probably that by David J. Farber, "Workers, Jobs and Statistics" (Study for the Department of Labor's Bureau of Apprenticeship and Training, 1966; unpublished).

and older in the labor force, but the number who actually worked in that year was 4.2 million!

Female labor force participation Participation of older females in the labor force is in large part a function of marital status and education. [*See Vol. 1, Chap. 3.B.3.b, pp. 58–59.*] As revealed by the data in Table 8, married women at each level of education have a lower participation rate than other women. But the higher the education, the higher the rate of participation in the labor force, as shown by comparison of educational categories within each marital status in Table 8.

HEALTH AND LABOR FORCE PARTICIPATION

Professionals dealing with problems of older workers are frequently confronted with generalizations about health as a factor in labor force participation. [*See Vol. 1, Chap. 3.B.3.a, pp. 57–58; Chap. 18.C.2.b, pp. 449–450.*] The aggregate data provide coincidental evidence that, over time (during the course of growing older), workers are increasingly "out" of the labor force. Cohort analysis from 1955 to 1965 demonstrates this. For example, in 1955, 230,000 men 25–34 years old were out of the labor force. Ten years later, the number of men 35–44 years old not in the labor force grew to 306,000. Similarly, in the case of men 35–44 in 1955 and 45–54 ten years later, the change was from 209,000 to 467,000 not in the labor force. And even more provocative, the numbers not in the labor force among men 45–54 in 1955, and 55–64 ten years later, rose from 326,000 to 1,227,000 respectively.

But the critical point here is that while most males out of the labor force report health problems, there is, nevertheless, a sizable proportion who report no chronic health problems or conditions that limit their activity. The National Health Interview Survey of 1964–1965 shows, as in Table 9, how these vary by age and labor force status.

The most striking aspect of this table may be that out of 5,431,000 elderly males not in the labor force, 38 per cent apparently have no health conditions that prevent them from working. In absolute numbers, this population amounts to two million persons. This figure, incidentally, *exceeds* by far—at a ratio of more than four to one—the number of younger men 45 to 64 years old who were also out of the labor force but without any work limitations imposed by health—523,000.

This analysis raises a variety of questions that cannot be answered on the basis of the data provided in the National Health Interview

TABLE 8 *Rates of labor force participation of older females, by marital status and education*

Age	8 years of school completed		9–11 years of school completed		12 years of school completed		1–3 years of college completed		4 or more years of college completed	
	Married	*Other*[a]	*Married*	*Other*	*Married*	*Other*	*Married*	*Other*	*Married*	*Other*
55–64	27.7	51.9	28.1	61.3	36.0	62.4	37.7	63.9	59.0	70.6
65+	5.5	9.8	8.1	14.4	11.6	17.9	13.1	13.6	16.7	23.1

[a] Widowed, divorced, and separated, excluding single women.
Source: Denis F. Johnston, "Educational Attainment of Workers, March, 1964," *Monthly Labor Review*, 88 (1965), Table H, A–12.

TABLE 9 *Health of adult males, by labor force status*
Per cent with each health characteristic

Health	Employed			Unemployed			Not in labor force		
	Age 25–44	*Age 45–64*	*Age 65+*	*Age 25–44*	*Age 45–64*	*Age 65+*	*Age 25–44*	*Age 45–64*	*Age 65+*
No chronic conditions	48	38	25	49	34	26	26	12	15
Activity not limited	45	47	41	37	36	33	23	17	23
Total	93	85	67	85	70	58	49	30	38
Number (in thousands)	(20,507)	(16,288)	(2,123)	(526)	(503)	(55)	(580)	(1,610)	(5,431)

Note: Percentages may not add to the totals shown, because of rounding.
Source: Carl Rosenfeld and Elizabeth Waldman, "Work Limitations and Chronic Health Problems," *Monthly Labor Review,* 90 (1967), 40.

Survey. For example, what were the preretirement occupations and industries of the older labor force nonparticipants? To what extent is their current nonworking status due to voluntary or compulsory retirement? [*See Ex. 18 · 25 in Vol. 1, p. 449.*] To what extent do they first become unemployed before the age of 65 and then, because of an extended inability to secure adequate reemployment, finally "drop out"? And, is there a limit to the number or proportion of such persons beyond which society will begin to feel the costs of their nonproductive roles?

THE OBSCURANTISM OF "65-PLUS"

The general reporting category of "65 and older" obscures the fact that this group is heterogeneous, consisting today of substantial numbers of persons in their 70's and older—many of whom are working. Future official statistics will need to provide more discrete breakdowns of such a classification, and on a more frequent basis than every ten years, as the tasks of older worker professionals become more specific and elaborated. The most recent detailed data available are from the 1960 Census. As of that date, nearly one million men 70 and older were in the labor force. As a way of testing our stereotypes about work and aging, it is interesting to note the kinds of jobs they held in that year, in comparison with the total experienced male civilian labor force and with other "older" male workers.

The data shown in Table 10 demonstrate again the concentration of older workers in agriculture. Nearly one-fourth of the very oldest workers (75 and older) are farmers, farm managers, laborers, or farm foremen, in sharp contrast to one-twelfth of the total male labor force of 1960. On the other hand, the table shows that outside these farm occupations, the oldest workers are widely represented in the "white collar" occupations—professionals, technicians, managers, officials, proprietors, sales and service workers.

Industries employing older persons   As indicated by Table 11, the industries (exclusive of agriculture, forestry, fishing, and mining) in which male elderly workers are well represented are clearly those in which manual labor is *not* an occupational characteristic: wholesale and retail trade; finance, insurance and real estate; personal services; professional and related services; and public administration. Furthermore, it should be stressed that in a nonagricultural economy such as ours, construction and manufacturing account for only about one-third of all males employed in the nonextractive industries, yet typical discussions concerning the "problem" of the older worker are often based on an out-of-date image of American industry, in which the

TABLE 10 *Occupational distribution of older male workers, 1960 (percentage distribution)*

Occupation	All males	Age 60–64	Age 65–69	Age 70–74	Age 75+
Professional technical, and kindred workers	9.9	7.1	7.8	8.1	9.2
Farmers and farm managers	5.3	9.0	12.9	16.5	19.6
Managers, officials, and proprietors	10.3	13.0	13.6	13.1	13.4
Clerical and kindred workers	6.9	6.4	6.4	5.9	5.4
Sales workers	6.7	6.4	7.5	8.6	8.8
Craftsmen, foremen, and kindred workers	19.6	20.6	16.6	13.9	10.6
Operatives and kindred workers	20.3	15.5	11.6	8.6	6.4
Service workers, including private-household workers	6.1	8.9	10.5	11.9	11.2
Farm laborers and foremen	2.8	2.1	2.9	3.5	3.5
Laborers, excluding farm workers	7.4	6.8	6.3	6.1	5.6
Number (in thousands)	(45,713)	(2,629)	(1,267)	(611)	(357)

Note: Percentages do not add to 100 because "occupation not reported" is not indicated.
Source: U.S. Bureau of the Census, *Occupational Characteristics*, 1960 Census of Population, PC(2)–7A (Washington, D.C.: Government Printing Office, 1963), Table 4, p. 31.

"worker" is a manual laborer and the employer is a manufacturer. The contemporary reality is an economy in which only a *minority* of the employed population is in construction or manufacturing—and even in those industries, roughly one-fourth are nonproduction workers.

In 1960, nearly a third of all employed elderly women (in nonextractive industries) were working in personal services (for the most part, in private households, as domestics—an occupation in which nonwhites predominate). This proportion is more than twice that for all employed females in 1960. Because of the upgraded employment opportunities for American women, and because of the changing skill demands of the general economy, it would be foolhardy to prophesy that older women in the future will be similarly employed in such low-status activities.

As of 1960, 70 per cent of all male older workers and 89 per cent of female older workers employed in the secondary and tertiary indus-

TABLE 11 *Industry distribution of employed persons, 1960 (percentage distribution)*

	Males			Females		
Industry[a]	*All ages*	*Age 45–64*	*Age 65+*	*All ages*	*Age 45–64*	*Age 65+*
Construction	9.8	10.1	8.7	0.8	0.7	0.6
Manufacturing	35.1	34.2	21.2	22.4	20.8	10.3
Transportation, communication, and public utilities	9.9	11.0	7.2	3.9	2.9	1.3
Wholesale and retail trade	19.8	18.8	22.1	22.3	22.7	19.9
Finance, insurance, and real estate	3.9	4.3	7.9	6.3	4.7	4.6
Business and repair services	3.4	3.1	3.6	1.7	1.5	1.3
Personal services	2.9	3.4	7.3	14.1	15.8	31.3
Entertainment and recreation	0.9	0.9	1.5	0.8	0.6	0.8
Professional and related services	8.1	7.9	12.5	23.2	25.2	26.0
Public administration	6.1	6.3	6.7	4.6	5.0	3.9

[a] Excludes agriculture, fisheries, forestry, mining, and "industry not reported."
Note: Percentages may not add to 100 because of rounding.
Source: U.S. Bureau of the Census, *Occupation by Industry*, 1960 Census of Population, PC(2)–7C (Washington, D.C.: Government Printing Office, 1963), Table 1, p. 1.

tries (those included in Table 11) were outside of construction and manufacturing, in contrast to 55 per cent of males of all ages, and 77 per cent of females of all ages. Although this comparison may be interpreted as an index of the lack of opportunities for (and/or discrimination against) older persons in manufacturing and construction, the more positive interpretation points to the *greater* potentials for employment of the older workers now and in the future, that exist in the *non*construction, *non*manufacturing sections of our economy.

The future is one in which employment for older workers will be concentrated in nonmanual, nonmanufacturing occupations and industries, with an increasing female component. Because of this changing composition, we can expect new problems and opportunities to emerge in the area of "industrial gerontology." Unemployment and educational upgrading supply compelling illustrations.

UNEMPLOYMENT

Once unemployed, an older worker runs a greater risk of long-term joblessness, even though unemployment rates themselves are generally lower for older workers as a whole.[24] [*See Vol. 1, Chap.*

[24] Rates are lower among workers in the more mature adult years, say after 30. Unemployment rates of men in their 50's and older, however, are frequently the greatest, as shown in Table 13 below.

TABLE 12 *Long-term unemployment, by age, 1957, 1961, and 1966*

Year	Age 14–19	Age 20–24	Age 25–44	Age 45–64	Age 65+	General unemployment rate[a]
			Per cent of unemployed out of work for 15 or more weeks			
Males						
1957	13	15	19	28	39	4.1
1961	22	31	35	41	57	6.4
1966	12	14	22	31	37	3.2
Females						
1957	11	13	18	23	21	4.7
1961	16	25	29	34	41	7.2
1966	11	10	17	22	34	4.8

[a] For labor force 16 and older.
Source: Manpower Report of the President (Washington: Government Printing Office, 1967), Table A–18.

3.A.3.c, pp. 47–48.] This greater long-term unemployment risk can be seen in Table 12 showing the percentage of the unemployed out of work for fifteen or more weeks for each of three selected years during the past decade. In each of these years the proportion with long-term joblessness increased with age. The table also shows how these proportions, regardless of age, rise and fall from one year to another, depending on the overall state of the economy. (The general rate of unemployment was comparatively higher in 1961.)

Since the high unemployment year of 1961, the overall rate of unemployment among men declined by 50 per cent (from 6.4 to 3.2). The decline was even greater for those between 35 and 64. But despite the subsequent opportunities for pre-65 retirement under recent social security amendments, the rate of unemployment for the 65 and older group declined by only 44 per cent. Regardless of these "opportunities," unemployment remained at a higher rate among such elderly workers than among all other adult workers 25 years of age and older.

But cohort analysis, which would be more pertinent to this issue, suggests that unemployment rates for male workers 45–54 in any given year will be higher ten years later; see Table 13. For example, in 1950, 4 per cent of all men 45–54 were unemployed; ten years later, in 1960, when these men were 55–64 years old, the rate was 4.6 per cent.These unemployment rates, moreover, do not include any count of men 45–54 in 1950 who, becoming unemployed during 1950–1960, gave up the search for reemployment and left the labor force entirely. Unfortunately, there are no longitudinal studies of work, un-

TABLE 13 *Unemployed rates of aging males*

	1947	1948	1949	1950	1951	1952	1953	1954	1955	1956
Rate for men aged 45–54 in each specified year	2.6	2.5	4.3	4.0	2.4	2.2	2.3	4.3	3.2	3.0
	1957	1958	1959	1960	1961	1962	1963	1964	1965	1966
Rate for men aged 55–64 ten years later	3.5	5.5	4.5	4.6	5.7	4.6	4.3	3.9	3.3	2.6

Source: Manpower Report of the President (Washington: Government Printing Office, 1967), Table A–12 (adapted).

employment, and labor force participation that could provide information on the full range of experiences of workers as they grow older.[25]

The problem of hard-core unemployment In the immediate present and for some years to come, increasing attention will be given to the difficult, individual-by-individual aspects of the "hard-core" unemployed, especially in our central city "slum" areas. As an example of the characteristics of the older men and women who are unemployed or "subemployed" in such areas, information from a Department of Labor survey for four days in December, 1966, in seven of our major urban areas justifies concern for the older worker.

Among all adults contacting local employment service offices in these seven cities, nearly one-third were 45 or older. Professional interviewers determined what they considered to be the major barriers to obtaining employment for such persons. Data on background characteristics included number of years of school completed, so that we are able to compare these barriers, holding age and education constant. Table 14 illustrates the problems of older unemployed persons in slum areas.

Among the unemployed older persons in these areas, the less educated are most likely to face the "age barrier," but even for individuals with a high-school diploma, interviewers judged age to be a significant factor for one out of every eight. The task ahead is to sensitize employment personnel at both the public and private levels to the peculiar "barriers" that impede older persons in their quest for security and status through the world of work, and to provide such personnel with the special skills needed to help the job-seeker overcome these difficulties.

THE EFFECT OF EDUCATION

Neither the occupational nor the employment status of older workers is a simple function of age. It is crucial that manpower specialists

---

[25] The most critical problem is among those older women still too young to retire, aged 45–54. Since 1961, women have constituted about 36 per cent of the total labor force 45–54 years old, but have consistently been disproportionately over-represented among the unemployed in the same age category. By 1966, 37 per cent of the 45–54 labor force was female, but females were 44 per cent of all unemployed in this age group. Data for older groups suggest that were it not for early retirement options under social security, the unemployment rates of older women might be higher than they are technically reported. It should also be noted that the overrepresentation since 1961 of women among the unemployed in this critical point in the work lives of the labor force (45–54) is largely a product of reduction in the general unemployment rate. Men tend to be overrepresented, in other words, when the economy is in a general recession or depression, but when the economy "picks up" the older women are not reemployed at the same rate as men, and thus become a substantial part of the remaining pool of unemployed job-seekers.

TABLE 14 *Significant barriers to employment, by age and education, in seven slum areas (percentage distribution of persons seeking employment)*

Barrier	0–7 years of school		8–11 years of school		12 or more years of school	
	Age 22–44	Age 45+	Age 22–44	Age 45+	Age 22–44	Age 45+
Age	0.7	19.2	0.4	19.3	1.0	12.1
Lack of necessary skill and/or experience	10.8	5.7	10.6	6.2	13.2	6.2
Lack of education or training	21.5	17.8	13.0	6.9	3.4	4.2
Obsolete skill; no demand for skill in local area	1.6	2.7	1.1	2.0	2.2	4.2
Health	4.7	6.6	5.2	7.6	3.9	8.7
Other barriers[a]	11.4	8.0	14.7	10.3	16.4	17.9
No discernible barrier	49.2	40.0	54.9	47.6	59.9	46.7

[a] Personal, transportation, care of child or other family member.
Source: U.S. Senate Subcommittee on Employment, Manpower, and Poverty, *Examination of the War on Poverty: Staff and Consultants Reports* (Washington, D.C.: Government Printing Office, 1967), II, 562.

recognize that correlations between age and these statuses may frequently be spurious, that is, due to factors other than age per se. One way of demonstrating this principle is to examine the wide variation in the occupational distribution of elderly workers according to their educational levels. Table 15 shows this distribution among males 65 and over in the experienced labor force, as of the 1960 Census.

The table shows, for example, that nearly three-fourths—73 per cent—of college-educated men 65 and older are in professional, technical, managerial, and related occupations (including officials and proprietors), in comparison with only 22 per cent of all elderly men, and 20 per cent of the total experienced male labor force of all ages in 1960. Nearly one-fourth of elderly men with less than eight years of schooling are in farm occupations, in contrast with less than one-eighth of those with some high-school education, and one-twelfth of the total group of males.

A second way of highlighting the role of education in the occupations of employed older males is to show the relatively narrower variation in occupations among different age groups with similar years of schooling. More precisely, *the higher the level of education, the less the degree of occupational variation.* This shows up clearly among men with four or more years of college, as Table 16 reveals.

With the exception of farm-related occupations (in which the proportion of higher-educated elderly males is roughly four times greater than that among the youngest college graduates in Table 16), there are no clear-cut discrepancies in the broad occupational categories among the various age groups of college graduates who were in the experienced male labor force of 1960. The relative occupational homogeneity, regardless of age, is obscured in aggregate tables comparing the occupations of young and old males which do *not* include the education variable. To repeat, age per se is not a useful variable in explaining many aspects of the occupational and work status of "older" workers.

Although projections into the future regarding aging are dangerous exercises when based on these types of data, it may nevertheless be worth the risk to speculate about some possible implications of the previous two tables. With general improvement in the level of education in the American labor force, along with the changing character of the economy's technology and occupational composition, age may make less difference in the occupational mix in the decades ahead. This greater similarity in occupational profiles among age groups is also likely to mean smaller differences in unemployment experiences among adult workers.

TABLE 15 *Occupational distribution of experienced male labor force 65 and older, 1960, by years of schooling completed (percentage distribution)*

		Years of school completed						
Occupation	All men 65+	0–7	8	9–11	12	1–3 college	4 or more college	All men 14+
Professional and technical workers	8.3	1.1	2.3	5.1	9.1	22.1	55.9	9.9
Farmers and farm managers	15.7	18.4	18.7	11.8	8.3	9.1	3.8	5.3
Managers, officials, and proprietors	13.9	8.1	11.6	17.5	22.8	23.7	17.3	10.3
Clerical workers	6.1	3.0	5.9	9.6	11.7	10.4	5.1	6.9
Sales workers	8.2	4.9	7.3	11.7	13.0	13.4	7.5	6.7
Craftsmen and foremen	14.3	15.8	18.7	16.5	13.0	7.6	3.2	19.6
Operatives	9.5	13.2	11.2	8.9	6.6	3.5	1.4	20.3
Service, including private-household workers	11.0	14.7	12.1	9.7	7.5	4.0	1.9	6.1
Farm laborers and foremen	3.1	5.6	2.7	1.4	1.0	0.8	0.4	2.8
Laborers	5.8	10.6	5.4	3.5	2.3	1.6	0.6	7.4
Occupation not reported	4.0	4.6	4.0	4.3	4.7	3.8	3.1	4.7

Note: Percentages may not add to 100 because of rounding.
Source: U.S. Bureau of the Census, Occupational Characteristics, 1960 Census of Population, PC(2)–7A (Washington, D.C.: Government Printing Office, 1963), Table 11, p. 144.

TABLE 16 *Occupational distribution of experienced male labor force with four or more years of college, 1960, by age (percentage distribution)*

Occupation	Age 25–29	Age 30–34	Age 35–44	Age 45–54	Age 55–64	Age 65+
Professional and technical workers	60.6	59.1	57.1	53.5	54.1	56.0
Farmers and farm managers	0.7	0.8	1.0	1.4	1.8	3.8
Managers, officials, and proprietors	11.0	15.7	19.7	22.9	22.0	17.3
Clerical workers	7.1	5.4	4.9	4.8	4.8	5.0
Sales workers	9.9	10.0	8.0	7.1	6.8	7.5
Craftsmen and foremen	3.6	3.9	4.1	4.2	4.3	3.2
Operatives	1.4	1.2	1.3	1.6	1.5	1.4
Service, including private-household workers	1.0	0.7	0.9	0.9	1.0	1.9
Laborers, including farm and farm foremen	0.7	0.5	0.4	0.5	0.5	0.9
Occupation not reported	4.0	2.9	2.6	3.1	3.3	3.1

Note: Percentages may not add to 100 because of rounding.
Source: U.S. Bureau of the Census, *Occupational Characteristics*, 1960 Census of Population, PC(2)-7A (Washington, D.C.: Government Printing Office, 1963), Table 11, p. 144.

Furthermore, such projections will be affected by the total age structure of the labor force. If birth rates in the next decade or so continue to decline, for example, it is quite possible that persons at upper age limits will be in greater demand among employers. Some slight evidence for this speculation may be gleaned from the fact that in 1960 more than 70 per cent of all urban men aged 55–64 and with 12 or more years of schooling worked the previous year for 50 to 52 weeks, in contrast to only 40 per cent of those with no schooling, 51 per cent of those with 1 to 7 years, and 63 per cent of those urban men with 8 to 11 years of education. These percentages are based on the total population in each education category, including those not working at all in the previous year. The corresponding proportions for the 65 and older urban males are shown in Table 17. [*See also Vol. 1, Chap. 3.B.3.b, pp. 58–59.*]

Such data warrant some speculation that work and retirement patterns characterizing the recent past may *not* be continued in decades ahead, as the general level of educational achievement among urban workers continues to rise.

Concluding note

This chapter began and now ends with a plea for a new perspective on the part of administrators, decision-makers, and practitioners whose

TABLE 17 *Work experience of urban males, 65 and over, by education, 1960*

Years of school completed	Per cent who worked 50–52 weeks in previous year
None	11
1–7	15
8	19
9–11	26
12	29
1–3 college	32
4 or more college	37

Source: U.S. Bureau of the Census, *Employment Status and Work Experience,* 1960 Census of Population, PC(2)–6A (Washington, D.C.: Government Printing Office, 1963), Table 20, p. 208.

professional lives have a bearing on the employment status of "older" workers. Such a new perspective must flow from the specific research studies and aggregative quantitative data forming the empirical and theoretical basis of "industrial gerontology."

These studies and data can provide a foundation for anticipating, preventing, or mitigating employment problems of older workers. Once the stereotypes about "older workers" are challenged (as a result of studies and analyses that go beyond averages) personnel practitioners and manpower specialists are free to develop new approaches to job placement, training, and job redesign. In addition, sensitivity to non-economic, nonskill aspects is indispensable: Psychological factors such as orientation toward opportunities, fears about being rejected for employment, and self-image as an older worker are realities to no less an extent than degree of job skill and chronological age—and they require consideration and possible modification along with training and job redesign measures.

7

Aging and financial management

JUANITA M. KREPS

Financial management differs from such fields as social work or the law in that it is not the province of a single, clearly established professional group. Yet a variety of experts (such as bankers, life insurance agents, investment counselors, or consulting economists) engage in financial advising and planning for old age—both at the level of the individual attempting to budget his personal funds, and at the corporate, union, or government levels of fiscal policy.

Professor Kreps, in the essay that follows, formulates the issues involved in building an income-maintenance program for the years of retirement—an ever-lengthening period as the average length of life increases while the age of retirement falls. As necessary background for financial decision-making and recommendations at both the personal and the organizational level, Mrs. Kreps analyzes patterns of income and saving—not only in the usual cross-section view—but also over the lifetime of cohorts of individuals in various occupational or educational categories. She concludes that, although under present conditions consider-

able individual saving may be possible during the last decade and a half of a person's worklife, public and corporate policies will continue to be a critical determinant of standards of living for most people in old age.

Advisers for this chapter were Herman B. Brotman, Administration on Aging, Department of Health, Education, and Welfare; and Sverre Roang, Rock County Court—Branch 1, Janesville, Wisconsin.

ON THE RELEVANCE OF VOLUME ONE

The importance of this field for persons in their middle and later years is documented in Volume One. The older person's financial status, in the same manner as his health status, is a primary limiting condition upon his entire way of life. For example, the connections between his income—past, present, and prospective—and his family living arrangements are indicated in Chapter 7, his life attitudes in Chapter 14, his life adjustment in Chapter 15, his adaptation to retirement in Chapter 18, and his use of leisure in Chapter 22. Social research dealing directly with financial resources, reported in Chapter 4, points to the difficulties faced by many older people in maintaining income over their retirement years sufficient to fill subsistence needs, meet emergencies, or to partake of the affluence of today's society.

Rising earnings provide the primary distribution of claims to the increasing quantities of goods and services in the marketplace. The primacy of jobs and equitable pay for work cannot be questioned.

Earnings, however, have a very poor fit over time to the individual's changing consumption needs . . . the times in the family life cycle when earnings and consumption needs are farthest apart come early and late.

—Ida C. Merriam

Introduction: the problem of humps and valleys

The subject of income distribution, a source of centuries of controversy, has in the past been primarily concerned either with differences in income levels or with the determination of functional shares: wages, rent, interest, and profits. Although the traditional income-distribution problems have not disappeared, equally urgent current issues center on the apportionment of the national product between workers and nonworkers, the latter including not only the sick and disabled but the young and the old as well.

Changes in the nature of the income-distribution dilemma are due in part to a certain ambivalence in our economic ideology. On the one hand we like to rely on the productivity of a man's labor or that of his capital to determine the size of his income; on the other, we recognize that some persons throughout their lives, and all persons during some part of their lives, do not receive income from either source. The confrontation of economic ideology with economic reality is taking place under the banner of guaranteed annual income, which is perhaps the most controversial economic issue of our day. While the debate rages around the minimum income proposals, the process of building an income-maintenance program for the lengthening period of retirement, although advancing in both the public and the private sectors, is a long way from evening out the humps and valleys in family income.

Retirement continues to bring sharp drops in income for most of today's aged. As a rough measure of their financial status, the aged's median income is now less than half that of the population under age 65; their median asset ownership is about $3,000 for married couples, when home value is excluded. Of the many issues of federal income-maintenance policy, perhaps the primary one is that of providing adequate income supplements to those persons who have already retired, and who are dependent almost altogether on public programs. Unfortunately, Congressional action on this issue during the second half of the 1960's has been constrained by many competing demands, particularly those of the military.

When questions are raised as to financial preparation for retirement in the future, competing claims are again evident; current consumption has a habit of absorbing whatever income is available to the family. Reliance on the accumulation of private savings for old age must thus presuppose either a marked change in attitude toward spending, or significant increases in income levels. Although there is conflicting opinion on the rationale of consumer behavior, predictions of personal incomes can be made which provide approximations of the income stream available through whatever portion of worklife remains. For purposes of financial planning it is this expected worklife income, reflecting increases attributable to experience and seniority on the job, and to the process of economic growth, that is relevant. Cross-sectional data indicating the occupation's present level of income for age categories may show, for example, a lower average income for 55–64-year-old males than for those 45–54. But the impact of economic growth will generally be sufficient to raise the incomes of particular individuals throughout the latter part of their worklife, with the result that a man's income at retirement will usually be higher, not lower, than that of previous years. [*See Vol. 1, Chap. 1, pp. 5, 7–8; Chap. 4.A.4, pp. 83–85.*]

Since the expenses of rearing and educating children are usually heavy during the parents' 20's, 30's, and 40's, there remain probably no more than fifteen working years during which savings for retirement can be accumulated. Annual income during these years of worklife may be as much as three times retirement income, given current projections of pension benefits. The budgeting problem is thus a long-range one: to apportion the earnings from the last fifteen or so years of worklife, plus retirement pensions and income from any previously acquired assets, over the remaining life expectancy. The ideal distribution of this total income would of course take into account differences in expenses during the working and nonworking years.

If the goal of long-term financial planning is to be approached, several steps are necessary. It is important to review, first, the income and asset position of today's aged, most of whom are outside the labor force and dependent upon pensions; and second, the income, expenditure patterns, and potentials for saving of families at different stages of worklife. The cross-section data used for these comparisons can then be supplemented with some illustrative projections of lifetime earnings, in order to show the probable behavior of income through the remaining worklife of the current labor force participants. Once the size of an expected earnings stream is estimated, the issue of consumption levels during worklife versus consumption levels in the retirement years can be considered. Finally, two questions remain: *How* the temporal reallocation of income claims might be accomplished and *how much* we choose to reapportion.

The current financial position of older people

The overall economic status of older persons, when compared with that of the population under 65, is at present quite inferior. Evidence can be drawn from the data on their relative income and asset positions. [*See Vol. 1, Chap. 4.A and B, pp. 70–95; Chap. 18.C.4.c, pp. 454–456.*]

INCOME LEVELS IN OLD AGE

In 1965 the median income for families headed by persons aged 65 and over was $3,460, or 47 per cent of the median of $7,352 for families with younger heads. For aged individuals living alone or with nonrelatives the median was $1,348, which was only 40 per cent of

Table X–1

	1960	1961	1962	1963	1964	1965
Families						
Head 14–64						
Amount	$5,905	$6,099	$6,336	$6,644	$6,981	$7,352
Per cent Increase	—	3.3	3.9	4.9	5.1	5.3
Head 65 +						
Amount	$2,897	$3,026	$3,240	$3,352	$3,376	$3,460
Per cent Increase	—	4.4	5.9	4.6	0.7	2.5
Per cent of 14–64	49.1	49.6	50.6	50.4	48.4	47.1
Unrelated Individuals						
14–64						
Amount	$2,571	$2,589	$2,644	$2,881	$3,094	$3,320
Per cent Increase	—	0.7	2.1	9.0	7.4	7.3
65 +						
Amount	$1,053	$1,106	$1,248	$1,277	$1,297	$1,348
Per cent Increase	—	5.0	12.8	2.3	1.6	3.9
Per cent of 14–64	41.0	42.7	47.2	44.3	41.9	40.6

Source: Herman B. Brotman, "Income of Families and Unrelated Individuals, 1965," Administration on Aging, Department of Health, Education and Welfare (Washington, D.C.: Government Printing Office, 1967).

the median ($3,320) for the comparable category of younger persons. Of the families with aged head, 43 per cent had money incomes below $3,000; of the aged unrelated individuals, 58 per cent had incomes below $1,500. The corresponding proportions of younger families and unrelated individuals were 12 per cent and 27 per cent. Moreover, it is evident that although the incomes of the elderly have risen during the first half of 1960, the increases have been somewhat smaller than those accruing to the younger population. The relative income position of the aged therefore worsened slightly during the first half of the decade.[1]

When family size, farm-nonfarm residence, and other relevant factors are taken into account, about 42 per cent of the noninstitutionalized aged are classified as low-income ($2,545 per year for a two-person nonfarm family); about 30 per cent have incomes below the poverty level ($2,100 for the same family type).[2] Another 10 per cent, who would be poor if they relied on their own incomes, share homes with relatives who are above the poverty line.[3] These proportions are approximately double the percentages for the population under age 65.

[1] The 1960–1965 changes for families and individuals were as shown in Table X–1.

[2] Percentages based on indexes developed by Mollie Orshansky, Social Security Administration. For a summary of the aged's position, see Herman B. Brotman, "Counting the Aged Poor, 1965," Administration on Aging, Department of Health, Education and Welfare (Washington, D.C.: Government Printing Office, 1967).

[3] Mollie Orshansky, "The Poor in City and Suburbs, 1964," *Social Security Bulletin*, 29 (1966), 22–37.

The sources of the aged's income have shifted markedly during the past twenty years, with earnings coming to be a smaller and income-maintenance programs a much larger proportion of the total. [*See Vol. 1, Chap. 4.A.3.b, pp. 80–81.*] About 46 per cent of their aggregate income in 1962 came from social insurance, veterans', and public assistance programs. Earnings accounted for another 32 per cent, and income from assets—rent, interest, and dividends—another 15 per cent of the total. Cash contributions by friends or relatives not living in the same household amounted to 1 per cent of the aggregate. Nonmonetary support in the form of home-sharing was most frequent for elderly couples and nonmarried women in the lowest income group; the median income of the aged single women living with relatives, for example, was only about two-thirds that of nonmarried women living alone.[4]

THE OWNERSHIP OF ASSETS

Median asset value of aged units in 1962 ranged from $2,900 for single men and $3,285 for single women to $11,180 for married couples. Noting further the two extremes: one-sixth of the couples and two-fifths of the nonmarried persons had less than $1,000 in assets; one-third of the couples and one-sixth of the single persons held $15,000 or more in assets, including home equity. Other than equity in a home, about one-fourth of the couples and two-fifths of the nonmarried had no assets. The median holdings for couples were just under $3,000 when home value was excluded.[5]

Since a large proportion of the elderly, particularly the couples, own homes, it is often suggested that a conversion of assets into income, prorated over remaining life, might improve significantly the well-being of the elderly. [*See Vol. 1, Chap. 4.B.1, p. 85.*] Ignoring for the moment the feasibility of this form of asset management, a measure of potential income increase has been prepared from 1962 data. Assets were assumed to command a 4 per cent return, and principal and interest then apportioned evenly over the remainder of life. The resulting effect on income would be to raise the potential median about 10 per cent above the actual median when home equity is excluded, and approximately 30 per cent when home equity is included. The income results, as in Table 1, reflect the relatively small asset holdings, except for home ownership, of most aged units.

[4] Lenore A. Epstein and Janet H. Murray, *The Aged Population of the United States*, Research Report No. 19, Social Security Administration (Washington, D.C.: Government Printing Office, 1967), Table 12. 14, 397.
[5] *Ibid.*, Chap. 4.

TABLE 1 *Potential income of older people, 65 and over, if prorated assets were included*

	Actual median income	Potential median income	
		Excluding home equity	Including home equity
Married couples	$2,875	$3,130	$3,795
Nonmarried men	1,365	1,560	1,845
Nonmarried women	1,015	1,130	1,395

Source: Lenore A. Epstein, and Janet H. Murray, *The Aged Population of the United States,* Research Report No. 19, Social Security Administration (Washington, D.C.: Government Printing Office, 1967), 71.

Income-expenditure patterns at different ages: the cross-section data[6]

Comparisons of median asset holdings and income levels of different age groups thus reveal the relatively poor position of the majority of today's aged. Such cross-section comparisons, particularly when they are supplemented by data on expenditure levels, are important for policy considerations of income distributions at a given time among age groups in the society. A more detailed account of the income expenditure patterns by age and occupation of family head reveals the problem of extremely low incomes for certain occupations at each level of working age, thus indicating the constraints on financial preparation for old age by families whose support is derived from these low-paying jobs. [*See Vol. 1, Chap. 4.C, pp. 95–105.*]

AVERAGE ANNUAL EARNINGS

Estimates of the 1960–1961 average annual money incomes (after taxes) in six occupational classes are shown in Table 2. These incomes are primarily earnings; income contributed from gifts, rents, and capital owned amounts to about 5 per cent of total money income.[7]

[6] Although age-related income data are available from Census reports, family expenditure data by occupation and age of family head may be drawn only from the Survey of Consumer Expenditures conducted by the U.S. Bureau of Labor Statistics. Because of the need for consumer expenditure patterns at different stages of the family cycle, the BLS data are used for the discussion immediately following. Estimates of lifetime earnings, which were recently published by the U.S. Bureau of the Census, are discussed later in the chapter.

[7] This calculation is based on money income before taxes, for all urban families and single consumers. Data on earnings as a proportion of income, by age and occupation, are not available. In addition to these major sources—earnings and the ownership of assets—public and private transfers (pensions, welfare payments, unemployment insurance, military allotments, gifts of cash, constitute about 9 per cent of money income before taxes. U.S. Bureau of Labor Statistics, *Consumer Expenditure and Income,* Supplement 3, Part A to Report No. 237–238 (Washington, D.C.: Government Printing Office, 1964), 12.

TABLE 2 *Mean annual family income, after taxes, by age and occupation, 1960–1961*

Age of head	Self-employed	Profes-sional	Clerical	Skilled	Semi-skilled	Un-skilled
Under 25	$4,528	$ 4,990	$4,459	$4,676	$4,602	$3,246
25–34	7,645	7,240	5,704	5,993	5,351	4,495
35–44	9,466	9,159	6,675	6,993	6,042	4,882
45–54	9,429	10,722	6,804	7,232	6,136	4,521
55–64	8,100	9,156	5,851	6,730	5,760	4,180

Source: U.S. Bureau of Labor Statistics, *Consumer Expenditures and Income,* Supplement 2, Part A to Report No. 237–238 (Washington, D.C.: Government Printing Office, 1964), 30–34.

The different occupational categories display similar patterns of income at various ages, as Table 2 reveals; in all classes of occupations, the lower incomes of the youngest, the differences in income, by age, and the age at which maximum annual earnings are received, while varying in absolute amounts, tend to be alike in structure.[8]

Consider, for example, the income-age pattern in two of the occupations. *Professionals* under the age of 25 receive an average of $4,990 per year after taxes. During the age span 25–34 the average is much higher: $7,240. The age group 35–44 has still higher incomes, although the differential over the preceding category is diminishing.[9] From an average of $9,159 for the 35–44 age group, earnings rise to a maximum of $10,722 for ages 45–54. Average incomes are significantly lower ($9,156) for those persons in the 55–64 age group—the cohort that is in its last full decade of work. For *clerical* employees under age 25 the average income is $4,459. In this occupation, too, the largest difference is that between the income of the under-25 and that of the 25–34 age group. The two succeeding age categories have still higher incomes: $6,675 for the 35–44 and $6,804 for the 45–54 year-olds. Again the average income for the oldest group in the full-time labor force is lower, almost $1,000 less than the average for the preceding age category. Roughly the same pattern holds for skilled and semi-skilled workers.

The percentage range in incomes of the self-employed and the

[8] Earnings from work are based on the average annual number of labor force participants per family, which differs by occupation. For the self-employed the average is 0.98; for professionals the average is 1.06; for clerical and skilled, 1.02; for semi-skilled, 0.96; for unskilled, 0.80. *Ibid.,* 30–34.

[9] Earnings for college-trained personnel rise particularly rapidly between the ages of 25 and 44. See Dorothy S. Brady, *Age and the Income Distribution,* Social Security Administration (Washington, D.C.: Government Printing Office, 1965), 33.

TABLE 3 *Mean annual family expenditures, by age
and occupation, 1960–1961*

Age of head	Self-employed	Profes-sional	Clerical	Skilled	Semi-skilled	Un-skilled
Under 25	$5,912	$5,088	$4,526	$4,814	$4,544	$3,469
25–34	6,905	6,941	5,632	6,144	5,367	4,599
35–44	8,701	8,795	6,668	6,733	5,947	5,051
45–54	8,694	9,933	6,815	6,945	5,971	4,540
55–64	7,639	8,281	5,672	6,251	5,629	4,064

Source: U.S. Bureau of Labor Statistics, *Consumer Expenditures and Income,* Supplement 2, Part A, Report No. 237–238 (Washington, D.C.: Government Printing Office, 1964), 30–34.

professionals is more than twice that in other occupations. For professionals, incomes are highest for persons aged 45–54; here average income is 115 per cent above that of the under-25 age group. For self-employed persons, differences in average income are somewhat less marked, the highest average (that received by the 35–44 age group) being 109 per cent greater than the lowest incomes. For the other occupations, the income range is much narrower. Within each occupation, the largest income differential between two successive age groups is that between persons under 25 and those 25–34.

AVERAGE ANNUAL EXPENDITURES

The data reported in the Survey of Consumer Expenditures provide a rough picture of the consumption levels achieved by the families headed by persons of different occupations and ages.[10] Although the level of expenditures is admittedly constrained by (among other things) income, age-related differences in income are not always paralleled by comparable differences in spending. In all classes of occupation, income exceeds expenditures for some age categories; conversely, expenditures are greater at some ages for all occupational groups.

Expenditures[11] at different ages of the family head are shown in Table 3. Taking the clerical worker as an example, expenditures in the family headed by the 25–34-year-old are about one-fourth again as high as the level for the preceding age group; for the 35–44 group

[10] See Sidney Goldstein, *Consumption Patterns of the Aged* (Philadelphia: University of Pennsylvania Press, 1960).

[11] Expenditures are calculated as after-tax income, less the net change in assets. Thus, if after-tax income is $5,000 and the net change in assets is $+$100, expenditures are taken as $4,900. On the other hand, if after-tax income is $5,000 and net change in assets is $-$100, then expenditures are taken as $5,100. Expenditures include current consumption plus outlays for durables.

consumption is higher still, by about one-fifth. Families with heads aged 45–54 spend only slightly more than those approximately ten years younger, while average expenditures by the families of the 55–64-year-olds are about one-sixth lower than the level maintained by the 45–54 age group.[12]

INCOME-EXPENDITURE DIFFERENCES BY AGE AND OCCUPATION

The relation between income and expenditure for families at different stages of the life cycle is depicted in Figure 1.

Self-employed and *professional* workers' incomes are well above expenditures for practically all age groups, as might have been predicted. Except for the early stages of worklife, after-tax incomes afford a wide margin for higher current consumption levels, or for savings and the purchase of future income claims. The amount of the excess of income over expenditures during a lifetime cannot, of course, be estimated from the cross-section data—the family head aged 55–64 did not have in his younger working years the income now accruing to younger cohorts. However, it is clear that a perpetuation of the current incomes going to the different age groups would result in lifetime earnings sufficient to guarantee today's self-employed and professional employee substantial discretionary margins.

Clerical workers' earnings and expenditures, on the other hand, are closely balanced for all age groups. In contrast to the margins available to self-employed and professional workers, the clerical worker will have substantial savings for old age only if consumption levels are reduced, or if incomes rise in the course of the coming decades. Among *skilled* and *semi-skilled* workers, spending exceeds income during the early labor force years; income is high enough to match the expenditure level only for those workers aged 35 and over. Persons aged 45–54 have incomes in excess of expenditures, some margin persisting through age 64. Although semi-skilled employees earn less than skilled workers during their working years, expenditures also absorb proportionately less of their after-tax income. *Unskilled* workers do not receive enough income to cover their expenditures at any age except the 55–64 span, and even then there is no significant income margin. As in the case of the clerical workers, no saving appears possible unless the expenditures are cut substantially, or money incomes rise. Moreover, it is evident that this occupational group re-

---

[12] There is some evidence that surveys such as the BLS *Survey of Consumer Expenditures and Income* understate income and overstate expenditures. See Irwin Friend, and Stanley Schor, "Who Saves?" *Review of Economics and Statistics*, 41 (1959), 221; and U.S. Bureau of Labor Statistics, *op. cit.*, 6, 9.

FIGURE 1 *Annual family income and expenditures, by occupation and age, 1960–1961*

——— Income

- - - - - Expenditures

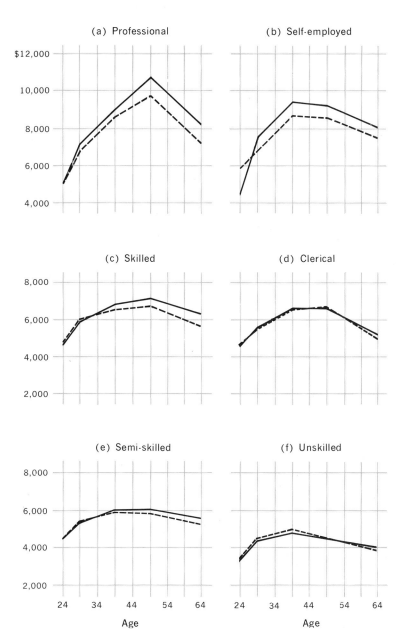

(a) Professional

(b) Self-employed

(c) Skilled

(d) Clerical

(e) Semi-skilled

(f) Unskilled

Age

Age

Note: Based on Tables 2 and 3.

Aging and financial management **211**

quires transfers of income, not only in the retirement years, but through most of worklife as well.

In summary, annual incomes exceed expenditures of the self-employed and professional workers' families for most of the age categories, leaving sources of savings at practically all stages of worklife. Semi-skilled workers, whose expenditures are held below income in the middle and later years, also have a small margin for saving. Clerical and skilled workers, by contrast, barely balance expenditures with income in total, with the years of slight deficits roughly offset by years of small savings. In the case of the unskilled worker, no balance of income with expenditure is achieved except for those in the brief 55–64 age period.

Data on the incomes and expenditures of different age groups and occupations show that although relatively low incomes accrue to the youngest group in the labor force, the incomes going to the next two age groups are substantially higher in all occupations. Incomes of those persons in the last several years of worklife are also noteworthy. During this period financial preparations for retirement are normally made. Since incomes of this age group are lower than those of the younger categories, however, there may be some tendency for 55–64 year-olds to sustain levels of living higher than can be afforded, given the need for concentrated saving for the retirement period. Finally, the volume of expenditures at all age levels is obviously dependent primarily on the income that is available. Further increases in disposable income during worklife may well be accompanied by higher levels of living during worklife, rather than increased saving for old age.

Income and expenditures through worklife: some projections

As suggested in the foregoing section, certain kinds of policy considerations may require analysis of cross-section data. These data shed but little light, however, on the flow of income and expenditures over the life course of particular individuals, and on the probable financial status of the old people of the future. The fact that in a given year, 1960, families headed by 55–64-year-olds had incomes lower than those with younger heads does not mean that workers actually suffer declines in income during their last decade of worklife. Indeed, earnings normally rise throughout worklife, and peak incomes are most likely to occur during the years just prior to retirement. [*See Vol. 1, Chap. 4.A.4, pp. 83–85.*] Viewed in comparison with the incomes of younger workers (who entered the labor force when productivity and wages were higher), the incomes of the oldest working group are lower; but in comparison with their own earlier levels, the 55–64-year-olds are receiving their highest incomes. The continued rise in income during the family head's 50's and early 60's (albeit a slower rise than he enjoyed in earlier years) may make financial planning for retirement possible. For it is also during this period that family size is likely to be reduced and living costs minimized.

Since incomes usually do rise throughout worklife, it is important to concentrate on the probable income-expenditure patterns of today's labor force entrant, and in this way to estimate his capacity for accumulating income for old age. In the course of his worklife, his income will be rising in some rough accord not only with his own productivity, but also with overall economic growth.[13] By the same token, it must be remembered, today's retiree did not receive the incomes during his past worklife that the cross-section picture indicates. If he came up through the ranks of his occupation, his income at each stage was lower than the income now being paid; economic growth has raised the earnings of each of the occupational levels he once occupied. The income problems of many of the present retirees can be explained by reference to their relatively low earnings in an earlier, less productive economic era.

POSSIBLE GROWTH IN EARNINGS

Until full longitudinal study affords data on lifetime earning and consumption patterns of individual families, one may direct attention to the income of the future aged by making some assumptions regarding the earnings of today's labor force participant as he moves through the worklife cycle, and by combining these projected lifetime earnings with probable expenditure patterns. On earnings, earlier work by Herman P. Miller may serve as a guide to the kinds of changes occurring for selected cohorts over the ten-year period between 1949 and 1959.[14] Table 4 reproduces his estimates of the changes in mean income for males between ages 30 and 40, 40 and 50, and 50 and 60. For example, he finds an average annual increase of 12.7 per cent

[13] H. S. Houthakker has observed that "every individual may expect an upward trend in his own earnings superimposed on the cross-sectional pattern for a given year." See his "Education and Income," *Review of Economic Statistics*, 41 (1959), 27. This growth factor is taken into account by Herman Miller in his estimates of lifetime earnings, which are indicated on p. 220. See the work by Miller and Richard A. Hornseth, *Present Value of Estimated Lifetime Earnings*, U.S. Bureau of the Census (Washington, D.C.: Government Printing Office, 1967).
[14] Herman P. Miller, "Lifetime Income and Economic Growth," *American Economic Review*, 55 (1965), 834–844.

TABLE 4 *Components of change in mean income*[a] *for selected cohorts of males,*
United States, 1949 to 1959
Average annual increase in income (as percentage of 1949 base)

Education	Between 25–34 and 35–44			Between 35–44 and 45–54			Between 45–54 and 55–64		
	Total	Experience	Growth	Total	Experience	Growth	Total	Experience	Growth
Less than 8 years	5.5	1.8	3.7	3.3	0.8	2.5	1.9	−0.6	2.5
8 years	5.3	1.9	3.4	3.3	0.7	2.6	1.8	−0.7	2.5
1–3 years high school	5.9	2.1	3.8	3.7	0.9	2.8	2.4	−0.6	3.0
4 years high school	6.3	2.4	3.9	3.8	1.7	2.1	1.8	−0.3	2.1
1–3 years college	9.1	4.6	4.5	4.4	1.4	3.0	2.9	−0.9	3.8
4 or more years college	12.7	7.6	5.1	3.5	1.5	2.0	1.2	−0.6	1.8

[a] In 1959 dollars.
Source: Herman P. Miller, "Lifetime Income and Economic Growth," *American Economic Review,* 55 (1965), 842–843.

of 1949 income for the college graduate who moves from the 30's to the 40's; an annual increase of 3.5 per cent for the graduate who moves from the 40's to the 50's; and a 1.2 per cent increase for the one who goes from the 50's to the 60's.

Miller's estimates suggest patterns of income growth of particular relevance to attempts to project income over the life cycle. First, it is clear that the annual rise in income is much greater during the male's 30's than during subsequent decades of his life, especially for the college graduate.

Second, the components of the income rise are of some importance to discussions of the aging process. Distinguishing between that portion of the increase attributable to the worker's added experience and other age-related factors,[15] and that portion due to economic growth, the author finds that the relative significance of the two sources shifts through the decades of worklife. For college graduates, experience accounts for a yearly income increase of 7.6 per cent for males moving from ages 25–34 to 35–44, while growth brings another 5.1 per cent. In the subsequent decade, however, experience gives rise to 1.5 per cent annual rise in income, and economic growth assumes the larger proportion of 2.0 per cent. Finally, experience has a negative impact on income during the male's later worklife, and this holds for college graduates as well as for the workers with less education; except for the growth component, all incomes would drop during a person's last decade of work.

Third, the Miller estimates, as derived from one set of actual data, suggest that both "experience" and economic growth have differential impact, not only for different stages in the life cycle, but also for varying categories of labor force participants. Such variations should be taken into account in selecting rates of increase for estimates of probable future income.

For purposes of isolating the least privileged segments of the population, these increases in income during worklife are perhaps best viewed by classifying workers on the basis of educational level, as Miller has done, rather than occupational category,[16] since education is easier to define and less likely to change over the life cycle of the individual. To give a rough income estimate for each of the occupa-

[15] The difference at a given point in time between the mean income of a cohort and that of the adjacent age group (as of 1949) was assumed to be attributable to experience and other factors associated with age. The remainder of the income increase of the younger cohort as it moved from 1949 to 1959 was imputed to economic growth.

[16] See James N. Morgan's review of *Income Distribution in the United States* by Herman P. Miller, in *American Economic Review*, 57 (1967), 626.

TABLE 5 *Estimated annual incomes through worklife,*
with economic growth component included, for workers
25 and under, 1960–1961

Age	Self-employed	Professional[a]	Clerical	Skilled	Semi-skilled	Un-skilled
Under 25	$ 4,528	$ 4,990	$ 4,459	$ 4,676	$ 4,602	$ 3,246
25–34	10,149	9,681	7,785	8,111	7,179	5,918
35–44	17,582	17,845	12,388	12,784	10,722	8,899
45–54	23,591	23,316	15,385	17,106	13,956	11,031
55–64	32,946	26,322	17,994	22,487	17,489	13,780

[a] [The assumption that professionals start their worklife later than all other occupational categories (at 22 rather than 20) tends to depress the income estimates for this category.—Editors' note.]
Source: Income data for workers under 25 taken from U.S. Bureau of Labor Statistics, *Consumer Income and Expenditures*, Supplement 2, Part A, Report No. 237–238 (Washington, D.C.: Government Printing Office, 1964), Tables 15a and 15e. Incomes for 25–34 and succeeding age categories calculated by compounding the growth rates indicated in Table 4, and adding the 1960–1961 cross-section differences in incomes of age categories (Table 2).

tions used in the earlier cross-section analysis, however, let us suppose that persons with 4 or more years of college enter the professions;[17] those with 1 to 3 years of college are the self-employed; persons with high-school diplomas become clerical workers; persons with 1 to 3 years of high school, skilled; those with 8 years of education, semi-skilled; and persons with fewer than 8 years of school become unskilled workers. Suppose further that the 1949–1959 trend in incomes continues; that economic growth raises income per year at the same rate during the male's 20's as during his 30's; that the average age of entry for persons entering professions is 22, rather than the 20 assumed for other occupations; that family income can be used as a basis for estimating income of male workers. (Moreover, no attempt is made to allow for possible difference between dollars received in the future and dollars received in 1960–1961.)

Under these assumptions, it is possible to illustrate the combined effects of economic growth and experience on worklife income by occupational categories as shown in Table 5. In the *professional* income profile shown in Table 2, for example, the 1960–1961 Bureau of Labor Statistics data show an average annual income after taxes of approximately $4,990 for the youngest age group and $7,240 for the 25–34

[17] It is interesting to note that the proportion of college-trained persons is increasing relative to those without college training, yet there is no indication that this relative increase has reduced the return on a college education. See Brady, *op. cit.*, 4; Herman P. Miller, "Annual and Lifetime Income in Relation to Education 1939–1959," *American Economic Review*, 50 (1960), 962–986; and U.S. Bureau of the Census, *Income Distribution in the United States* (Washington, D.C.: Government Printing Office, 1966), 163.

group. To this difference of $2,250, attributable to whatever experience, maturity, skill, etc., the older group has acquired, must be added an economic growth factor (applying the analysis for Table 4) of 5.1 per cent per year for eight years, giving an average annual income of $9,681 for the 30-year-old male.[18] During the next decade growth again adds 5.1 per cent per annum, which, when added to the experience differential of $1,919, raises the average income of the 40-year-old to $17,845. Both growth and experience add noticeably less to income for the 45–54-year-olds. The annual growth component is 2.0 per cent, which raises average annual income (when the experience factor is added) to $23,316 for the man aged 50. Since the experience factor is negative between 55 and 64, the effect of growth is only to offset this tendency and raise income slightly. By the time the professional workers reach retirement age, earnings average $26,322 per year.

Similar computations yield the estimated incomes at various ages for the different occupations. Under the assumptions upon which these computations are based, average incomes at the time of retirement for most workers in all occupations would be quite high by today's standards, once the impact of economic growth is taken into account, as suggested for the professional category in the contrasting cross-section and lifetime estimates in Figure 2. Other growth assumptions could be made, yielding different future incomes for the various occupations; the assumption of no growth factor is, however, clearly invalid.

EXPENDITURES: HOW FAST WILL THEY RISE?

The 1960–1961 data on income and expenditures at different ages give a rough indication of the extent to which income constrains spending. The cross-section data in Figure 1 above show the close correlation of expenditures with current after-tax incomes at most ages between 20 and 64, and for most of the occupations. In order to gauge the income potential for the retirement period, however, it is necessary to determine the probable pattern of consumer expenditure through the life span, given the much higher real incomes that are likely to be forthcoming. We know from Goldstein's work that the consumption patterns of persons now middle-aged are different, even

[18] Estimates of the contribution of economic growth are taken from Miller, "Lifetime Income and Economic Growth," *op. cit.* Cross-section differences ($2,250 in this instance), assumed to be due to experience, are taken from Table 1. [Miller's growth rate, however, originally calculated on a decennial basis, appears here to have been compounded annually—thus exaggerating the income estimates considerably, particularly for the later years.—Editors' note.]

FIGURE 2 *Cross-section view of family income and expenditures, by age in 1960–1961, contrasted with estimated income through worklife for workers 25 and under in 1960–1961*

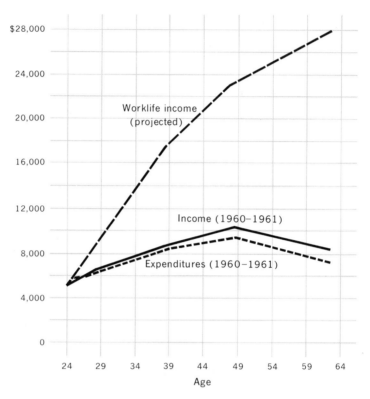

Note: Based on Tables 2, 3, and 5

Note: Data for the professional category only. Similar graphs for other occupations suggest consistently marked discrepancies between cross-section and estimated worklife income.

when income is held constant, from the patterns observed by aged persons [*and the cohort comparisons presented in Vol. 1 suggest a general excess of income over expenditure in the years just prior to retirement—see Chap. 4.C.1.d, pp. 100–101.*] How will the consumption patterns of this middle-aged group be affected by the rise in incomes that will accompany continued economic growth? More specifically, what portion of the higher incomes will be preempted for consumption during worklife and what portion will be available for savings or transfers?

If economic growth should raise future incomes well above present expenditure levels, and if levels of living were to remain fixed through even a decade of such growth, the greater margin of income over consumption would make possible expanded investment, including investment in the education of the young, or increased consumption by other groups (for example, retirees). The supposition that workers' expenditures will remain at something close to their present level is unwarranted, however, on the basis of past experience; nor would such a freezing of living levels be necessarily desirable.

Most people agree that they should save more heavily for retirement; most people fail to do so. Indeed, the widespread reliance on public and private pensions may reflect the premise that most people fail to make systematic provisions for retirement income voluntarily. As incomes rise, the consumption of new types of goods quickly becomes a part of the standard of living; today's luxuries are tomorrow's necessities. The high propensity to consume,[19] documented by earlier studies, continues to be a deterrent to saving for retirement, despite the gradual rise in income levels.

Perhaps the most reasonable assumption as to future expenditures is to suppose that their increase will be proportional to the rise in income. Goldsmith found that the personal rate of saving "failed to show a marked upward or downward trend during the past half century."[20] Modigliani and Brumberg have hypothesized a constant saving-income ratio.[21] They argue that households wish to maintain a certain level of saving to provide for emergencies, retirement, etc. Thus, a 10 per cent increase in income would be matched by a 10 per cent rise in expenditures.[22] Any departure in this proportional relationship is due to short-term or unanticipated fluctuations in income, and is not typical of the usual relationship between income and expenditures.[23]

If consumer expenditures do continue to absorb the proportions of income used for that purpose in 1960–1961, the bulk of the grad-

[19] See, for example, Ruth Mack, "Trends in American Consumption and the Aspiration to Consume," *American Economic Review*, 46 (1956), 57 ff.

[20] Raymond W. Goldsmith, *A Study of Saving in the United States*, I, National Bureau of Economic Research (Princeton: Princeton University Press, 1955), 7.

[21] Franco Modigliani and Richard Brumberg, "Utility Analysis and the Consumption Function: An Interpretation of Cross-Sectional Data," in Kenneth K. Kurihara (ed.), *Post Keynesian Economics* (New Brunswick, N.J.: Rutgers University Press, 1954), 430.

[22] *Ibid.*, 419.

[23] *Ibid.*, 430. On the possible inaccuracies associated with data collected over a relatively short period, see Harold Lydall, "The Life Cycle in Income, Saving, and Asset Ownership," *Econometrica*, 23 (1955), 145; and Ralph B. Bristol, "Factors Associated with Income Variability," *American Economic Review*, 48 (1958), 279–280.

ually rising incomes of labor force participants will obviously be absorbed by their rising consumption, but the residual will nevertheless be significant for men in some occupations. For the professional and self-employed persons, the worklife totals would of course be quite high; skilled and semi-skilled would also have substantial balances, and the clerical workers somewhat less. Since expenditures exceed income for the unskilled workers at most ages, a portion of the projected rise in incomes would need to be used to equate expenditures and income. Some net saving could result in the last ten years of worklife, should the projected expenditures-income ratio be the same as that observed in the cross-section data.

For persons who remain in the low-paying jobs throughout their worklives, there seems little hope of accumulating private savings in sufficient quantity to make significant improvements in retirement incomes. Not only are the annual incomes low when full-time work is available; the threat of unemployment, which quickly erodes any past savings, is ever present. It is questionable, moreover, whether the limited savings that are available to these families should be earmarked for retirement, given the competing need for, say, the children's education. It is well to identify those groups—occupational or educational—whose earnings even during their most productive years are likely to be inadequate to maintain reasonable living standards. For these families, as well as those without wage earners, income supplements are required throughout most or all of life. The income problem in such cases is of course not caused by old age or by retirement from work, but by low productivity and its root cause in turn, a low level of education and skill.

A LIFETIME INCOME STATEMENT

The foregoing projections of changes in the incomes of age cohorts as they move through worklife provide one type of estimate of the capacities of different occupational groups to support their consumption needs through retirement, as well as through the working years. All such projections are mere approximations, of course, and vary greatly depending upon the particular assumptions they make about the applicability of current income structures to the unknown conditions of the future. Another approach to the question of how much future earnings will be, and hence what volume of savings are possible, is used by Miller and Hornseth in the calculation of projected earnings over the entire worklife. This analysis, rather than calculating economic growth from analysis of Census data as in Table 5 above, simply assumes alternative levels of growth (as well as alternative discount rates to adjust for the fact that a dollar to be received in the future is not worth a dollar received today). These estimates indicate, for example, that the lifetime earnings of a male service worker aged 18 and with eight years of school are $143,000 when discounted at 4 per cent, assuming also a 4 per cent rate of economic growth. Similarly, the professional worker at age 22, with four or more years of college, has a presently valued earnings expectancy of $400,000 under the same growth and discount assumptions.[24]

Savings and income transfers for the aged

Financial preparation for retirement would ideally begin no later than age 45, when there are at least twenty years of worklife remaining. But for families at or below the current median income of under $9,000, it is unlikely that savings for old age (beyond mortgage payments, OASDHI taxes, and life insurance) will be accumulated until somewhat later. If the youngest child is born when the father is 28, and if the child goes to college, he will not be through school before his father is 50. In practical terms, therefore, the period in which savings may be accumulated is probably no longer than the last fifteen years of worklife [as suggested also in Vol. 1, Chap. 4.C.1.d, pp. 100–101].

THE ROLE OF PERSONAL SAVING

In addition to the length of the period of financial preparation, two other variables are crucial: the annual income during these preretirement years, and the level of expenditures. Average incomes can be estimated, as we have seen, under varying growth assumptions; annual expenditures can preempt any proportion of this income up to (or even beyond) 100 per cent. The essence of financial planning is to allocate at least the last fifteen years of earnings in such a manner that, when added to retirement benefits and income from any previously acquired assets, the income stream most nearly meshes with desired expenditures through the remainder of life.

Budgeting for a twenty- to thirty-year period is perhaps too far-fetched a goal; most families have difficulty budgeting on an annual or even a monthly basis. [See Vol. 1, Chap. 18.C.1.b, pp. 444–445.] But it would be possible, once earnings during the latter part of worklife have been projected, to estimate also the size of retirement benefits and thus to note the amount of drop in income at age 65. Such a

[24] Miller and Hornseth, op. cit., 1, 2, 14, 40.

forward look would probably serve to encourage some form of long-term planning.

As an illustration, suppose we take a male clerical worker, high-school graduate, who is 50 years old in 1969. He was 40 years old in 1959, a year in which the average annual income for his occupation and educational level was known to be $5,695.[25] If we assume that his income changed in accordance with the age-related change for his occupation, and that he also enjoyed an annual growth-component increase of 3 per cent, his income at age 50 would be $7,727. Extending the same assumptions for the remaining fifteen years of worklife, his annual income during the financial preparation would increase slightly each year so that, at the time of retirement in 1983, his annual pretax income would be $11,376.

In contrast, his retirement benefits will probably be not more than one-third the estimated income at the time of retirement. A recent simulation projection of incomes in old age estimates that in 1980 about half the couples and more than four-fifths of the unmarried retirees will receive $3,000 or less in annual pension income, both public and private.[26] It is of course true that the most recent retirees have the highest retirement benefits, and in addition the earnings figures used here extend to 1983. Even so, it is clear that retirement benefits are unlikely to approach even one-half the immediate preretirement income average, unless benefits rise much faster than in the past.[27]

Data on current income levels of older people, presented on pages 204–206 above, indicate that their median is less than half that of younger persons. There is little reliable information on the behavior of a particular family's income after the head passes age 65. [*See Vol. 1, Chap. 4.A.4.c, pp. 84–85.*] During the early years of this period, income is more likely than later to include some earnings, and is therefore higher than it will be during the family head's 70's and thereafter. But the important determinant of relative income status is again the rate of economic growth and hence the pace at which earnings continue to rise. This growth, during a retirement period of fifteen or twenty years, allows a substantial deterioration in the aged's relative income even when prices remain stable.

As an example, assume that an income recipient sets aside each

[25] *Ibid.*, 25.

[26] James H. Schulz, "The Future Economic Circumstances of the Aged: A Simulation Projection," *Yale Economic Essays*, 7 (1967), 145–217.

[27] In the study cited, social security benefits were assumed to increase by 4 per cent annually (based on average creditable wages) between 1962 and 1980. *Ibid.*, 211.

year that fraction necessary to provide a retirement level of consumption equal to the level *of the current year*. Upon retirement, he takes his saving (the cumulated sum plus interest) and buys an annuity providing whatever annual income can be purchased for the remainder of his life. But whereas he then has a fixed payment per year for as long as he lives, persons in the labor force continue to enjoy rising incomes. Making the simplifying assumptions that the average age of entry to the labor force is 20, retirement occurs at 60, and death at age 80, that the relevant rate of interest is 5 per cent and the rate of economic growth 2 per cent, the amount he will have available for consumption at the beginning of the retirement period is only 60 per cent of the average spent by workers in younger age groups.

But this proportion available at the time of retirement is not likely to be maintained during the retirement period. If the economic growth rate continues at 2 per cent, the older person's average potential for consumption will have fallen to 45 per cent of the worker's consumption after ten years of retirement; by the end of life the proportion is only one-third. If incomes of the economically active are rising at a rate of 3 per cent annually, the relative deterioration occurs even faster. From a 48 per cent level at the beginning of retirement, consumption falls to 36 per cent after ten years and eventually to 27 per cent of the worker's level.[28]

Personal savings can of course soften the financial blow at the time of retirement, both by adding to pension income and by holding down consumption in the later working years, so the actual change in consumption level is minimized. Since it is apparently quite difficult to reduce a level of living once it is established, the least painful method of saving for old age may be to view increases in income after age 50 primarily as retirement income, holding the standard of living as nearly fixed as possible during the latter part of worklife. In the case of the clerical worker, if expenditures could be held to whatever disposable income a gross income of, say, $8,000 affords, savings from age 52 through 64 would amount to more than $21,000. This amount with interest could then be prorated over the retirement years. If life expectancy [*see Vol. 1, Chap. 2.3, pp. 24–35*] for the male at age 65 is 13 years and that of his wife (whom we will assume to be younger than he) is 20 years, the accumulated savings and interest would need to be spread in some reasonable manner over roughly two decades.

[28] The model from which these estimates were derived is shown in Juanita M. Kreps and John O. Blackburn, "The Impact of Economic Growth on Retirement Incomes" (Report prepared for the U.S. Senate, Special Committees on Aging, 1967).

For many reasons, income requirements may vary during the last one-third of the life span. Tax liabilities are heavier during worklife when income is higher, as are insurance premiums, and the costs associated with working. Mortgage payments may continue during the 50's, but probably not during retirement. Expenses during retirement may be higher if travel and recreation expenditures are made [*see Vol. 1, Chap. 4.C.2.a and b, pp. 102–103; Chap. 22, pp. 511–535*] and if medical expenses not covered by Medicare are incurred. Studies by Sidney Goldstein provide some basis for estimating differences in expenditures by age and income level.[29] The smoothing-out of disposable income in later life need not make each year's income the same as its predecessors, therefore; rather, the goal is to prevent the extreme fluctuations that now occur.

THE NATURE AND VOLUME OF INCOME TRANSFERS

Although personal savings are likely to grow, particularly for those families whose incomes rise in accordance with the economy's growth, the major source of retirement income for most families will continue to be public and private pension benefits.

But total pension income for couples in 1980 is not expected to increase at a rate sufficient to be of much help in closing the gap between earnings and retirement income. By 1980, three-fourths of the couples will be receiving pension incomes of $4,000 or less, with only about one-eighth having pensions of more than $5,000. When the 1980 estimates are corrected for price change (assuming that the 1955–1965 price rise of 1.6 per cent yearly continues till 1980), 81 per cent of the retired couples are expected to have a real pension income plus asset income of $4,000 or less; the comparable proportion for 1962 was 84 per cent.[30]

Continuation of past rates of growth in pension benefits, or even some slight acceleration in rate, will probably do little more than offset price rises. Moreover, the family cannot determine the size of its pension, but is bound by legislative action in the case of social security payments and by the employer's retirement plan where private pension coverage is provided.

Public pensions, which in this country are financed by payroll taxes on the incomes of persons still at work, operate to transfer income claims against the nation's total output from workers to retirees. It is important to note that the transfer is from the workers in 1969 to the

[29] See Goldstein, *op. cit.*; and "Urban and Rural Differentials in Consumer Patterns of the Aged," *Rural Sociology*, 31 (1966), 333–345.
[30] Schulz, *op. cit.*, 181.

retirees in 1969, and not from a man who works in 1969 to the same man when he retires in 1989. The retiree of 1989 will have an income claim against the 1989 output, and his claim will be financed by a tax on the workers of that year. Transfers of income claims thus reallocate the annual output between workers and nonworkers (including the young as well as the old), the measure of this redistribution being dictated largely by Congressional decision.

Public policy in the United States has provided for a floor of income for retirees, but there has not yet been an attempt to use social security benefits as a means of smoothing the humps and valleys of income in any broad, life-range manner. The problem of poor fit between earnings and consumption needs persists, and is in fact accentuated by the rise in productivity and real earnings of persons at work. A shortening of worklife relative to total life span further complicates the problem of lifetime financial planning. [*Cf. Sheppard, Chap. 6 in this volume.*] For a relatively small proportion of families, private pensions have eased the problem of retirement income. But coverage is quite limited, and estimates indicate that in 1975 only about one in four retirees will have a private pension.

PUBLIC AND PRIVATE TRANSFERS

Reluctance to provide more generous public pensions for retirees reflects in part a failure to recognize the lengthening retirement period as a new life-stage, and in part a belief that each family is in charge of its own financial destiny. [*See Vol. 1, Chap. 4.D., pp. 105–106.*] Hence, private savings are expected to achieve whatever income smoothing, beyond certain minimum pensions, is desired. The private method has the advantage of allowing the family to do its own lifetime budgeting and saving for old age; it also has the disadvantage of allowing the family to do neither.

Recent studies, however, suggest that planning for retirement income may be at about the same stage today as was planning for protection against the hazard of death a half century ago. Although people typically do not want to think about either death or old age, they will, if the needs are brought into focus, enter into contracts that provide important elements of security against both hazards. Furthermore, as the joint survivor years are extended into retirement, husbands and wives seem to be increasingly interested in the prospects of their retirement years. [*See Vol. 1, Chap. 4.C.1.e, p. 101; Chap. 18.C.1.b, pp. 444–445.*]

But the accumulation of private savings in sufficient amounts to keep retirement income in step with earnings is extremely difficult, as earlier discussion has shown. The barrier to such a volume of saving is twofold: (1), we are a highly consumption-oriented society, with an apparently insatiable appetite for present goods and services; and (2), even if we depress current consumption levels in order to enjoy higher future incomes, our savings are likely to maintain during retirement only a fraction of the earnings of persons who are employed. The threat of erosion of purchasing power through price increases is a further deterrent.

Private pension arrangements face much the same difficulty, since they also require more saving now for more consumption during retirement. In order to provide future benefits commensurate with future incomes, and further, provide benefits that would keep pace with earnings during the retirement period, private pension schemes would have to exact much heavier contributions from employers and employees than they now require. Unless these larger contributions are made, employers will find it difficult unilaterally to raise pension benefits above the levels financed by past contributions.

The goal of achieving a better fit of income with needs, particularly during the last third of life, can be realized only if family financial planning is accompanied by appropriate income-maintenance programs. Since such a large proportion of retirement income is derived from these programs, public policy is clearly a critical determinant of levels of living in old age. It would be possible, for example, for much of the necessary income-smoothing to be achieved through higher benefits that would be financed from higher payroll (or other) taxes. In this case, some of the productivity increase would be diverted from wage income into retirement pensions.

Social security benefits will obviously need to rise as earnings rise; debate hinges on the questions of how fast the increase should be, and on the proper direction of tax policy. As to the desirable extent of benefit increase, the wide gap between earnings and present retirement benefits indicates the range within which income "smoothing" might advantageously occur. But even if benefits were raised so as to minimize the gap, the improvement would be temporary unless policy also deals with the relationship of earnings and benefits through time. Until benefits are in some way tied to the growth in real income, retirees' incomes will lag behind the incomes of workers.

A critical question of equity is involved: Whose growth is it? In the present scheme of income allocation, which offers financial rewards primarily on the basis of productivity, lies the implicit assumption that the gains from economic growth are due altogether to the efforts of persons who are currently at work. But the validity of this assumption can be questioned. Increases in the productivity of the employed may have very little to do with their own actions and initiatives; they result, rather, from capital accumulation and advances in technology, to which the retired have already made their contribution.

Income gains from intraoccupational promotions and from advances into higher occupational ranks, which are due to knowledge and job experience, may be considered the rewards for individual effort. Further increments accrue to those persons who are willing to undergo extended education and training. The income differentials attributable to education, skill, and experience can be maintained, however, without also imputing to the current generation of workers that portion of output that derives from scientific and technical progress.[31]

The question of tax policy is also a much-debated one. Further increases in payroll taxes will of course be necessary if benefits are to be financed exclusively from this source. Raising the taxable base, as in the 1967 Amendments to the Social Security Act, helps to reduce the regressivity of the payroll tax. But significant increases in the rate raise the question of whether we are not taxing heavily one low-income group in order to raise the incomes of another. It is obviously necessary to consider general-revenue financing, if benefits are to continue to rise.[32]

Division of the total output between the economically active and the retirees is achieved, ideally, by a set of financial arrangements that do not interfere with the achievement of the economy's other goals: a high rate of economic growth, full employment, price stability —to take the three most often cited. At any particular point in time, the pressure toward one of these goals may constitute a major constraint on the nation's capacity to raise the incomes of any particular group. During the period of the Vietnam war, total expenditures have generated a price inflation of serious magnitude; an objective of social policy is to contain the price rise by reducing total expenditures.

---

[31] For a fuller discussion of the equity question, see Joseph J. Spengler and Juanita M. Kreps, "Equity and Social Credit for the Retired," in Juanita M. Kreps (ed.), *Employment, Income, and Retirement Problems of the Aged* (Durham: Duke University Press, 1963).

[32] Eveline Burns has recommended a "two-decker" system of public benefits, with a demogrant (a uniform cash payment to all persons in a given age group), which would be paid regardless of income or employment status, plus a contributory wage-related benefit that is actuarially calculated. See her "Income-Maintenance Policies and Early Retirement," in Juanita M. Kreps (ed.), *Technology, Manpower, and Retirement Policy* (Cleveland: The World Publishing Co., 1966), 125–140. Needless to say, the amount of the second tier of benefits is dependent upon the amount of income foregone during worklife; agreement on how much current consumption should be foregone is seldom unanimous.

If the total demand for goods can be restrained, price changes will be minimized.

In a different economic climate, it may be equally important to increase total expenditures in order to stimulate output and create jobs. Unemployment has been a serious problem throughout most of the two decades between World War II and Vietnam. Confronted with the need to spend instead of save, public policy can afford financial arrangements involving, where necessary, federal deficits. What it *cannot* afford is increased saving. For under depressed economic conditions, attempts to save more heavily—for retirement or whatever—reduce the level of effective demand and incomes further still. Payroll taxes, exacting a percentage of earnings, should not be increased in such a period; ideally, they or other taxes would be reduced.

Neither the accumulation of private savings for old age nor the financing of social security benefits can be made dependent on the need to achieve the fiscal goals of the economy. Yet it is important to note that both the financing of retirement benefits and the volume of private saving have important consequences for the economy, and their implications for the economy as a whole will certainly influence public policy. Similarly, the management of pension funds, whose total volume has grown so rapidly in recent years, will surely have an influence on aggregate saving and yields in capital markets.[33]

Regardless of the financial arrangements, it is productivity increases that provide the goods and services with which to raise levels of living for all age groups. Retirees can share in this economic growth in accordance with their income claims. Income claims, in turn, accrue to retirees via the tax mechanism or the medium of private saving; in either case, consumption is foregone during worklife in return for consumption during retirement. The more evenly we choose to regulate consumption through the life cycle, and the longer the retirement period relative to worklife, the greater is the necessary transfer of income through either public or private methods.

---

[33] See John O. Blackburn, "Pensions, The National Income, and The National Wealth," in Kreps (ed.), *Employment, Income, and Retirement Problems of the Aged*, 178–197; see also his "The Macroeconomics of Pension Funds," in U.S. Congress, Joint Economic Committee, 90th Cong., 1st Sess., *Old Age Income Assurance*, Part V: *Financial Aspects of Pension Plans* (Washington, D.C.: Government Printing Office, 1967), 1–14.

8

Aging and the fields of architecture and planning

JOHN MADGE

In this essay, Mr. Madge, an English architect and sociologist, organizes the social science findings of Volume One around five stages or turning points at which older adults confront basic choices of how and where to live. Within this framework Mr. Madge points to many exciting possibilities and raises many issues for architects and planners who must determine the policies, develop the programs, and design the housing and other facilities appropriate to older age groups.

The five stages are, briefly: (1) The departure of grown children *reduces the housing requirements of a family, but it is difficult at best to design homes which contract or expand. It is not unthinkable, however, for communities or neighborhoods to be so "balanced" as to permit a change of residence without major disturbances in established networks of friends and neighbors. (2) With all the problems and issues inherent in meeting the housing needs of* retired *people, one conclusion seems to emerge. Retirees want to keep in touch with everyday life, but at the same time they want to maintain their own sense of privacy.*

They want "intimacy, but at a distance." (3) Although bereavement *is an almost universal experience of the married couple (save where both spouses die together), little if any systematic attention has been given to the consequent adjustments in housing needs and living arrangements. (4) In sharp contrast, much work has been done to develop housing criteria for* infirm *or disabled older people, largely centered on considerations of comfort, convenience, and safety. (5) Finally, if and when the time comes that an older person can* no longer care for himself, *new arrangements must be made either at home or in an institution. Despite much experimentation, the situation today is such that these arrangements typically reflect either outmoded medical practice, or inadequate understanding of the patient's needs, or both.*

Advisers for this chapter were Robert L. Geddes, Dean, School of Architecture, Princeton University; and Huson Jackson, Sert, Jackson and Associates, Architects, Cambridge, Massachusetts. It was also reviewed by Glenn H. Beyer, Center for Housing and Environmental Studies, Cornell University.

ON THE RELEVANCE OF VOLUME ONE

Much of the social science knowledge about older people, as set forth in Volume One, is of crucial interest to the architect or planner who would provide the optimal residential setting. In particular, Chapter 6 describes the geographical concentration of older people in certain types of communities, the tendencies of the aged to be less mobile than the younger population and to own their homes, the characteristics of these homes, and the implications of housing for the range of human contacts, day-to-day activities, and available community facilities and services. More generally, Chapters 8 through 11 provide background on the physical limitations of older people, Chapters 7 and 23 on family and household relationships, Chapter 24 on ties to neighbors and friends, Chapter 22 on leisure activities in retirement, and Chapter 25 on the roles of that fraction of the aged who live in institutions.

Architects and planners sometimes act like gods. Just as Jeremy Bentham said of his own Panopticon prison design, "Morals reformed, health preserved, industry invigorated, instruction diffused, public burdens lightened . . . all by a simple idea in architecture,"[1] so too our contemporaries are liable to claim that poverty, delinquency, and racial tensions can be dissipated by the simple act of tearing down the slums.

We must also be on guard against the belief that improvements in the physical environment can remedy the intrinsic problems of aging. But this does not mean that the physical environment and the layout of a community are irrelevant. Architecture and planning cannot create friendships or cure physical handicaps, but they can make or mar the opportunities for the individual who wishes to conserve his independence and active social life. Good design can provide an appropriate setting, and it is up to the architect to learn all he can of the needs and desires of the aging rather than to impose on them his own ideas.

This chapter is mainly about housing and other residential needs of the elderly. In terms of capital investment, manpower, and land use, housing and substitutes for housing constitute the most important task for architects, planners of policy and design, and the construction industry. Important though they are, nonresidential facilities such as clubs and clinics are subsidiary to housing, and the clearest picture of this field of architecture and planning for older people is gained by highlighting residential needs.

There are five critical phases in the life cycle that have a particular bearing on residential requirements as these relate to aging, though naturally by no means all aging individuals encounter all five. These stages are: the phase when children are growing up and leaving the parental home; retirement, including the period leading up to it; widowhood; disablement connected with the aging process; and dependence, when the individual, no longer able to look after himself, may or may not need skilled medical and nursing care. For various reasons there may be a tendency for these phases to become increasingly differentiated from each other. For example, with earlier retirement and improved medical care there is a growing interval after retirement and before serious physical disablement is likely to occur.

It is convenient to discuss the architecture of aging in the light of these phases. Each stage has distinctive implications for the individual's residential needs, and particular design requirements become especially pressing at one phase or another. The challenge to the architect and planner is, then, to respond imaginatively and sensitively to these changing needs through the latter half of the life cycle.

[1] Jeremy Bentham, "Panopticon or the Inspection House," in Bowring (ed.), *Works* (1791), IV, 39, quoted by Max Grunhut in *Penal Reform* (Oxford: Clarendon Press, 1948), 51–52.

The departure of grown children

The first phase involves the often unanticipated changes in living routine and space requirements that are precipitated by departure of children into homes of their own. This spatial fission of the family is a feature of all industrialized countries, with the result that only a minority of households still contain under the same roof both an aging parent or parents and one or more of his children. To be sure, this is an important minority. In the United States, about one-quarter of persons over 65 share a household with their offspring, with the older generation more likely than the younger to act as household head. Combined households may consist of a father being looked after by a widowed or unmarried daughter. There will also be cases in which one or both parents continue to provide a home for a physically or mentally handicapped child. Other types of unusual households include a few with three generations of adults. Yet it is most common by far to find all children leaving home when they grow up. [*See Vol. 1, Chap. 7.B, pp. 167–183.*]

This fragmentation of the household has been steadily increasing in recent decades. On the one hand, the younger generations are marrying earlier in their life cycle, and are both demanding and achieving total independence at an earlier age than was formerly the case. On the other hand, the parents are surviving to increasingly older ages, and many of them too are seeking and maintaining independence. [*See Vol. 1, Chap. 23.B.1.f, pp. 549–550.*] What was once a relatively short period in the dusk of life has now stretched, in many cases, to a third share or more of the whole life span.

Thus the couple, while still in middle life, is confronted with the possibility that their home may be too large.

THE QUESTION OF MOVING

Yet the normal aging couple may find it particularly difficult at this stage to make fully rational adjustments in residential arrangements in response to the departure of their children. Both parents are likely to be completely active and the man, at least if he is not a manual worker, will probably be at the peak of his earning capacity. Because he is still hard at work, he will be discouraged from making a radical move to some other district. Furthermore, the pressures to stay put may well be matched by a fond desire to maintain an amply large house so that there will be no difficulty in accommodating frequent and prolonged visits from children and their families. [*See Vol. 1, Chap. 6.B.6.a, pp. 136–138.*] Whether or not these visits take place, there is a likelihood that more couples than logically should will decide not to move, and thus miss what might be an excellent opportunity to plan for their old age accommodations at a time when they are fully active, more or less fully adaptable, and still possessing a higher capacity for financial maneuver than they will possess in later life. [*See Vol. 1, Chap. 6.C, pp. 143–155.*]

THE OVERSIZED HOME

It is a well-documented fact that many older people are living in houses that are larger than they want or need. Chapter 6 in Volume One cites evidence at various points to show that "substantial minorities of older people who are home-owners . . . feel they have more rooms than they need"; "moving to a smaller residence heads the list of retirement plans . . . made . . . in advance"; "older people who move or renovate their homes are more likely to reduce, than to increase, the number of rooms." According to Beyer and Wahl,[2] "authorities generally agree that 2- or 3-room units are sufficient and desirable for the aged."

This does not of course mean that all older people should be pressed to move to smaller homes. Needs and tastes differ widely. For the very old, for example, who are often sustained by familiar sights and sounds, a move might be traumatic, perhaps fatal. Except for urgent financial or physical reasons, it is clearly undesirable to move such individuals.

The problem of the oversized home may be particularly acute in the case of poorer families, whose mainly manual job prospects may already have begun to show a downturn by the phase in their life cycle at which their children are just moving away. Such families may be still more reluctant to leave their oversized older houses because newer houses or apartments, though they may be smaller, are likely to have a higher rental or to require mortgage outlays at an age when mortgages are in any case difficult to arrange. [*See Bernstein, Chap. 9 in this volume, for suggestions for new forms of "property."*] In the British and European context, many of the poorest urban householders—and particularly the older ones—are owner-occupiers of outworn central-area property, and their old homes, though not possessing much capital value, do provide relatively inexpensive accommodation.

Similar considerations apply to rented housing. In Britain, for example, there has until recently been a persistent tendency to give

[2] Glenn H. Beyer and Sylvia G. Wahl, *The Elderly and Their Housing* (Ithaca, N.Y.: Cornell University Agricultural Experiment Station and New York State College of Home Economics, 1963), 25.

priority in public housing construction to two-generation family units with young children, typically requiring three bedrooms. In many areas it is unfortunately still true that the supply of smaller homes in the same locality is quite inadequate. For this reason, and also because such smaller houses or apartments as there are—being newer —have a disproportionately high rental value, there is often considerable resistance by older people to accepting a transfer.

An apparently obvious alternative solution to the problem of the overly-large house should be noted in passing. This is the taking in of boarders, who live and eat with the family; or of lodgers, who rent rooms and are given access to bathrooms or other joint facilities. In some localities there is considerable demand for accommodation for single, or temporarily single, people such as students, young clerical workers, seasonal laborers, and others who have no fixed workplace. There is also the traditional trade in providing accommodation for vacationers or travelers. As a solution to the problem of the excess spare rooms this is, however, comparatively rare in the United States and of decreasing importance generally. There seems to have been a simultaneous decline in the popularity of the status of landlady, and in the willingness of students and others to be child surrogates in private homes. There are even institutional discouragements to the making of such arrangements; in rental housing, many leases prevent and many public authorities prohibit tenants from taking in boarders or lodgers.

ARCHITECTURAL SOLUTIONS

The question remains whether there are any measures in the fields of architecture and planning that can mitigate this problem of the oversized home. Two possibilities immediately suggest themselves. The first is the architectural point that houses themselves should be designed from the start in such a way as to make them easy to divide when the time comes. The second, to be discussed below, is the planning or development point that every area should have houses in a good range of sizes so that couples at this critical phase can at least stay in the same area even if they decide to move into a smaller house.

In practical terms it is probable that the architectural solution is often difficult of realization. Although the idea of a divisible or contractible house design is an attractive one, it is often found in practice that versatility of this kind can be too dearly bought. It is difficult enough to design a house type that satisfactorily fulfills one set of needs, and to introduce further constraints may produce a result that is not satisfactory in either form.

COMMUNITY PLANNING SOLUTIONS

Since we are thus forced to conclude that it may be too difficult to devise houses that shrink as the family contracts, let us consider the planning possibility that neighborhoods are so designed that the aging individual can find a home in his existing community that is suitable for his newly reduced needs.

The question of whether or not the individual finds suitable accommodations and remains in his own neighborhood, rather than moving away, has important implications for the architect and planner in terms of the older person's "integration" into the community—a concept that we shall encounter repeatedly in the ensuing discussion. Each individual must choose (either at this stage or at the later stage of retirement when his freedom of choice is enhanced) either to stay in his old community as long as he lives or as long as he can find a home there, or to move into a new and presumably final neighborhood.

How the individual makes this choice will depend on the strength of his social ties or his integration into the community. This integration may be a reflection partly of his personality and of his attitude to his own circle, and partly of the objective realities of his social environment. This is ground well covered by various researchers, that seems to arouse strong feelings among students of aging. Some, like Peter Townsend, produce evidence to suggest that the emphasis on the disintegration of modern communities has been exaggerated and that old people are not substantially more isolated today than formerly —a position that may hold generally true of relationships with kin, as is mentioned later (pp. 247–248). Others, noting the continuing friendships of those older people with long-established residence in the community, question whether new friendships can be readily developed if a move is made. [*See Vol. 1, Chap. 24, pp. 561–575.*] Some gerontologists even question the desire of the aged to be integrated, suggesting instead that many prefer to become disengaged. [*See Vol. 1, Chap. 15.6, pp. 353–356.*]

Irving Rosow, who has examined integration from the point of view of the architect and planner, points to the tendency for older people to choose friends of the same age as themselves. Thus he sums up the conditions that must be fulfilled if the aged are to be socially integrated into the normal community: long-term residency; stable, unchanging neighborhood; social homogeneity; and primary groups of friends relatively intact. For those without these social ties (the group for which he believes there is a housing problem), Rosow advocates a concentration of older people in the housing complex—a concentration that is insulated, rather than separated, from the community.[3]

We shall consider here how realistic a policy it is to retain or to restore the balance of older and younger people in the traditional cores of cities or in their modern planned counterparts, deferring to the next section (pp. 245–246) an examination of how large these local concentrations should be. There is no doubt that this policy of age balance in the community finds widespread favor. It was endorsed, for example, by the United Nations Economic Commission for Europe (ECE) Colloquium held in October, 1965.[4] It is the official view of the British Ministry of Housing and Local Government.[5] Despite obvious difficulties, it also has the support of at least one American authority, Huson Jackson, who expresses the opinion that:

> The idea of flexibility in community planning and programming to create dwelling types suitable for families of a variety of age levels merits careful examination. The desires of older people for privacy and for convenience to transportation and community facilities parallels in many respects the needs and preferences of young couples and of childless families. Housing units can be located and planned to meet simultaneously the needs of a variety of age groups, and such dwellings, by appealing to a variety of family types, would work against the isolation of the aged who live there and towards their continuing involvement in the wider community.[6]

The fact that the space requirements of an older couple may be much the same as those of a newly-married or a childless couple naturally simplifies the task of providing the correct range and diversity of dwelling types, and has useful implications in both existing and new communities. One feature of older existing communities is the presence of numbers of houses which, though structurally sound and capable of modernization and sanitary upgrading, are below

[3] Irving Rosow, "Retirement Housing and Social Integration," quoted by Marilyn Langford in *Community Aspects of Housing for the Aged* (Ithaca, N.Y.: Cornell University Press, 1962). See also Irving Rosow, *Social Integration of the Aged* (New York: Free Press, 1967), 29.

[4] United Nations Economic Commission for Europe, *Housing for the Elderly* (Proceedings of the colloquium held in Belgium and The Netherlands, October 4–15, 1965).

[5] Stated in an article "summarising the official view" by M. Empson and N. J. Sheppard, "Housing for Old People, I. Siting," *Architects' Journal* (London), 146 (1967), 177–180.

[6] Private communication.

modern space standards for family living. In sections of some cities these houses are now being bought by enterprising young couples who improve them and sell them again in a year or two. An extension of this program, geared to existing systems of funding, could provide a useful pool of low-cost homes for low-income elderly families in locations that would enable them to remain within the community which they know and in which they are known.

In the case of new and reconstructed balanced communities, it is clearly not possible to lay down general laws as to the proper size distribution of houses and apartments to accommodate families at differing stages. It is worth noting, however, that quite sophisticated demographic projection programs now exist and are being increasingly used to achieve dynamic balance in housing provision within large developments. The first major application in Britain was in the plan for the abortive New Town of Hook;[7] but work in this field has been developing fast and the program for housing in at least one British New Town takes into account the major phases in the family cycle as well as the size and type of house or apartment, the density of development, and the form of tenure (for example, private and public housing). With a forecast and plan of this kind there should be no difficulty in insuring a set of properly balanced communities that make adequate provision for the needs of aging and contracting families.

Retirement

At the second critical stage, when the husband retires, the couple may enjoy freedom to choose among a wider range of alternatives in location and life style. If retirement is not deferred until too late, this opportunity for a degree of severance from past associations may be seized by those who, though geographically mobile by temperament, have been restrained by circumstances.

In many respects the moment of retirement may seem a suitable occasion to adjust to changed housing needs. In all reasonably affluent countries there is a considerable migration of postretirement people to areas regarded as more favorable, both climatically and in terms of other amenities. These migrations and the consequently skewed age distribution of the population are familiar topics in demographic studies of migration areas, and sometimes approach dramatic

[7] London County Council, *The Planning of a New Town* (London: L.C.C., 1961), 18–21.

proportions, as in St. Petersburg, Florida. [*See Vol. 1, Chap. 6.A, pp. 122–128 and 6.C, pp. 143–145.*]

On the whole, the typical new suburban housing developments are overwhelmingly designed for younger families, thus holding little attraction for older people.[8] For example, British New Towns, in spite of special provisions, have succeeded in attracting only a small minority of the elderly, and it is clear that a similar reluctance to move out to such developments is found in the United States. Gans reports, for instance, that of the first 3,000 families to move into Levittown, New Jersey, only 6 per cent of the men were over 55.[9]

RETIREMENT COMMUNITIES

This discrepancy between the desire to move out and the unsuitability of typical new housing developments has led to the spectacular and controversial emergence of various kinds of packaged retirement communities, on either a commercial or a semi-charitable basis, which have the almost unprecedented policy of excluding from residence all below a certain age, generally fixed in the lower fifties. The first such retirement communities were built in favored parts of the United States—in California, Florida, and Texas—but one developer in this field is already extending its Leisure World communities to include one in Switzerland, and there seems every reason to suppose that some version of the same idea will, in due course, establish itself in various parts of Europe.

This trend should not, however, lead to the conclusion that segregated villages for retired people are likely to become the only, or even a major, form of new community provision for old age housing. An assessment of this solution is given in the following paragraphs in which we shall examine some of the basic housing needs of those who have passed the age of formal retirement.

The first point is that individuals do not shed all their commitments at the moment of retirement. Particularly now that the date of retirement is being advanced so that the question of serious mental or physical impairment is less likely to intervene, many will probably wish to continue with some work, whether paid or voluntary. [*See Vol. 1, Chap. 18.C.3, pp. 452–453.*] For those with certain types of skill, such as school teaching, such commitments may not act as a constraint on choice of retirement location; but for others the necessity for continuity of employment will effectively prevent the individual

---

[8] See, for example, M. Meyerson, B. Terrett, and W. L. C. Wheaton, *Housing, People and Cities* (New York: McGraw-Hill Book Company, Inc., 1962).

[9] Herbert Gans, *The Levittowners* (New York: Pantheon Books, Inc., 1967), 42.

from moving away from his former workplace. In other instances, local family or social ties will deter moving.

How consistent is life in a retirement community with the need to retain such occupational and social commitments? The answer will naturally depend on the location of the community, but an interesting recent analysis of two Californian communities by Michael B. Barker[10] shows that less discontinuity is often involved than might be expected. One of these communities (A) is clearly a highly sophisticated and successful example; the other (B) is located some distance to the north of San Francisco, farther from the metropolitan labor center, and aimed at a less wealthy sector of the market. In spite of the differences between these two examples the following statements apply in each case:

1. The principal housing market area is the metropolitan San Francisco Bay Area (90 per cent for A, 80 per cent for B). This calls in question the widespread stereotype of the typical resident as an early-retired farmer from Iowa or some other northern state.

2. The majority of households (practically all for A, 65 per cent for B) have relatives in the Bay Area.

3. A substantial proportion (80 per cent for A, though only 40 per cent for B) of the households have one member gainfully employed.

In general, the survey makes it clear that it was possible to move to each of the so-called retirement communities without having to renounce patterns of work or family relationships.

Naturally, many social commitments are of a very specific and local character and will have to be replaced on moving. It must be recognized, however, that there is seldom a clear identity of social needs between the young (or even young marrieds) and the elderly. As Rosow and others have pointed out,[11] the concept of peer-group culture which has mainly been applied to youth is equally applicable to age, and it may be argued that a retirement community is particularly propitious to the emergence of a consistent old-age peer-group culture. This type of culture is particularly likely to appeal in a country such as the United States in which the prevailing rejection of old age almost compels some defensive reaction on the part of older people.

In at least the better planned retirement villages, every encourage-

[10] Michael B. Barker, *California Retirement Communities* (Berkeley: Institute of Urban and Regional Development, University of California, 1966), 62.
[11] Rosow, *op. cit.*, 20 ff.; Elaine Cumming and William E. Henry, *Growing Old: The Process of Disengagement* (New York: Basic Books, Inc., 1961), 65–66.

ment is given to the peer culture through promotion of community activities. At Community A, for example, there is an elaborate system of facilities, both central and decentralized. The "main clubhouse" has a 2,500 seat auditorium-theater, a shopping arcade, an administration center, and a television studio where a closed-circuit system provides programs and disseminates information geared to the elderly residents. There are also clubhouses serving each "mutual" of 600 dwelling units, each of which is equipped with game room, sewing room, hobby room, wood shop, ceramics studio, croquet courts, shuffleboard, billiard room, and cooking facilities. Other major facilities designed to serve the whole community include a library, riding stable, 18-hole golf course, Olympic-sized swimming pool, a lawn bowling green, a putting green, and a hotel to accommodate visitors.

In addition to such physical facilities, there is an energetic program run by the staff, who are always on hand to suggest leisure activities, from karate for the men to flower arranging for the women. There is so much to do that apparently some new residents are completely overwhelmed. Steps are taken to insure that no newcomer shall remain lonely, including a notice-board signposted "Your New Neighbors" to which photographs of all recent arrivals are pinned.

There seems little doubt that the more elaborate retirement communities have proved popular with their residents, whatever feelings of distaste or guilt they may have aroused in at least a proportion of those children who have seen their parents make the decision to enter. In addition to the "peer-group" incentives already mentioned, there are certain practical merits: a knowledge of the extent of future financial commitments; a full maintenance service; specially tailored health and hospital arrangements; and the security provided by perimeter wall, gatehouse, and patrol. At present the average age of residents is quite low, and it remains to be seen how the communities will be working out in twenty years' time when the average age may be nearer 75 than the present 55.

Behind all these practical issues there remains the basic question whether it is a desirable social policy to segregate, even if only partially, a large fraction of the population and to relieve them from total involvement in the life of the larger community. In this respect, the retirement community could fairly be regarded as a reflection of social pressures that favor social segregation, rather than as a cause.

SOCIALLY INSULATED HOUSING

If, following Rosow's suggestion, the aim is to be social insulation but not segregation of older people, the probability is that the greater part of such housing for the aged will be provided within towns and may even be concentrated in the older areas near to community facilities and services. Donahue and Ashley[12] suggest that it might often be sited in slum clearance areas.

There is clearly scope for active programs providing various forms of nonsegregated housing specifically designed, located, and equipped with special facilities and services to suit the needs of the elderly. Successive United States Housing Acts have provided for a variety of financing arrangements for low-profit or nonprofit sponsors of housing for the elderly. [*See Vol. 1, Chap. 6.B.8, p. 142.*] Nevertheless, old people are to be found in such a wide range of circumstances that no simple set of programs could fit all their needs. At one extreme, for example, is a category of relatively affluent aged persons whose housing needs appear, at least in the United States, to occupy increasing prominence in planning considerations. Research has indicated that a growing proportion of those reaching retirement age own, in addition to other assets, their houses, generally free of debt. [*See Ex. 4 · 20, p. 91 in Vol. 1.*] This now substantial proportion of old people who, already being house-owners, can often afford to buy the retirement housing of their choice is one reason for the success in the United States of the packaged retirement communities previously discussed. Many others will avail themselves of the various government programs authorized, for example, under successive Housing Acts, particularly the Section 203 program for those who wish to purchase and own an individual home, and the Sections 202 and 231 program for those who wish to rent.

Some experts, including Huson Jackson, believe that besides suburban retirement communities there will be an increasing recourse to condominium developments offering apartment or town house dwellings near the traditional centers of cities.[13] The most prevalent use of the condominium form of organization is in the context of the multifamily, high-rise structure, offering to each purchaser individual fee ownership of the living unit within the structure together with an appropriate share of the common ownership of the site and of all shared facilities. It is felt that this arrangement, which overcomes some of the difficulties attached in the United States to the cooperative form of ownership, reflects the American preference for home ownership

---

[12] Wilma Donahue and E. Everett Ashley, III, "Housing and the Social Health of Older People," quoted by Langford, *op. cit.*, 32.

[13] Private communication. See also Herbert J. Friedman and James K. Herbert, "Community Apartments: Condominium or Stock Cooperative," *California Law Review*, 50 (1962), 299–341.

over renting. In European countries similar forms of common ownership have been developed.

Such facilities as retirement communities or condominium developments, despite their growth, clearly fit the needs and financial
capacities of only a minority of older people, while housing for the
aged as a whole is not particularly attractive to a developer who is
looking for profits. This means that much of the task of providing new
housing for the elderly, particularly high-rise apartments, falls either
on nonprofit agencies or on the public housing authority.

Public housing, which is making such a vital contribution to solving housing problems in most European countries, is still plagued
in the United States by the stigma attached to living in a "project."[14]
Although public housing is used predominantly by those in greatest
need, and currently accounts for half of all federally assisted housing
for the elderly, it still appears to serve only a small proportion of all
urban elderly households with incomes under $2,000 (4 per cent of
this group according to the 1960 Census of Housing, Volume VII,
Table B–3). However, current programs of public housing for the
elderly may be expanded as a result of recent legislative and administrative developments in the social welfare field. The pioneer Victoria
Plaza public housing project in San Antonio, Texas, may then prove
its value as a prototype of many such projects in other American
cities.

By any standards, Victoria Plaza is an impressive housing development, not only because of the range of on-site facilities that it offers
but also because of the care that went into the detailed design. Furthermore, we have the advantage of the excellent investigation and
report by Frances Carp,[15] which gives a detailed account of the initial
reactions of the tenants and of their subsequent adjustments to their
new life. Victoria Plaza is a nine-story T-shaped block containing 184
dwelling units for the elderly (16 two-bedroom, 16 efficiency, and
152 one-bedroom). These apartments have been very fully equipped,
with heights of shelves and refrigerators designed to eliminate the
need for bending or stretching, with easy cleaning surfaces, and with
wide doors and an emergency bell system. Each resident provides his
own furniture, and is able to add an air conditioner and telephone.
There are laundry facilities and an incinerator chute for waste dis-
posal on each floor. There is also a senior center, comprising such

[14] Paul L. Niebanck, *The Elderly in Older Urban Areas* (Philadelphia: Institute
for Environmental Studies, University of Pennsylvania, 1965), 77.
[15] Frances Merchant Carp, *A Future for the Aged: Victoria Plaza and Its
Residents* (Austin: University of Texas Press, 1966).

communal facilities as a hobby room, a library, a small post office, two counseling offices, a community kitchen, and a well-equipped recreation room. In accord with Federal policy, the senior center is open to all senior citizens in the area and not just to the residents of Victoria Plaza. Also attached to the building is an eight-room clinic which is used by the Public Health Department to serve both the residents and persons of all ages living in the neighborhood.

The modern conveniences, the easy upkeep, and the communal facilities were appreciated from the start; and it is interesting that most of the residents were delighted that the location provided such easy access to churches and downtown stores, though some questioned the related fact that such a beautiful building was not in a safer and more attractive part of the town (compare the recommendation, already quoted, that such developments should take place in urban renewal areas). Naturally there were a number of complaints about specific points, and these are taken into account in the detailed recommendations given later in this chapter (pp. 254–259); but the general reaction appears to have been extremely favorable. Furthermore it was possible to construct a set of adjustment criteria that could be used to select residents most likely to fit into such a development, whether publicly or privately financed.

Victoria Plaza has been described at some length, but many other American examples could be given. Some of these, like Springbrook Apartments in Cleveland and the Anthony M. Webbe Apartments in St. Louis, are public housing projects. There are also a number of important nonprofit developments, mainly FHA Section 202 projects, including York House North in Philadelphia (Philadelphia Geriatric Center) and the beautiful Menlo Park Retirement Apartments near Stanford University in California. One interesting feature of a number of these, including Springbrook and York House North is that, like Victoria Plaza, they are combined with other services ranging from a medical clinic to optional meals.

At the same time, it remains astonishing to an Englishman to discover how limited the total public effort remains. In England, in recent years, a quarter of all new public housing is in the form of one-bedroom dwellings. Since public housing constitutes about one-half of all new housing in England and Wales, perhaps 10 per cent of all new dwellings are being specifically designed for elderly single persons and married couples. Furthermore, this proportion is being raised: For example, a 50 per cent increase in the share of old people's dwellings by 1972 has been declared to be the target in Northern Ireland, while the Ministry of Housing in England has stated that 15 per cent of all housing (not just public housing) in New Towns in Britain should henceforward be in the form of old people's dwellings.

These figures could be paralleled by the achievements of a number of other European countries. Admittedly, circumstances in America and Europe are different, but it is remarkable that, according to evidence presented to the United States Senate Special Committee on Aging on August 18, 1965,[16] the administration's proposed total budget for 1966 for housing and community development amounted to only .001 per cent of total output, or five cents per capita. To use another index, the total number of units for the elderly aided by all Federal programs including public housing from inception through December 31, 1966, appear to have amounted to less than 200,000, probably less than 2 per cent of all new units in the past ten years.[17] In spite of the indications that the rate of public provision is increasing, there is clearly still an enormous disparity in this respect between the United States and Europe.

LOCATION REQUIREMENTS

As has been seen, one of the advantages claimed for retirement communities, or for such centrally located sites as Victoria Plaza, is the convenient location of shopping, social, and recreational facilities. [See Vol. 1, Chap. 6.A.3.b, pp. 127–128.] For young and middle-aged adults, modern mobility has reduced the importance of proximity for such facilities, but with aging the walking radius shrinks and private transportation is decreasingly used. It is therefore of major importance that houses for the aged should be conveniently located in relation to shops, post offices, pubs, clubrooms, and other social and recreational facilities, either by insuring public transportation or by locating old people's dwellings within easy walking distance. Surveys on both sides of the Atlantic have shown the emphasis that should be given to convenient shopping facilities for the elderly, and a maximum walking distance of one-quarter mile is often suggested.[18] In addition to its instrumental function, the shopping expedition is used by old people, as it is by mothers tied by young children, to

[16] Leon Keyserling, President, Conference on Economic Progress, U.S. Senate, Special Committee on Aging, *Services to the Elderly on Public Assistance* (Washington, D.C.: Government Printing Office, 1965), 41.

[17] U.S. Senate, Special Committee on Aging, *Developments in Aging, 1966* (Washington, D.C.: Government Printing Office, 1967).

[18] Barker, *op. cit.*, 87. See also Product Planning Limited, *Housing: Tenant Survey* (London: P.P.L., 1966), 20: "Some general shopping availability, say within a quarter of a mile and including a Post Office, is most necessary."

satisfy the expressive need to keep in touch with the local community and to confirm their place in society.

There is a temptation for planners to allocate to old people the less desirable lots, such as land in the middle of large blocks. This is clearly questionable practice, and where an area is being comprehensively planned, as in a major renewal project, it should be mandatory to reserve some good sites for old people's dwellings close to the most local center (which may be serving a total of 5,000 persons within a quarter of a mile radius). There is nothing new in this idea, which is common practice in Sweden[19] and some other countries. The difficulty is that the interests of the elderly are not always voiced with sufficient power to bring about what is patently the most equitable arrangement.

SIZE OF THE HOUSING COMPLEX

The question as to how many units should be contained in a housing facility for older people again confronts the basic issue as to whether there should be local segregation of old people's dwellings, or whether old people should be spread as evenly as possible throughout groups of family houses. On this matter of size, there seems to be radical disagreement in the policies of different countries. The Victoria Plaza project contains nearly 200 dwelling units, and some American developments for the elderly contain up to 750 units, the larger size apparently being chosen on the grounds of economic management; for, according to the United Nations ECE Colloquium, the ideal size is regarded in the United States as lying between 75 and 150 units.[20] In several European countries, notably Denmark, Holland, and Switzerland, large-scale projects are favored on economic and other grounds, while a figure around 100 units is fairly widespread. In contrast with this, in Britain, and to a lesser extent in France, there are very definite official pressures in favor of smaller aggregates. Recent statements from the British Ministry of Housing and Local Government have reiterated this policy.

Neighborly help from younger families is more likely to be forthcoming where housing consists of the smallest groups, such as two to six bunga-

[19] F. Gutheim, *Architectural Considerations in the Design of Housing for the Elderly* (mimeographed; Paper for the Brookings Institute Conference Study on Housing for the Aging, n.d.).

[20] United Nations Economic Commission for Europe, *op. cit.*, I, 70. According to the Group of Rapporteurs, "schemes of 150 dwellings for 170 persons would appear to be most suitable from the sociological point of view, as the younger elements of the population do not wish to have too many old people around them" (p. 69).

lows or flats. Where the services of a warden are provided it has been found that dwellings for about thirty old people in one group is a reasonable maximum since this appears to be the number which one warden can look after. If additional bungalows or flats, outside the warden's services, are to be provided this should not bring the number of old people living in one group above a total of about fifty.[21]

The case for small groupings has been argued so effectively and is so widely accepted in Britain that it is difficult to find more than a dozen projects in Britain containing over 75 units, while the hundreds of thousands of old people's dwellings built in recent years have virtually all been arranged in small groups of 20 to 30 units or even less. With such a radical divergence of opinion, it might be thought that strenuous research efforts would be going into an objective study of the merits and disadvantages of different sized housing groups. In fact, very little is being done; the writer, with the support (moral but not financial) of the Ministry of Housing and Local Government and of the National Old Peoples Welfare Council (Britain's senior social welfare agency for the old), has been trying since 1966 to interest a funding body in such a project, but so far without success. Meanwhile, there are signs that the same economic pressures that have led to the acceptance of large projects in the United States are beginning to carry more weight in Britain as well, with consequences that at the moment are only to be guessed.

HIGH-RISE OR LOW-RISE

Akin to the size of the retirement housing project is its vertical arrangement. Although for obvious reasons there is an initial advantage in a house on one floor or ground-floor apartment for the elderly, this does not mean that the high-rise apartment building is to be ruled out. A number of British surveys have shown than an appreciable proportion of old people may even prefer living on upper floors.[22] A similar finding is hinted at in the Victoria Plaza report; although the study does not distinguish clearly between the satisfaction felt by those living in different parts of the building, it is reported that the two top floors were the first to be fully selected.[23] In general it is commonly found that floors above street level are preferred, particularly if there is a suitable elevator installation. This confirms the impres-

---

[21] Empson and Sheppard, *op. cit.*, 178. The functions of a "warden" are described on p. 259 of this chapter.

[22] V. Hole and P. G. Allen, "Dwellings for Old People," *Architects' Journal* (London), 135 (1962), 1017–1026; Product Planning Limited, *op. cit.*, 19.

[23] Carp, *op. cit.*, 70.

sion that while most elderly people like to keep in touch with every-day life, they also place great store on privacy and quiet, or "intimacy at a distance" as it has been aptly described.[24] They would rather look down from a detached position onto children playing below them, than be exposed directly to the rough and tumble or the constant anxiety that a football will be coming in through their window.

RETIREMENT HOUSING AND THE EXTENDED FAMILY

When new communities are planned or old ones redeveloped so as to meet the desiderata we have been discussing, several aspects of the daily lives of older people must be kept in mind. The question of segregation, insulation, or isolation from age-mates has already been mentioned in several connections. A still more significant factor is the proximity of kin. Any comprehensive redevelopment, even if it leaves the old people themselves undisturbed, is likely to precipitate another unwanted effect, that is, the physical separation of elderly parents from their children and their families. [*See Vol. 1, Chap. 23.B, pp. 541–559.*] The importance of maintaining the traditional mother-daughter relationship has been stressed by a number of sociologists and evidence has been adduced to show that married children, particularly daughters, moving out to new suburban homes have been distressed over the loss of regular contact with parents that this has entailed.[25]

Taking the population as a whole, the extent of such daily contacts may seem rather surprising: For example, the recent cross-national study covering Denmark, the United States of America, and the United Kingdom showed that of the three samples of parents with living children, 62 per cent of the Danes had been visited by at least one child in the previous twenty-four hours, while the corresponding figures for Americans and British were 65 per cent and 69 per cent. [*See Ex. 23 · 2, p. 541 in Vol. 1.*]

In the tight-knit community of Bethnal Green in the East End of London, with its continuing emphasis on the extended family, the figures suggest that as many as 75 per cent of parents had been visited by at least one of the children in the previous twenty-four hours.[26] In Bethnal Green the child would typically be a married

[24] L. Rosenmayr and E. Köckeis, "Propositions for a Sociological Theory of Ageing and the Family," *UNESCO International Social Science Journal*, 15 (1963), 410–426.
[25] M. Young and P. Willmott, *Family and Kinship in East London* (London: Routledge and Kegan-Paul, 1957); Peter Townsend, *The Family Life of Old People* (London: Routledge and Kegan-Paul, 1957).
[26] Young and Willmott, *op. cit.*, 29.

daughter living in a nearby street, but a survey in Swansea in South Wales has shown that such proximity is not essential for a high level of daily visiting. The Swansea survey was designed to replicate the Bethnal Green study in a rather different urban area, and found that, "though the families we visited were a good deal more spread out than those described by Young and Willmott for Bethnal Green, the patterns of visiting appeared remarkably similar."[27] Here the effects of relatively wide geographical dispersal of families were counteracted by the widespread and rapidly increasing use of cars. All in all, the authors of the Swansea study found no evidence of a breakdown in the extended family network irrespective of social class; this would be highly reassuring if it could be shown to be true of communities of other types as well.

CLUBS AND OTHER SOCIAL FACILITIES

Although family ties are of first importance to many people, the normal sociable individual at the age of retirement is also likely to retain, and in some cases because of greater leisure to extend, his voluntary pursuits outside the home. [*See Vol. 1, Chap. 21, pp. 501–510; Chap. 22, pp. 511–535.*] Several researchers have noted a gradual shift with age from instrumental activities to those concerned more with enjoying the company of other older people with similar interests. There is recent evidence from various countries of an impressive number of clubs for the 65's and over, which may be known as Senior Centers, Golden Age Clubs, Darby and Joan Clubs, and so forth. These vary greatly in their sponsorship and in the activities that they promote, but they share the vital function of combating loneliness. A recent survey in Lancashire and Derbyshire in England showed that elderly members gave the desire for company as the commonest reason for attending.[28] Clubs of this kind are obvious candidates for a central site in the housing complex or community, and for location on a public transport line, so that they are within easy reach of as many of the elderly as possible.

Circumstances vary so widely that it is not possible to lay down any precise guidelines as to what the physical plant of a senior center should comprise. The accommodation and activities provided at the Senior Center attached to Victoria Plaza have already been briefly described, and note taken of the fact that when Federal grants

[27] C. Rosser and C. Harris, *The Family and Social Change* (London: Routledge and Kegan Paul, 1965), 219.

[28] E. E. White, *Clubs for the Elderly* (London: National Old People's Welfare Council, n.d.).

are involved, the center must be open to all old people in the vicinity. As a general rule, programs are likely to include some group games and other social leisure pursuits; some instruction in arts, crafts, and hobbies; music and entertainments; outings; simple eating arrangements. Sometimes a counseling service for personal and health problems is also offered. [*See Vol. 1, Chap. 21.4, pp. 508–509.*]

The United States Department of Health, Education and Welfare has recently published a National Directory of Senior Centers, and for this purpose has adopted the following definition:

A center is a program of services offered in a designated physical facility in which older people meet at least three days or more each week under the guidance of assigned leaders performing professional tasks. The basic purpose of such centers is to provide older people with socially enriching experiences which help to preserve their dignity as human beings and enhance their feelings of self-worth.[29]

Inevitably many such centers are located in converted houses or in public or church halls rented at regular times each week; but it is clearly preferable to have accommodations built especially for this purpose, including, if possible, a number of smaller rooms in addition to the main hall. [*See, however, Hammond, Chap. 10 in this volume, on possible advantages in church location of such centers.*]

One of the difficulties with such clubs is the problem of cost, not only of the buildings themselves but also of staffing them and of sustaining morale. According to circumstances and country, the actual buildings will probably be paid for by a voluntary agency or by a public authority. As far as staffing is concerned, more use should be made of the voluntary help of old people themselves; now that more and more people are retiring while they are still active, it seems common sense to enlist their help in running programs for others with less energy and initiative.

This raises a point of principle that should perhaps be placed in a wider context. Quite apart from club work, there are various other neighborhood activities which are semi-commercial in character but which cannot offer sufficient income to attract someone with career ambitions. The corner shop, for example, is being squeezed out of existence by economic pressures; yet it is often an extremely popular gossip-center as well as a useful shopping facility, so that it is easy

---

[29] U.S. Department of Health, Education and Welfare, Administration on Aging, *National Directory of Senior Centers* (Washington, D.C.: Government Printing Office, 1966), iii.

to imagine circumstances in which it behooves a local community to give financial support to a retired person by supplementing the inadequate earnings accruing from a corner shop. Another suggestion is that older persons should be used more to give direct aid as teachers of others.[30] Activities such as these would not only supply the needed service, but would also perhaps make the old person taking part in them feel still wanted.

SUPPORTIVE SERVICES

In addition to meeting places designed to meet social and semi-commercial needs, there are other socially and medically supportive services that can best be provided on a localized basis. The need for many of these may not be great during the early postretirement years, but particularly on the medical side the value of old people's clinics for regular check-ups and advice, together with simple forms of medical and perhaps dental treatment, has been demonstrated. In some cases these clinics are attached to old people's housing projects, even though they may be separately administered and available for use by other old people living in the area. Housing developments incorporating medical clinics include the previously mentioned Victoria Plaza, Springbrook Apartments, and York House North, as well as La Guardia Homes in New York, and various projects under construction.[31] But most out-patient facilities for the elderly are attached to hospitals or in special institutions removed from the old person's dwelling place.

A similar situation exists in Britain, where one consequence of the operation of the National Health Service is that most strictly clinical geriatric services are either attached to hospitals as out-patient clinics or are clinics run by hospitals. One possible result is that out-patient attendances by the chronically sick and geriatric patients are counted in hundreds whereas the attendances for general surgery are counted in millions.[32]

Partly in order to overcome the reluctance of old people and

[30] Daniel M. Wilner and Rosabelle P. Walkley, "Some Special Problems and Alternatives in Housing for Older Persons," in John C. McKinney and Frank T. de Vyver (eds.), *Aging and Social Policy* (New York: Appleton-Century-Crofts, 1966), 221–259.

[31] Doctor M. Powell Lawton of the Philadelphia Geriatric Center stated recently that his team had literally scoured the entire eastern half of the country looking for sites offering on-site services that will open during the term of a current research project, but had only come up with the three eastern examples mentioned.

[33] Kenneth Hazell, *Social and Medical Problems of the Elderly* (London: Hutchinson & Co., Ltd., 1965), 87.

others to attend centers for purely clinical out-patient care there has been a drive during the last decade on both sides of the Atlantic to set up day hospitals that provide a much wider range of facilities than out-patient clinics and are designed as the place where patients will spend their days, returning to their homes (or to hostels) only at night and probably at weekends. Already by 1959 a British survey counted over forty day hospitals and major day centers, of which at least a third had geriatric facilities.[33] One good example is the Oxford Day Hospital, a small modern building which has maximum accommodation for forty day patients and offers occupational therapy, including basketry, weaving, sewing, knitting, carpentry, printing, and pottery; physiotherapy and remedial exercises where necessary; meals, bath, social activities, activities of daily living, and estimation of social competence. This day hospital is on the grounds of a geriatric hospital in which most of the day patients were formerly in-patients.

The advantages claimed for day hospitals that are particularly relevant to the present discussion are that they may help to keep old people living in the community longer than would otherwise be the case; that they enable in-patients to be discharged earlier; that they provide a substitute for hospital admission in some cases; and that they relieve the strain on the relatives with whom the old people live. Furthermore, by increasing social contacts, the day hospital can improve the mental attitude of lonely, elderly chronically ill patients, particularly those who would otherwise be alone at home all day.[34]

It has to be admitted that such a set-up has an added attraction for the social gerontologist, in that the opportunity for regular contacts with a sample of old people over a period of years would provide opportunity for studying in greater depth than is generally possible the processes of aging of people still living at home under comparatively normal conditions.

Even after all the necessary forms of medical and personal attention have been provided (including hearing aids, opthalmic services, and chiropody), there are still other supportive services that can help to keep the individual living in his own home. Chief among these are arrangements for daily cleaning and some kind of "meals on wheels" service. If there is a genuine intention to preserve the independence of the elderly as long as possible, it is surely better to provide such

[33] James Farndale, *The Day Hospital Movement in Great Britain* (Oxford: Pergamon Press, 1961), 71.

[34] Ministry of Health Circular, "Geriatric Services and the Care of the Chronic Sick" (London: Her Majesty's Stationery Office, 1957).

forms of partial assistance than to leave no alternative except departure to institutional settings where the provision of all meals and domestic services may be unavoidable.

To summarize this section, it can be said that the phase of retirement provides what is in many ways the most natural opportunity for a change of home. Just as preparation for retirement is widely advocated, so also retirement itself may be a preparation for aging over the final decades of life. Special retirement communities are seen to have both attractions and dangers, and the arguments in favor of the older person's continued integration with the wider community and of his continued participation in its affairs are taken into account. Finally, mention is made of the city planning implications of continued integration and of the need to provide certain local community buildings and facilities in order to permit the elderly to remain in their own homes.

Widowhood

The stage of bereavement presents new problems to the concerned planner: how to enable the surviving spouse to maintain privacy and individuality and at the same time to counter his loss with increased orientation toward the community. At this stage, too, those residential problems that have not previously been resolved (the over-large home, or the need to be near to relatives, friends, and facilities) become even more acute.

Bereavement, an almost universal experience of the married couple, naturally varies in its impact according to the degree of interdependence of the spouses and the age and health of the survivor. It must, however, be recognized as one of the greatest climacterics of the family life cycle, with far-reaching implications for the health and adjustment of the surviving spouse.

The survivor is more likely to be the wife than the husband, because typically she is both younger and also has a longer expectation of life. Furthermore, a bereaved husband, even quite an old man, has a not negligible chance of remarrying. [See Vol. 1, Chap. 7.A, pp. 158–166.]

What are the implications for achitecture and city planning? This is the stage at which the older person often decides, through choice or through necessity, to live entirely alone. [See Bernstein, Chap. 9 in this volume, on cooperative communal living as an alternative.] Among persons 65 and over in the United States, for example, one-third of the women and one-sixth of the men live either alone or with nonrelatives, and these proportions are still higher in the most advanced age groups. [*See Vol. 1, Chap. 7.B.1.a, pp. 167–168, and Ex. 7 · 10, p. 167.*] If, prior to the bereavement, the couple had already moved into a small house or apartment with one or at the most two bedrooms, the need for a further move to curtail living space is not likely to be pressing. On the other hand, there will be many who will want to combat the loneliness of single living by moving close to the home of a daughter or other relative, and every neighborhood should include some dwellings suitable for this purpose. [*See Vol. 1, Chap. 7.B, pp. 167–183.*]

Sometimes the surviving mother or father will move into the home of a married offspring. Joint households of this kind are notoriously explosive, particularly in the case of mothers and mothers-in-law, and they sometimes demand superhuman tolerance. For this reason, there have been various experiments in attaching small self-contained apartments to family houses, or locating mobile homes in the family lot, so that these can be lived in by surviving parents. Although such arrangements have up to a point worked quite well, for obvious reasons the need for them is impermanent, and care has to be taken to insure flexibility and to protect against serious invasion of the family's privacy through subsequent use by someone else. In any case, it is obvious that an annex of this kind could not be attached to every family home.

Disablement

For the fourth stage, that of disablement, thoughtful planning can also have special significance. To be sure, it is sometimes suggested that proper attention to the normal principles of good design is all that is needed to insure that a house is suitable to be lived in by elderly people. There is of course an element of truth in this assertion. As the General Rapporteur to the UN Colloquium put it:

> Age alone is not a criterion for determining housing needs. As the process of aging is sometimes drastic in its effects and sometimes scarcely perceptible it is impossible to plot a curve of progressive individual needs. But any population will be found to contain at any time two broad categories of old people: those whose housing needs are the same as for the rest of the population and those with special housing needs.[35]

Whether or not forms of disability have begun to emerge, it should go without saying that every house designed should be perceived by the

[35] United Nations Economic Commission for Europe, *op. cit.*, I, 48.

architect as a home—as a center of both rest and activity capable of bringing comfort, reassurance, and even joy into its occupant's life— especially so for the old as their outside commitments decline. At the same time it must be accepted, by the designer as by the aging individual, that the occupant's physical powers are declining with age whether slowly or dramatically, so that attention to the special design points needed by those who survive to very old age is advisable—even though only a minority will have serious disabilities by the time of retirement. [*See Vol. 1, Chap. 9.2, pp. 204–218.*]

Design requirements have been exhaustively treated in the literature, mainly in pamphlets or articles and, as Beyer and Nierstrasz point out, there is general international agreement on the desirability of adopting certain design features.[36] These can best be considered under the three broad headings of comfort, convenience, and safety.

COMFORT

Space standards As indicated, elderly couples often occupy old houses that are larger than they need or desire. In the case of new construction, however, the opposite is sometimes true. Partly for reasons of economy, space standards for some new units for old people have tended to be lower than those for younger households, whereas it could be argued on several grounds that space standards for the elderly, while avoiding extremes of expense or difficulty in keeping warm and clean, should be comparatively high. In the first instance, old people are likely to spend more time indoors. Second, in most cases they will be reluctant to discard many treasured possessions, and the furniture that they bring with them will often be heavy and space-consuming. There will always, of course, be some demand for the simplest possible accommodation for those with particularly limited means and capacities, but a general rise in minimum space standards may be reducing the demand at this end of the scale. In

---

[36] Glenn H. Beyer and F. H. J. Nierstrasz, *Housing the Aged in Western Countries* (New York: American Elsevier Publishing Co., 1967), 48. Some years ago Doctor Wilma Donahue compiled an excellent annotated bibliography for Senior Citizen Housing that includes a valuable section listing twenty-three references on Design, Standards, Siting. These references include the following: Edith Alt, *Standards of Care for Older People in Institutions, Sec. 1* (New York: Committee on Aging of the National Social Welfare Assembly, n.d.); American Public Health Association, Committee on the Hygiene of Housing, *Housing an Aging Population*, Public Health Service, Federal Security Agency (Washington, D.C.: Government Printing Office, 1953); I. S. Loewenberg, "Designing Homes for the Aging," in Wilma Donahue (ed.), *Housing the Aging* (Ann Arbor: University of Michigan Press, 1954); N. Musson and H. Heusinkveld, *Buildings for the Elderly* (New York: Reinhold Publishing Corp., 1963); Architects Safety Committee, *Check List on Home Safety* (Albany, N.Y.: Department of Health, n.d.).

Britain, for example, the standards, as laid down by the Ministry of Housing and Local Government, are now encouraging the provision of some two-bedroom houses for elderly couples in public housing projects but will no longer accept efficiency units for couples.

Windows   It is pleasant to have windows that admit the sun, and it is also pleasant to have windows that look on to a sunlit view. Often a choice has to be made, and sometimes the view may be thought to be more important than direct sunshine. In either case, the aim should be to offer a view to an old person who is lying in bed or sitting in an armchair. This can readily be done without neglecting the need for safety.

Privacy   Nothing in the last paragraph should be taken to diminish the importance of privacy, which to many older people is of paramount importance. It is significant, for example, that among the design features of Victoria Plaza (see pp. 242–243) that aroused critical comments, the lack of more privacy was prominent, particularly because of the window arrangement which gave no protection from the common hall, and because of the absence of bedroom doors. As has already been mentioned, the elderly often want to be able to look down on the world, with all its bustle of activity, but they also like to be able to retire from the hurly-burly when they feel like it. House designs with sheltered internal patios or outdoor rooms may be well suited to the needs of the elderly, but balconies and open galleries— particularly on high-rise buildings—have apparently not been a great success.

Noise   Old people are often light sleepers and it is important that they should not be disturbed by noises at night. Even during the day they are probably more sensitive to noise than most younger people. Some disturbance by noise is inevitable under modern conditions in urban areas, but relief can be gained through intelligent design and allocation of apartments. There is no excuse except lowered cost for inadequate standards of sound insulation which allow excessive sound transmission through walls and floors.

It has been suggested that extreme quiet can be even more disturbing than excessive noise, particularly if the older individual's sight is poor and he must depend on hearing for his cues. This consideration has to be balanced against the fact that a loss of hearing may cause him to turn up his radio or TV and so disturb his neighbors.[37]

Heating   It is now fully appreciated that accidental hypothermia,

[37] White House Conference on Aging, *Background Paper on Housing* (prepared in March, 1960, under the direction of the Committee on Housing [Washington, D.C.: Government Printing Office, 1961]).

that is, underheating, is a common source of discomfort among the old and is in some circumstances a contributory cause of death. It is understood, even in relatively spartan countries like Britain, that houses for the elderly should be heated in every room and that access to any communal rooms should be along properly heated corridors. Central heating is part of the way of life of American and most European countries. In Britain, its general acceptance is quite recent, and doubts were at first expressed as to whether people might yearn for the traditional open coal fire. In the event, the elderly in Britain have been quick to adapt to central heating, which they value for its simplicity and cleanliness, though they like to have an electric fire in the living room for "topping up" in exceptionally cold weather or during a cold spell when the central heating is not on.

There are naturally some differences between countries as to the actual room temperatures that should be attained. It seems generally agreed that old people need temperatures of five to eight degrees Fahrenheit higher than younger adults. In the United States this suggests a standard of between 70 and 75 degrees, while in Britain the recommended standard is 70 degrees.

If heating provision is inadequate there is a danger that old people will try to maintain temperatures by restricting ventilation. Normal precautions should be taken to ensure adequate ventilation without causing drafts or excessive loss of heat.

Lighting Standards of artificial illumination have increased steeply in recent decades, and some older people are accustomed to what by modern standards appears to be very poor lighting. However, failing eyesight can be countered to some extent by high levels of lighting, both natural and artificial. Although particular attention should be paid to the prevention of glare, there is nothing in this or in the other lighting requirements that conflicts with good illumination practices.

CONVENIENCE

In the main, the measures needed to achieve maximum convenience for the disabled elderly are the same matters of good practice as apply at all life stages. Thus kitchen sequences should assist workflow, and there should be work surfaces on both sides of sink and stove. Refrigerators should be of ample size to reduce the number of shopping trips needed. There should be plenty of electric outlets fitted at waist-height. The dining area should be planned in convenient relationship to the cooking and dishwashing area. All surfaces should be easy to clean and maintain.

In addition, two special requirements may be mentioned. One is that door openings and circulation space should be wide enough to maneuver wheelchairs, and thresholds should be avoided, so that the home is usable even if one member of the household is confined to a chair. The same eventuality clearly favors keeping accommodation on one floor. Also for this reason, it is an advantage to install clothes washers, dishwashers, and other appliances of a suitable design.

The other requirement, which concerns both convenience and safety, is that all shelving and closet space should be designed to be within easy reach, obviating the need to stretch up or bend down.

SAFETY

The scare headlines that appear from time to time purport to show that homes are more dangerous than roads, since more people have fatal accidents in the home than elsewhere. The argument is, of course, fallacious: The truth is that, in addition to the greater expenditure of time in the home than on the road, the majority of fatal accidents occur to older people typically through a combination of frailty and of impaired senses——a fact that has been confirmed in a number of analyses of coroners' certificates, and that must almost certainly apply equally to nonfatal accidents.[38]

Some of these accidents are beyond the control of the architect. If an elderly man or woman falls out of bed or trips on a hole in the carpet this may lead to complications that end in death, but the design of the house can hardly be blamed. There remain, however, a number of planning and design precautions that should be adopted, and the main ones are indicated below.

Falls The greatest risk of accident is from falls. Falls, apart from those without an external physical cause or from the causes mentioned above, are mainly associated with stairs, fixed steps inside and outside the house, and movable steps and ladders. Fixed steps and other changes of level, if avoidable, should not be permitted. Stairs are clearly unavoidable in houses on more than one floor, but they should be made as shallow as possible and attention should be paid to

[38] Doctor C. A. Boucher of the Ministry of Health in London stated in 1957 in an Address to the Medical Society for the Care of the Elderly that 57 per cent of fatal home accidents in England and Wales in 1955 affected old people aged 75 years and over and a further 16 per cent affected those aged 65–74 years. Females to males were affected in the proportion 2.4 to 1.0. (See Hazell, *op. cit.*, 25–26.) Comparable figures for the United States show that among accidental deaths in the home nearly half pertain to older people over 65. (See *Accidental Facts* [Chicago: National Safety Council, 1963], quoted by Glenn H. Beyer, *Housing and Society* [New York: The Macmillan Company, 1965], 287.) See also Barbara Gray, *Home Accidents among Older People* (London: Royal Society for the Prevention of Accidents, 1966).

landings and banisters. It has also been found that some old people have fallen downstairs during the night when visiting the bathroom or returning to their bedroom, a risk that can be reduced through careful planning. In all cases stairs and other changes of level should be properly lit with night lights where appropriate.

Windows should be designed to prevent the older person from falling out. Falls from movable steps and chairs typically occur when old people are attempting to reach shelves or closets that are too high for them. The way to prevent these falls is to make it unnecessary to use such inaccessible positions for storage.

It should go without saying that all floor surfaces should be non-slip, and that there should be plentiful grab-rails, not only in the bathroom, but throughout the house.

Burns and scalds   These constitute another common source of danger. Open fires or appliances with exposed flames or elements should be discouraged, whether for heating or for cooking. Whenever possible, materials used should be incombustible. Kitchens should be designed to reduce the danger of scalds from overturning saucepans or kettles. Stove controls should be easy to reach. The temperature of the hot water supply should be regulated so that it cannot cause serious scalding.

Other accidents   Where gas is used for cooking or heating, some fatal accidents are bound to occur. Old people often have an impaired sense of smell, and may doze off without remembering to light or re-light the gas. Cooking by electricity is generally regarded as safer.

Alarm systems   It too often occurs that old people sustain a fall or some other accident but are unable to attract attention. Although there is no way of insuring that this will never happen, provision should be made for a suitable warning system that the victim may be able to reach. This could be a direct-line telephone, a bell, or both.

SPECIAL DESIGN POINTS FOR GROUP HOUSING

Thus far we have been considering design requirements for self-contained accommodation. For various reasons, however, certain elderly people prefer to live in a house with some shared facilities. This can have the advantages of lowered cost and greater sociability, it may give relief from unwanted chores such as meal preparation, and—of particular importance for the disabled—it gives access to help in an emergency.

One example of this type of housing is afforded by the British flatlet program. Flatlets are small dwelling units sharing bathrooms and common rooms; grouped together into 20 to 30 units; and supervised by a warden, who is responsible for cleaning the communal rooms, attending to the heating plant, answering emergency calls, and providing help with shopping, making meals, and even nursing. Sociological surveys have shown that this arrangement suits many elderly people who value their independence but also enjoy the companionship and support of the warden and their fellow residents.[39] In their original version these flatlet buildings offered only shared toilet facilities. To many outsiders, including the writer, this seemed a highly objectionable feature: The elderly have a particular need for private and readily available toilet facilities, and it is encouraging that all new flatlets are to have individual toilets.

The question of individual or shared bathrooms is not quite so straightforward. Today's old people were brought up at a time when daily baths were not yet customary.[40] It may be argued that shared bathroom arrangements have the advantage of providing a variety of types of bathtubs and showers and make it easier for staff to supervise elderly bathers. It should be mentioned that the private bathrooms were singled out for special praise at Victoria Plaza, whereas one British survey of elderly people's satisfaction with new housing showed that "somewhat surprisingly, there was no difference in the proportions who appeared satisfied between those who had a bathroom for their exclusive use and those who shared these facilities."[41]

Dependence

The time may finally come when the old person is no longer able to take care of himself, and some new living arrangement may be required either at home or in an institution. Existing facilities typically reflect outdated medical practices and social attitudes toward the aged and their problems, and many improvements are needed both in the design of geriatric facilities and in community planning for maintaining the old person in a home that he can still call his own.

There is much evidence that (given proper encouragement, and except during episodes of illness) most elderly people are able to look after themselves until a very advanced age, that it is almost always

[39] Ministry of Housing and Local Government, *Grouped Flatlets for Old People: A Sociological Study* (London: Her Majesty's Stationery Office, 1962). The Ministry of Housing has produced a number of other booklets on the flatlet program of which they have been the sponsors.

[40] The Ministry of Housing's survey (see n. 39, above) shows that use of the bath falls off steeply with age: 74 per cent of residents aged under 75, 38 per cent of those aged 75–79, and 26 per cent of those aged 80 or over. *Ibid.*, 17.

[41] Hole and Allen, *op. cit.*, 5.

beneficial to encourage them to do so, and that most prefer it this way. [*See Vol. 1, Chap. 6.B.7, pp. 141–142; Chap. 25, pp. 577–596.*] Indeed, there is near consensus for the view that "home is still the best place for old people." For example, Beyer and Nierstrasz quote a number of recent statements by authorities in Europe and the United States to this effect.[42]

The possibility of retaining the elderly in their own homes was demonstrated by Doctor van Zonneveld in his celebrated survey of 3,000 aged men and women living in Groningen in northern Holland. With the aid of seventy senior medical students, he assessed the housing requirement of this sample and showed that, up to the age of 80, as many as 80 per cent of men and 74 per cent of women could live at home. Two comments about this study are in order. The first is that Doctor van Zonneveld's figures have been criticized mainly on the grounds that they were too cautious. The second is that all these estimates presuppose the existence of an extensive network of social and domiciliary supportive services of the kinds already mentioned.

It often happens, however, that infirmities, at least at first, are intermittent in their effects. What is then needed is a form of medical and nursing support that can be brought into operation, often for quite short periods and with a minimum of fuss. In view of the estimated large proportions of older people who might, under appropriate conditions, be taken care of in their homes (or in communal facilities without nursing care) the remaining proportion of men and of women who need to enter nursing homes or hospitals is small.[43]

COMMUNAL OR RESIDENTIAL HOMES

Existing facilities for dependent older people have developed in large part, however, without benefit of supportive community services. A wide variety of homes for the aged, nursing homes, hospitals, and other types of institutions are now in existence. Theoretically, such institutions can be subdivided according to the stage of dependency of the residents, or according to the type of ownership and control. In practice, however, such distinctions are blurred. Accordingly we shall deal first in this section with communal or residential homes generally, as these attempt to meet the needs of the very old (aged 80 or more) or of those other old people whose chronic disabilities call for special care. Unfortunately, most nursing homes must be treated together with communal homes supplying nonnursing care, since these two

[42] Beyer and Nierstrasz, *op. cit.*, esp. p. 13.
[43] R. J. van Zonneveld, *Health Problems of the Aged* (Assen: Gorcum & Comp., N.V., 1954), Table 6. Reproduced by Beyer and Nierstrasz, *op. cit.*, 8.

types are not clearly distinguished in practice. However, we shall isolate for separate discussion later those chronic hospitals (and geriatric units of general hospitals) that specialize in providing active nursing and medical care for acute cases.

Peter Townsend has pointed out in *The Last Refuge* that there is a lack of clarity of purpose in determining the social role of the residential home.

Is it to be a permanent refuge for infirm persons who cannot be supported in their homes by any practicable system of domiciliary services, and yet who are not in need of continuous nursing care and medical treatment in hospital? Is it to be a temporary refuge for frail persons recovering from illness or malnutrition or seeking to give relatives or workers in the domiciliary services a hard-earned rest or perhaps a chance of improving the facilities available at home? Or is it to be simply a rescue device for the present generation of old people whose differing needs cannot be met because good housing, adequate pensions, and comprehensive local domiciliary services are not yet provided?[44]

He argues that the first of these three choices is conventionally assumed to be the correct one, but that logic favors the second or third choice. Particularly now that the modern hospital geriatric unit is allotted a therapeutic function, it seems ironic that the communal or residential home, which is designed for those in less need of medical and nursing care, should be regarded as the terminal resting place of those who enter.

The British Ministry of Health has attempted to draw a distinction between infirmity and sickness, to guide decisions as to who should enter a residential home and who should go into a hospital. In practice this decision proves extremely difficult. The same elderly person may vary from day to day in his condition and requirements, and in any case the nursing and medical care needed by old people is very different from that appropriate in an acute general hospital. Apart from clinical considerations, a special kind of compassion is required of those who look after the very old and infirm; a son or daughter may develop this in dealing with an aging parent, but others who are merely doing a job may sometimes be so affected by the suffering and growing infirmity of their charges that they react by assumed indifference, by punitive attitudes, and, in extreme cases, by almost bestial maltreatment.[45]

[44] Peter Townsend, *The Last Refuge* (abridged edn.; London: Routledge and Kegan Paul, 1964), 193.
[45] Barbara Robb, *Sans Everything: A Case to Answer* (London: Nelson & Sons, Ltd., 1967).

Quite apart from the manner in which the elderly in homes are treated, there is the wider question as to whether or not the administrative and institutional set-up provides, or could be made to provide, the best living conditions for those old people who are no longer capable of looking after themselves.

TYPES OF COMMUNAL HOMES IN THE UNITED STATES

No nationwide data for the United States describe in detail the nature and distribution of communal homes. The number of old people living in them is known, however, through special reports of the United States Bureau of the Census and the United States National Center for Health Statistics [*as illustrated in Ex. 6 · 19, p. 141, and Ex. 25 · 1, p. 579 in Vol. 1*]. In 1950, a total of 217,536 persons 65 years old and over resided in all of the several types of homes for the aged and dependent (in addition to 141,346 in mental hospitals),[46] including 28 per cent in Federal, state, and other publicly operated homes; 30 per cent in private nonprofit homes (principally homes for the aged operated by religious, fraternal, and nationality groups); and 42 per cent in commercial homes of all kinds. Since 1950 there seems to have been a shift in this balance of ownership and control, with steep increases not so much in the publicly operated institutions as in the commercial and the nonprofit homes; thus by 1960 the comparable percentages were 61 per cent in private proprietary homes, 24 per cent in private nonprofit homes, 12 per cent in county and city homes, and 3 per cent in Federal and state homes. In 1960 also about 45 per cent of the old people in homes for the aged of all types were known to have access to skilled nursing care. [*See Vol. 1, Chap. 6.7.b, pp. 141–142; Chap. 25.1.a, pp. 579–580.*]

While no comprehensive picture of the programs of such institutions is available,[47] it has been said of institutional group housing for the aged in the United States generally that, "if it has discriminated, [*it*] has tended to favor either the very rich who could afford to pay unusually high prices for care and service (usually in exclusive commercial nursing and convalescent homes), or to favor persons of very low income, particularly in those areas of the country where old age

[46] U.S. Bureau of the Census, "Institutional Population," *1950 Census of Population*, Special Reports (Washington, D.C.: Government Printing Office, 1953), Vol. IV, Part 2, Chap. C.

[47] Nevertheless, some information is available about several states; for example, Wilner and Walkley, *op. cit.*, give some interesting data gathered in the 1964 California Survey. Further facts can be gleaned from the Hearings before the U.S. Senate Special Committee on Aging and its Subcommittees that have taken place since 1965.

assistance grants were liberal and standards of services were minimal."[48]

The same broad categories of ownership and control exist in Britain as in the United States, and it is of interest to examine the findings of Peter Townsend's careful survey of British residential institutions and homes for 1960.[49] Townsend's findings are based on a mail questionnaire addressed to and answered by all 146 local authorities (that is, Counties and County Boroughs) in England and Wales, and on reports of visits to 173 of a random sample of 180 institutions and homes in all regions of England and Wales.

He found that—apart from hospital geriatric beds—there were 110,000 beds in over 3,000 institutions, of which 33 per cent were in former public assistance institutions, 33 per cent in other local authority homes, 23 per cent in voluntary homes (that is, nonprofit), and 11 per cent in private (that is, commercial) homes. The characteristics of each of these groups are outlined in the following paragraphs.

1. *Former public assistance institutions* These are the gradually diminishing survivors of the workhouses of the 1830's and 1840's designed to accommodate all those—vagrants, mentally ill, or old people—who had to be cared for with public money. There are still about 300 of these institutions in England and Wales and some are very large, more than a quarter having at least 250 elderly residents. More than half of the residents sleep in dormitories with at least ten beds. Of the staff, only a small minority (3 to 4 per cent) have nursing qualifications, and the day-to-day duties are almost entirely entrusted to untrained attendants.

2. *Other local authority homes* The former workhouses survive only because it is so expensive in both capital and running costs to replace them. Since World War II local authorities have gradually been supplementing, if not replacing, them by providing much smaller communal homes which seldom have more than fifty beds. Most of these original postwar homes were conversions of buildings previously used for other purposes—former country mansions or hotels, for example—with the result that they are often remote or badly sited in other respects; in recent years there has been a rising proportion of newly built homes, and this trend will probably continue. Residents seem to constitute a more homogeneous group than those in the workhouses, but sex-segregation remains the normal rule and many difficulties have been found in integrating the residents into local communities so that they can enjoy a reasonable

[48] White House Conference on Aging, *op. cit.*, 33.
[49] Townsend, *The Last Refuge*.

amount of sociability. But perhaps the biggest problem is the persistence of ambiguity in the intended role of these homes and their staffs. This was expressed to Townsend by the more compassionate and thoughtful of the matrons and wardens to whom he spoke, who were uncertain as to whether they should conduct their home as a well-drilled hospital or as a warmer and more informal place in which the individuality and self-expression of its residents could flourish. Nevertheless these local authority homes are clearly much preferable to the older public assistance institutions.

3. *Voluntary homes* The voluntary homes are associated with well-established religious and charitable institutions. These homes have increased their capacity nearly threefold since the end of World War II. Like the local authority homes they tend to be small (e.g., not more than sixty beds) and, being mainly converted stately homes or country hotels, they are often isolated. Their standards of amenity vary greatly according to differences in ideology and the amount of endowment. Some adopt a very strict regime, with the formal and authoritarian rules imposed by some religious orders; others are understanding and permissive in a manner that local authority homes with their political supervision can hardly afford to be. Almost all are haunted by the shortage of money which prevents them from achieving the standards in physical plant and in staffing that they feel to be necessary. Typically they are run as havens for those old people still able to manage without nursing care, and this entails a distressing disruption of the resident's way of life when he must be removed to a hospital or nursing home in case of severe illness.

4. *Private homes* These differ from voluntary homes in that the primary motive of their owners is to make them pay. The best ones are luxurious nursing homes, and are correspondingly expensive. The worst are trashy shacks, with the minimum of furniture, heating, or other basic necessities of civilized life, and the charges are correspondingly low. To a greater extent than for other types of home, these residents are mainly survivors from middle-class (nonmanual) families. The atmosphere tends to be informal if not casual, an impression which may sometimes be traced to the personality and background of the matron and to the flexibility of the staffing arrangements. The residents of private homes, unlike those of other types of institutions, are paying patients and, as they are also typically older and frailer, they are not expected to help the staff in house and garden, in the way that residents do elsewhere. In all but the most expensive homes, the paid staff are short in number and in qualifications, although the homes must be registered with the local authority and must maintain standards at the level acceptable to these authorities, thus providing some safeguard against exploitation. But perhaps the most effective safeguard is the fact that such homes are not a source of easy profits. Indeed, the general belief in Britain is that economic pressures are likely to force the private home out of business, except at the upper end of the market, and that local authorities will in due course have to take over direct responsibility for many residents now looked after in these private homes.

CROSS-NATIONAL DIFFERENCES

This comparison between American and British arrangements is revealing both in its similarities and in its differences. The trend in the United States is clearly toward private ownership and control (including sale to occupiers) while that in Britain is probably toward rental housing provided by local authorities. This difference reflects disparities in affluence and ideology. It also means that communal housing in Britain is more locally-based, and hence more geographically dispersed, whereas in the United States it is gravitating toward climatically more favored areas, such as southern California.[50]

Perhaps the feature that most clearly differentiates the British examples from those in the United States (or in some European countries such as Sweden) is that in the latter the residential homes are far more often modern buildings with a high proportion of single rooms, individual toilets, small dining and other communal rooms, and a generally domestic design scale.

ARRANGEMENTS THAT INCLUDE NURSING CARE

Despite the difficulty of drawing any clear line of distinction between the communal home and the nursing home, planning and design will of course be affected by the specific combination of services and facilities provided in particular institutions. The overlapping provisions for nursing and other types of care arise in many instances because it is the same older people who at one time are quite capable of the limited self-help expected of them in a communal home, and who at other times, perhaps for quite short periods, require easy access to intensive medical and nursing care. Furthermore, as the Swedish Committee on Social Policy pointed out in a report published in 1963,[51] there is a complex interrelationship of factors making up the demand for alternative forms of provision: More communal homes mean less demand for community care; subsidized health service will fill hospital geriatric units and nursing homes at the expense of communal homes; and the like.

One conclusion that can be drawn from these considerations is that combined provision should be made on a single site for the various types of accommodation that old people need. As pioneered in

[50] Wilner and Walkley, *op. cit.*, Table 5.
[51] Quoted by Beyer and Nierstrasz, *op. cit.*, 133.

West Germany, using the term "three-step projects," three stages of physical ability are taken into account by including normal housing for those old people who can look after themselves, a communal home for those who need general care, and a nursing home for those who need nursing attention. Careful planning is required to insure that the non-infirm can use their accommodation without unwanted contact with the communal and nursing homes, though it is clearly an advantage to them to have meal service and other facilities on the site.[52]

One example is a project in a busy residential area of Stuttgart; this is known as Ludwigstift and Karl-Mailänder-Heim, the former comprising a communal home for 92 old persons and a nursing home for 50, while the latter consists of a block of 35 one-room apartments, 28 of which have a full kitchen. Both buildings are on the same site, and some facilities are shared. Another example is Moerwijk in The Hague, which has 76 apartments, a communal home for 90, and a nursing home for 49.

A similar arrangement is being tried out in the United States, notably at Presbyterian Village in Detroit which is being built according to a master plan for a community of 450 to 600 aged persons, offering a choice of individual homes or apartments for the independent, a community residence for those who need to have meals and housekeeping service provided, and a nursing unit for those requiring nursing but not hospital care. The Philadelphia Geriatric Center, whose York House North has already been mentioned, can also be regarded as a combination facility since it includes as part of the complex the 376-bed Home for the Jewish Aged which combines a communal home and geriatric hospital.

There are both advantages and disadvantages in arrangements of this kind. The advantages are the more obvious ones of flexibility in facilities provided, increases in the sense of stability and security of the residents who feel that they will continue to be looked after whatever may happen to their health, together with economies of scale and efficiency in organization. Against this there is the question whether or not the standards of a small medical facility attached to a typical combined project can match those of a unit attached to a large general hospital with its range of consulting, diagnostic, and therapeutic facilities.

It seems therefore that a distinction has to be made between the needs of those who are basically healthy but have episodes of minor illness, and those who are suffering from more serious illnesses. For

[52] *Ibid.*, 41, 204–209.

the former, combined projects may well prove very suitable, but a different type of accommodation is required for the latter.

GERIATRIC UNITS

When we come to the question of accommodation for the elderly ill, we have to bear in mind that medical opinion today is much less tolerant than it was of the idea that physical and mental degeneration of the elderly is inevitable and progressive. The emphasis has shifted, at least in certain medical circles, toward a policy of active therapy for patients who would previously have been written off as bedridden and helpless.

The pioneers of this new geriatric approach have had to work out their forms of treatment and their rehabilitating regimes under what has often been the totally unsuitable environment of the old-type hospital for chronic patients. These long-stay hospitals were the counterpart of the former large workhouses but, with their high walls and isolated locations, were the institutions to which those certified as mentally ill were committed. Grossly understaffed and with few facilities for treatment or rehabilitation, they were places without hope. The new active forms of psychiatric therapy have tended to sort out many of the younger and less debilitated patients who, since they respond faster to treatment, now have a good chance of admission to short-stay geriatric units attached to acute general hospitals. The result is that the chronic hospitals have more and more become vast dumps for the senile. In spite of optimistic forecasts by politicians and others, it will be decades before these obsolete institutions can be replaced, and thousands of old people are without appropriate treatment while even progressive geriatricians have to do their best in thoroughly unsatisfactory physical settings.

In spite of this unsavory heritage, it has been possible in most countries to provide new facilities, which may or may not be keeping pace with increases in numbers of the elderly population. This new provision may be of various kinds to suit the three main categories of elderly patient—acute cases, short-stay cases, and long-stay cases. Hazell has estimated that two-fifths of the geriatric beds should be for acute patients, one-fifth for the short-stay patients, and two-fifths for long-stay patients;[53] but this may be an optimistically low estimate of the long-stay cases unless there is a fairly drastic policy of discharging chronic patients to other types of institution with a less active therapeutic program.

[53] Hazell, *op. cit.*, 78.

It is an important question whether these geriatric patients should be concentrated in special hospitals, or treated (as at the Philadelphia Geriatric Center) in hospitals that are an integral part of combination facilities, or accommodated in special geriatric units attached to acute general hospitals. The policy in Britain and in some other European countries seems to have swung strongly toward the last of these three courses, in some cases with the addition of an adjacent long-stay annex whose residents remain under the charge of the hospital medical staff. This contrasts with the position in the United States and some other European countries where the emphasis is on private nursing homes. Perhaps the main determining factor in the decision is the direction in which each particular medical system has developed, whether toward a national health service or toward an insurance system operating through private agencies. If there is a nationwide health system, it is likely that the initiative will be with the hospitals; if not, there is far more scope for private nursing homes.

Is has to be recognized that in addition to patients whose main symptoms requiring hospitalization are physical, some forms of senile dementia are bound to be quite widespread in geriatric units and in nursing homes for the elderly. Patients exhibiting mild symptoms may be acceptable to the other patients in a general geriatric unit, particularly perhaps to those who may be more tolerant because they are not paying directly for their own hospitalization; but there will be a minority of the mentally impaired whose impact on other patients is disturbing and who will then have to be provided with special accommodation. [*See Vol. 1, Chap. 16, pp. 361–406; Chap. 25.1.c, pp. 580–583.*]

Summary of implications

We have aimed in this chapter to indicate the kind of guidance that the social sciences can give to those who have the task of designing or planning a physical environment for the aging. These guidelines have been put forward in all modesty, for two good reasons. First, not nearly enough is yet known about how people respond individually and in groups to their environment; and second, circumstances can vary so enormously that however much we knew we should still fight shy of detailed prescriptions. Guidance can thus only be provisional, consisting of a three-cornered dialogue among designer, client, and social scientist, which ideally should be continuous, starting as part of the planning process and continuing by way of further research and feedback after the physical environment has been created and inhabited.

In spite of these limitations, much experience has accumulated to suggest which solutions are likely to succeed in specific circumstances and which should be avoided, and our purpose is to bring together the main threads of this experience. Three sets of typologies are involved: types of person, types of community, and physical and environmental needs.

ACTIVITIES AND THE LIFE CYCLE

The analysis of types of person has been organized in this chapter in terms of stages in the life cycle, in the belief that this is the most significant general descriptor of the individual since the stage that an individual has reached in the life cycle tells us quite a lot about his typical current roles and activities. This typology is summarized in a simplified form in Figure 1, though it must be recognized that any such diagram will inevitably oversimplify and distort the extent of regression among old people in particular instances. It should be noted that these activities and roles apply to individuals in various external social and economic circumstances, from the affluent to those on relief.

In order to make use of the full implications of this typology, the architect and planner must be given clear guidance by the developer as to the age and activity groups his facility is intended to accommodate, so that appropriate decisions can be made about location, size, and specific requirements for individual dwelling units (such as garage or yard).

TYPES OF COMMUNITY

Since local situations vary tremendously, the nature of any particular facility must offer some reflection of the types of community it is to serve. The typology of communities outlined below is based on that presented in the Background Paper on Housing prepared for the White House Conference on Aging, 1961.[54] These six types, though overlapping and not entirely cognate with one another, are useful in examining the American context. They would apply also to Europe, except perhaps that the European time-scale is more extended.

1. The new communities of mid-twentieth century
   Characteristics: Concentration on young family homes at expense of older people (who are not tempted to move to them by what is currently provided).

[54] White House Conference on Aging, *op. cit.*, 63–67.

FIGURE 1 *Activities and the life-cycle*

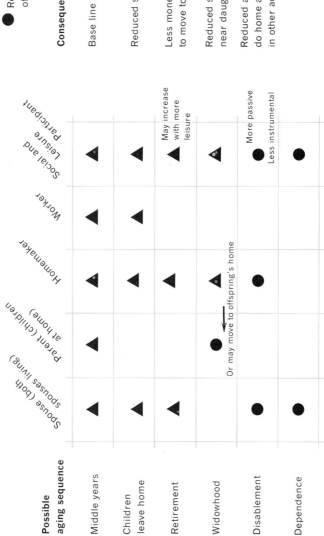

Possible aging sequence	Spouse (both spouses living)	Parent (children at home)	Homemaker	Worker	Social and Leisure Participant	Consequences
Middle years	▲	▲	▲	▲	▲	Base line
Children leave home	▲		▲	▲	▲	Reduced space needs
Retirement	▲		▲	▲	▲ May increase with more leisure	Less money. More freedom to move to new community
Widowhood		● Or may move to offspring's home	◭		◭	Reduced space needs. Desire to locate near daughter or other relative
Disablement	●		●		● More passive Less instrumental	Reduced ability to: read, drive car, do home and yard chores, participate in other activities
Dependence	●				●	

Activity

▲ Full activity

● Reduced activity (or some probability of lost activity)

Needs: (a) Well-located sites for older people, close to local centers.
   (b) More smaller dwelling units, grouped more closely.
   (c) Appropriate financial and marketing arrangements for individual and group house purchase and rental.
   (d) Provision of social and community facilities with needs of the elderly in mind.

2. Twenty- to thirty-year-old communities
Characteristics: Many homes too small for younger families, but suitable for elderly. Well-developed community services and activities.
Needs: (a) Some additional, even simpler housing for those who need relief from home and yard maintenance chores.
   (b) Persuasion of local governing bodies that all segments of the population should be provided for.

3. Thirty- to forty-year-old communities
Characteristics: Some old-type houses, spacious and well built but arranged vertically with many stairs. Also apartment buildings with good range of sizes. Also some jerry-built low-cost housing. Invasion of commercialism.
Needs: (a) Use of these communities for the low-cost housing that can be provided by modernization.
   (b) Enforcement of municipal housing codes and sanitary standards.
   (c) Provision of senior centers and medical and dental facilities.

4. Older residential neighborhoods
Characteristics: Much illegally converted housing, rundown, ill-equipped, and unsafe; some excellent, top-quality homes, very suitable for older householders. Good access to community facilities.
Needs: (a) Use of every possible resource to shore up the quality of the environment.
   (b) Concerted effort to achieve large-scale relocation and balanced redevelopment.

5. Downtown
Characteristics: Buildings, used mainly for commercial purposes, allow only for residence in clubs, hotels, or substandard or illegal dwellings. Excellent access to facilities, but these are often rundown.
Needs: Concerted redevelopment action, retaining downtown ad-

vantages. Potentially an area of special suitability for older citizens, if modern facilities are made available.

6. The small town

Characteristics: Problems most like those in suburban communities; social structure relatively satisfactory, but services and facilities may be inadequate, particularly as public transportation facilities will often be poor. Most small-size dwelling units achieved by subdividing larger family structures.

Needs: (a) Build more houses to suit needs of older people, close to Main Street but also conveniently placed near family residential areas where children and grandchildren may live.

(b) Support local initiatives for senior citizen programs.

GENERAL PHYSICAL AND ENVIRONMENTAL NEEDS

Requirements for architecture and planning may also be summarized according to variety of provisions needed by older people, range of supportive facilities, and quality of design and execution.

1. *Variety of provision for the elderly* There is scope for grouped schemes, and for houses suitable for older people interspersed with younger family homes. There is a market for one-story houses, for two-story row houses, for high-rise apartment buildings. There is a need to provide for fully independent living and also for various degrees of dependence. There can be a choice among individual house-purchase, various condominium and cooperative arrangements, and private or public rental housing.

2. *Range of supportive facilities* Needs are not satisfied merely by providing dwelling units. Other buildings for recreation, for social interaction, and for medical and associated care are an essential part of any comprehensive attempt to meet the problems of aging. Even beyond physical provision, the achievement of a proper range of supportive servives—such as facilities for meals, cleaning, or house maintenance—is an integral part of any program designed to maintain the dignity and independence of the elderly.

3. *Quality of design and execution* Beyond the need to achieve normal high standards of design, attention must be paid to the special requirements of older people imposed by widespread and often progressive physical and economic handicaps. Over and above the avoidance of strains and safety hazards, there are the amenities that can bring comfort to the old: sunny, well-planted oases of quiet outdoor space for those who like to sit and contemplate; attractive intimate rooms where old cronies can sit and talk without disturbing others; carefully thought-out closets for the storage and the display of treasured possessions. Features such as these often cost little, but they can demonstrate that the architect has contributed his own fond sympathy and care to the welfare of his elderly clients.

9

Aging and the law

MERTON C. BERNSTEIN

This wide-ranging and provocative chapter by Professor Bernstein is designed to stimulate practitioners in all branches of law to examine the impact of an aging population on their profession. It is argued that lawyers, acting in their varied roles, can assist both the elderly and the society at large to realize valued ends, despite the profound changes of status that accompany aging in a changing society.

Emphasizing the function of lawyers as architects of the law, Professor Bernstein presents selected examples of problems to which they might contribute needed solutions. A powerful integrating factor in his discussion is the question of how the law may help older people "maintain a sense of dignity and purpose after their years of regular employment are past." Although he offers no simple solution, he does bring to attention a host of new legal remedies that bear upon work opportunities and postponement of retirement, income substitute programs, new roles for retirees, living arrangements, and the rights of the mentally impaired.

Yet, lawyers are not only legal architects and draftsmen; they also serve as individual and family counselors in a variety of contexts. Professor Bernstein's discussion dramatizes the need for diverse legal services among the mass of individuals today, in contrast to the selected few of earlier decades, who not only survive into old age but also retire from the labor force. The legal aspects of asset management and estate planning, for example, offer attorneys new opportunities for serving their older clients. Social security benefits and private pension plans must increasingly be integrated with individual saving programs and income-maintenance plans which extend across the life cycle of the individual and the family.

Advisers for this chapter were Max Rheinstein, School of Law, University of Chicago; and Alvin L. Schorr, Brandeis University.

ON THE RELEVANCE OF VOLUME ONE

Many of the research findings reported in Volume One are important for the lawyer in his capacity both as designer of legal arrangements affecting the lives of older people and as legal counselor to aging individuals. For example, Chapters 4 and 6 specify the relation of age to income, assets, and housing arrangements. The four chapters in Part 2 and Chapter 16 describe the physical and mental impairments that can affect the entire range of the older person's competence, from automobile driving to financial management to self-maintenance outside an institution. Finally, attitudes toward death are examined in Chapter 14, and tendencies toward suicide and criminal behavior are treated in Chapter 16.

Law takes many forms and lawyers perform many roles. The law must accommodate to profound changes in age distribution that have occurred since the turn of the century and will continue at least until its close. Associated changes in patterns of work and leisure, productivity and dependency, family life and residence all have implications for legal structures and the practice of law. The Inventory provides orientation and basic information suggesting and sketching many problems, some amenable to treatment by the law-trained.

Lawyers as counselors and draftsmen must take account of changes in law prompted by an aging population, both those that already have taken place and those that will occur in the future. Lawyers as judges must interpret both old and new laws with understanding of what societal changes have shaped them. Lawyers as architects of the law—in legislatures, administrative agencies, and universities—must try to design new legal arrangements, possibly whole institutions, to ease the burdens of aging and to maximize the opportunities of the elderly, in their own interests and in those of society as well. And, as with other professions, the legal profession must seek ways to induce and enable lawyers to keep pace with the many changes that take place throughout their own lengthening careers. For example, practitioners might pool their experiences through bar association committee studies; in this way invaluable day-to-day experiences could be collected and organized for the guidance of practitioners and those concerned with law reform.

Lawyers in all their capacities must be sensitive to the possible requirements of adaptation and innovation occasioned by the growing ranks of the elderly. Specialists in each branch of the law must seek out the relevant information and attempt to respond. What follows provides selected illustrations from the Inventory, which also contains other patterns and problems that only other lawyer specialists can recognize. Such recognition is the necessary predicate of efforts to ameliorate, remedy, and build.

Work and leisure: problems and possibilities

A democratic society seeks to maximize the freedom of choice of the individual. But a complex, industrialized society also seeks large-scale production and dissemination of goods and services at lowest unit cost. This ideal of efficiency may tend to reduce the choice of the elderly as to whether they will continue to work full time, year round. Thus, paradoxical though it may seem, as more people live on into old age [*see Vol. 1, Chap. 2.1, pp. 16–20*], the normal working life of the American male shrinks. [*See Vol. 1, Chap. 18.A.1, pp. 422–424.*] A number of factors contribute to and reinforce such a tendency: social security and private pension benefits [*see Vol. 1, Chap. 3.B.4.a, pp. 59–61*] enable some who desire to do so to stop work; availability of such benefits enables employers to require retirement at age 65 and sometimes earlier; social security, among other institutions, exerts constraints upon the extent of work in "retirement"; and failing health [*see Vol. 1, Chap. 9.2, pp. 204–218; Chap. 18.C.2.b, pp. 449–450*] and obsolete skills motivate both employer and employee to terminate employment.

As a result of trends in longevity and retirement, the average white man at age 65 confronts thirteen years of nonwork life. [*See Vol. 1, Ex. 2 · 11, p. 29.*][1] Those who survive to age 70 will, on the average, last another ten years. For most, regular full-time work will cease. [*See Vol. 1, Chap. 3.A.1 and A.3, pp. 40–43, 46–49.*] A substantial minority will work into their 66th and 67th year, but most will be retired by age 68; another substantial group ceases regular work *before* 65—probably because of ill health or chronic involuntary unemployment. The averages conceal, however, variations in longevity, work patterns, and types and amount of income substitutes for earned income according to occupation.

Among older women, while recent history shows a dramatic upsurge in employment, the great bulk of women in their 60's do not work and the proportion who do diminishes with age. [*See Vol. 1, Chap. 3.A.2, pp. 43–46.*] Moreover, women live longer than men [*see Vol. 1, Chap. 2.3.b, pp. 30–32*] and hence face a more extended period of leisure, a portion of it without the support and companionship of a husband.

Retirement means leisure, possibly for enjoyment; but it also means the cessation of earned income; it often means a change from physical and financial independence to dependence; and it involves some profound changes in social role and status.

Accumulated evidence suggests that there is not one work-leisure problem of the aging, but many. For some, the physical aging process may necessitate cessation of work. [*See Vol. 1, Chap. 18.C.2.b, pp. 449–450.*] For others, obsolete skills [*see Vol. 1, Chap. 3.B.3, pp. 57–59*] mean that the financial problems of aging set in early quite apart from physical condition or predilection. Others remain able to work and quite a few of these desire to do so; while still others prefer retirement in varying degrees. [*See Vol. 1, Chap. 18.C.2 and C.3, pp. 447–453.*]

Although financial and economic problems of retirement should not be underestimated, probably the greatest challenge to society precipitated by technological and demographic change is how to enable the new millions of the elderly to achieve and maintain a sense of dignity and purpose after the years of regular employment are past. As people differ in temperament, values, skills, education, and physical endowment, this goal must be achieved in varying ways.

[1] On the average, nonwhites die earlier, one index of their disadvantaged status.

A number of innovations may foster self-esteem and improve income for those to whom work is more congenial than nonwork or less onerous than leisure with inadequate income. [*Cf. Sheppard, Chap. 6 in this volume.*] Each would require imaginative legal skills to render it fully operational.

Postponing automatic retirement   For example, automatic retirement could be postponed under certain conditions. A large part of industry prefers automatic retirement at specified ages [*see Vol. 1, Chap. 3.B.4.b, pp. 61–62; Chap. 18.C.2.a, pp. 448–449*], most frequently 65 and to a lesser extent 68, in good part for reasons of administrative convenience. Some unions have sought inducements for retirement at even earlier ages in response to rank-and-file anxieties about job security; the inducements (in the form of larger than normal retirement benefits up to a specified age) plus shop pressure may result in *de facto* compulsory retirement. Interestingly enough, not many unions have emulated the United Auto Workers in such experiments with early retirement. These arrangements are not readily adaptable to changed circumstances such as greater demand for a product or a shortage of particular skills, situations rather common today. To meet these exigencies, the continued employment of older workers might be encouraged under special circumstances (such as unemployment in an industry below a certain level, or a certain number or percentage of job openings in a particular skill) that would not prevent the employment or advancement of younger workers.

Partial retirement   In addition, various kinds of "partial employment, partial retirement" may be desirable to enhance status and income for the elderly without disadvantaging younger workers. Employees at a given age could cease regular full-time employment and be assigned to other tasks *not* being performed because of prohibitive costs. For example, standby replacements for absent employees are a rarity in industry, but their availability could effect savings to both employers and other employees working on piece work or incentive rates who are dependent upon the flow of supplies or parts from the absentee. This partially retired replacement would receive part of his retirement benefit and thereby could afford to accept call-in pay too low for regular experienced employees when regular rates would be prohibitively costly to the company. When unscheduled, temporary absences occur, the partially retired employee would go to work at regular rates. Thus the retirement system would effect savings that could be translated into higher benefits, the retiree would have more income than his social security and private pension would pay by themselves, and he would have the opportunity to be in the workplace, where so much of his life has been centered. Perhaps most important, he would be needed. The company would have lower unit costs and assurance of steadier production. Employers might also find partial-retirees valuable as training instructors (perhaps in connection with otherwise too costly anti-poverty, in-plant programs), as part-time or occasional plant guides, as out-of-plant employment recruiters, and as occasional liaison with community groups.

Experiments with phased-retirement, possibly useful for acclimating employees to imminent retirement or delaying it for a period, deserve study to see how they have worked and what modifications and adaptations may be necessary or desirable.

These and possibly other devices may be developed to give greater purpose and income to some older people who would find complete retirement unwelcome or premature. Apparent obstacles—in union agreements, social security, or other laws—may be soluble or require change. Such accommodations are grist for the lawyer's imagination and require his technical skills just as new building requirements call upon the talents of the architect.

Implications for retirement age of retraining Rapid technological change could serve to prolong, rather than to abridge, employment of older workers. Neil Chamberlain has suggested that, before long, all or most of us will need periodic retooling to remain fit to practice our professions and trades.[2] If, indeed, major portions of the population were to undergo periodic interruptions of employment in order to receive additional education and retraining, society would require new kinds of schools, new kinds of compensation arrangements, new concepts and mechanisms of employment, new tax and income transfer mechanisms. For some, perhaps many, of the elderly, a major reorganization of normal worklife might mean fewer years of retirement at the end of life. Such periodic retraining would also reduce the competitive educational and skill disadvantages that characterize many of today's older workers.

NEW ROLES

But conventional work is not necessarily the sole means of providing useful activity for the elderly. On the contrary, new roles, outside traditional occupational structures, may be far more satisfying to many and may provide richer returns to the community. Future pat-

[2] Neil W. Chamberlain, "Retooling the Mind," *Atlantic Monthly*, 214, No. 3 (September, 1964), 48–50.

terns of preference cannot be foretold, but nonwork roles may become more highly valued than they now are. We should, at the least, plan for the contingency and perhaps even seek to shape our legal institutions (such as taxation and social security provisions) to encourage such a development.

The provision of scarce but valued community projects and services by new organizations in the private sector may be one of the important innovations of our day.[3] [*See Morris, Chap. 2 in this volume.*] For example, limited experience with "foster grandparents" for institutionalized children supports the possibility of creating roles that provide useful, satisfying, and remunerative activity for older people and, at the same time, new and important services for deprived members of our society. Such programs have, up to now, been financed by government but could also be funded by private groups. Their structure, functions, and relationships—with government at all levels, employees, beneficiaries, and contributors—all require legal invention. Under existing law, such as Title III of the Older Americans Act, funds are available for local programs, including those in which older citizens provide volunteer services. Organizations and individuals can fashion new roles for themselves. But they often will need legal guidance to point the way and to fit their undertakings to existing law, which itself may require modification; for example, some experts believe that child-care agency requirements should be recast in the interests of both children and foster grandparents.

Leisure, living arrangements, and "property"

A frequent irony of being elderly is having unprecedented leisure but insufficient funds with which to enjoy it. Clearly more adequate income maintenance programs, as discussed below, are the major answer. In addition, adoption of certain alternative ways of organizing their lives may prove both more economical and more satisfying to many older people. [*See Madge, Chap. 8 in this volume.*]

THREE-GENERATION HOUSEHOLDS

For the most part, adult children and their parents prefer to maintain separate homes. [*See Vol. 1, Chap. 7.B.4.e, pp. 182–183; Chap. 23.B.1.f, pp. 549–550.*] There are some families, however, perhaps especially those in particular ethnic groups, who prefer to live in three-

---

[3] For some suggested structures and programs, see Merton C. Bernstein, "Putting Automation to Work Making Jobs: A Challenge to Enterprise," *Challenge*, 13 (1964), 23.

generation households that may offer a degree of economic security [*see Vol. 1, Chap. 4.A.2.b, pp. 77–78*] and companionship to the grandparent; child-care services, as well as companionship, to younger members of the family; and opportunity for the mother to work if she prefers. Encouraging this family association may require adjustment in public assistance (perhaps by providing a bonus for "live-in" grandparents), in public housing laws (by mandating apartment design to accommodate such arrangements, as with supplementary kitchen and entrance facilities for a modicum of grandparental privacy), and in zoning laws (now often inhospitable to joint households). Spotting and solving these problems are lawyer's work.

SUBSTITUTES FOR FAMILY LIVING ARRANGEMENTS

Even if traditional family living arrangements prove beneficial to some, new family-substitute associations may seem more promising for others. Widows and widowers, lacking the comforts and the economies of living with a lifelong mate, may find it satisfying to participate in cooperative communal living to which contributions could be made both in services and funds. Cooperative communal living would differ from the typical old age or nursing home in that administrative control—and perhaps ownership of facilities—would be retained by residents, a factor that could prove of immense importance in enhancing the psychological well-being and personal freedom of those elderly who must seek communal living arrangements as the alternative to living entirely alone. The undoubted problems of such an arrangement would test the skill of many specialists—psychologists, physicians, dietitians, architects, and lawyers. Yet, the game may be worth the candle, and the traditional tools of housing and hospital legislation, loans, guarantees, and various tax advantages could be employed to stimulate experimentation with such a new institution.

RESIDENTIAL MOBILITY

A major element of inefficiency in the enjoyment of leisure may be the fixed abode. During working years, living in one place reasonably close to the place of work not only makes sense but usually is necessary. Although family ties and long association may make one location attractive for retirement, it may also be ill-adapted to the elderly for full-time residence. Inclement winter weather, too great distances from recreational areas or other points of interest, remoteness from available part-year work are all examples of factors that might recommend living in more than one location during a year in the interest of comfort, health, income, a feeling of purposefulness, or just plain enjoyment. But seasonal changes of residence are today the option only of the fairly well-to-do and those hardy enough for trailer living. Control and use of property by some means other than outright ownership might effect both economy and flexibility of living arrangements.

Indeed, given the needs for different kinds of housing at different stages of life, the outright ownership of a home (if mortgaged property can be so regarded) seems a cumbersome, even a fictitious, arrangement for what is really only temporary residence. Meanwhile, the individual home "owner" must cope in the most inefficient way with repairs and local regulations affecting his interests as an owner, often without adequate community facilities such as parks. Preferential tax treatment given to mortgage interest payments and real estate taxes foster these current arrangements. A new form of property ownership for apartment dwellers, condominium, has been invented to combine these advantages with some economies of centralized administration. Utilizing this model or other new devices, multiple residences may perhaps be made available to the elderly (at well below the motel rates that relatively few can afford).

The legal ramifications of such new "property" arrangements makes the mind boggle. State residence requirements for public assistance, local tax advantages to elderly property owners, and the desirability of avoiding estate taxes in more than one state are just some of the problems attendant upon such a new scheme as certain of these problems now attend the movements of the well-to-do. Yet, ways may be found of accommodating to existing law and, in addition, new and principled legislation may be required of lawyer-architects. If we truly are in a population revolution, perhaps revolutionary changes in property arrangements and property law are needed.

Financial independence and dependency

Advancing age frequently signals the loss in varying degrees of full individual independence due to declining income or declining physical or mental fitness. We set a high value upon the individual's capacity to conduct his own affairs and to choose how and where he will live, free of unwelcome intrusion or coercion in making choices about these matters. Yet, unfortunately, our present institutions do not assure that our ideal of independence will be enjoyed by the elderly.

Financial security is a great problem for the elderly [see Vol. 1, Chap. 4, pp. 69–109; Chap. 18.C.4.c, pp. 454–456]; modest assets and current income substitute programs, taken singly or in combination, fall far short of enabling the retired to maintain preretirement standards of living. [*See Kreps, Chap. 7 in this volume.*] Probably two out of five of the poor are elderly.

MANAGEMENT OF ASSETS

An analysis made by the Social Security Administration suggests that, if the value of the elderly's assets could be spread over the years remaining to their owners, median incomes could be increased 10 per cent, or even 30 per cent if owned homes are taken into account. [*See Vol. 1, Chap. 4.B.1, pp. 85–88.*] While assets tend to be concentrated among the comparatively well off, any means of raising living standards for substantial groups of the elderly deserve careful attention.

Presumably, the best off have little trouble in turning assets into income. But those of modest means and small managerial and financial experience are ill-equipped to extract earnings from assets. Indeed, homes and small amounts of assets do not lend themselves readily to individual income-producing efforts.

Some proposals to derive income from such assets have been made. Professor Yung-Ping Chen, for example, proposes what he calls an "actuarial mortgage" plan.[4] Under it the owner of a home would borrow against its value, the proceeds, in effect, to be invested in a lifetime annuity. Thus the owner can remain in his home as long as he lives, in the meantime receiving a regular "income" from his property that is computed on an actuarial basis. Upon his death the property reverts to the lender. Although such proposals involve obvious difficulties, such as problems of subrental or adequate maintenance of property not to be handed on to the heirs of the incumbent, these problems may be worked out with the help of knowledgeable property and insurance lawyers. The proposal has the advantage of requiring only a few venturesome participants to launch a trial.

Homes and other nonliquid assets may have slight utility in the hands of their immediate owners and little revenue-producing power by themselves. However, managers could supply expertise and economies of scale if many homes and nonliquid asset holdings were pooled. In some instances, the owners would be able and well-advised to occupy part of their own premises and even perform some of the maintenance services required (thereby reducing the fee paid for

[4] Yung-Ping Chen, "Potential Income from Home-Ownership: An Actuarial Mortgage Plan," in U.S. Congress, Joint Economic Committee, 90th Cong., 1st Sess., *Compendium: Old Age Income Assurance* Part II (Washington, D.C.: Government Printing Office, 1967), 303. Another version appears in Yung-Ping Chen, "Taxation of the Aged: Some Issues and Possible Solutions," in R. W. Lindholm (ed.), *Property Taxation: U.S.A.* (Madison: University of Wisconsin Press, 1967).

management), while in other circumstances a different home in a different location, made possible by the net earnings of the managerial arrangement, would be preferable. Managerial services of this sort could be provided by relatively small enterprises, perhaps encouraged by favorable tax treatment as an initial inducement. Should private initiative prove wanting, local, state, or Federal agencies could be empowered to undertake the task. The legal arrangements for such undertakings, I venture to say, would have to be rather special, taking into account the relative financial innocence of many who would receive such services, and assuming that many would be unrepresented by counsel of their own in concluding the arrangement. Lawyers might draft model contracts to protect the interests of all parties and to prevent overreaching where the services are rendered for profit, as they may very well be.

SOCIAL SECURITY AND OTHER PUBLIC PROGRAMS

The great majority of elderly Americans (79 per cent in 1962) derive cash income from the Old Age, Survivors, Disability, and Health Insurance Program (OASDHI); indeed, nearly one-third of the aggregate income of older people comes from social security, a proportion exceeded only by the earnings of the minority still employed. [*See Vol. 1, Chap. 4.A.1, pp. 70–74.*] For beneficiaries, OASDHI is the principal source of cash income.[5] The proportion of the elderly who will benefit from social security will increase. While benefits have been improving, the large number of men who "retire" before age 65— with actuarially reduced benefits—slows the improvement markedly and probably will continue to do so. For the neediest beneficiaries, OASDHI benefit improvements merely mean that beneficiaries obtain larger amounts from social security but smaller amounts from Old Age Assistance, with little or no net gain.

I have proposed that the involuntary nature of much pre-65 retirement be recognized and that unreduced benefits be accorded those whose lack of work results not from choice but from physical or economic necessity.[6] The proper definition of that status, which would borrow heavily from unemployment compensation but would necessarily differ in some respects, and the design of procedures for its administration are lawyers' tasks.

Additional proposals under consideration for liberalizations of so-

---

[5] Lenore A. Epstein and Janet H. Murray, *The Aged Population of the United States: The 1963 Social Security Survey of the Aged* (Washington, D.C.: Government Printing Office, 1967), 43, 292.

[6] William G. Bowen *et al.* (eds.), *The American System of Social Insurance* (New York: McGraw-Hill Book Company, Inc., 1968).

cial security include supplementation of the payroll tax with general revenues to help finance larger benefits; automatic cost-of-living or standard-of-living benefit increases (or a procedure elsewhere recommended by the author under which the President would inform Congress of cost-of-living index increases and of his recommendations, and Congress would be required to hold hearings on the relevant issues);[7] and exemption of employee and self-employed payroll taxes and taxation of benefits instead. Such changes would require lawyers' talents both in drafting and in analyzing possible impact upon other rights.

Moreover, as the aged population grows [*see Vol. 1, Chap. 6.B.7, pp. 141–142*], we will be faced not only with Medicare payments (under OASDHI) for hospital and nursing home care required by illness, but also with the issue of new benefits to defray the costs of institutional care for those who have chronic but not acute conditions. This essentially new program for the institutionalized population will require a fresh rationale for OASDHI and a special set of provisions, especially if the institutions, like most nursing homes today, are to be under proprietary ownership.

Possibly even more profound changes impend. Although the design of new income-substitute programs is regarded as the economists' job, the experience of legislative draftsmen and administrator-bureaucrats is needed to shape workable structures and to plan many of the important details of new programs.

Proposed sharing of Federal revenues with the states, for example, poses some difficult problems of adapting and changing the dozens of Federal grant-in-aid statutory programs (some of which are of great importance to the elderly and grow as their ranks grow) to insure, if possible, that needs now met by them are not wholly neglected while allowing maximum flexibility to the states to use their new resources as they think best (but without merely relieving some of their taxpayers). Although such a set of goals appears unattainable, nevertheless some imaginative and skilled lawyers may come up with devices to do the trick.

Additional proposals for new income substitute programs which have received considerable attention and which, if implemented, would require the services of the legal profession include the negative income tax (NIT) and minimum income guarantees. Some warn that the negative income tax presents insuperable problems of potential fraud by those, principally the elderly, who would seek to qualify by transfer-

[7] *Ibid.*

ring their property and diverting their income to others. The laws of taxation and bankruptcy have had long experience with fraud. Possibly lawyers experienced in these fields can help design the anti-fraud devices necessary for these proposed programs; or they may counsel that their customary tools are not adequate to a mass program of this sort.

There is, moreover, serious question as to how such new programs would incorporate OASDHI benefits.[8] It may be argued that "un-earned" guarantee or tax payments and "earned" social security benefits are incompatible. Their coexistence would be decidedly un-easy and could lead to demands for social security-style benefits without payroll taxes and the insurance mechanism. Must we, then, begin to think the unthinkable—of dismantling OASDHI? Such a development would shatter a major premise upon which OASDHI has proceeded, that of the program's immortality. It would be premature to suggest just what experience with the liquidation of large undertakings, if any, might be pertinent to a consideration of the problems which tumble out of the larger question of scrapping OASDHI or of transforming it into the new programs under speculative consideration.

PRIVATE PENSION PLANS

Over one hundred and twenty-five thousand pension plans are operative today. Thousands of new ones are established each year, while some are discontinued. They command over one hundred billion dollars in assets, and their potential benefits over the next several decades are far greater. Most importantly, the financial security of innumerable future retirees depends heavily upon their proper functioning.

Analysis of how private pension plans operate and how well they meet possible future exigencies,[9] as well as understanding of the principles of finance and actuarial science underlying plan construction, are in part the task of the lawyer. It is the counselor's job to ascertain his client's expectations from such plans and to counsel upon contemplated employment in the light of their provisions. The lawyer,

---

[8] While controversial, incorporating cash benefits would be far easier than taking account of other program service benefits, which might simply be excluded from consideration.

[9] The principal analyses and critiques are not optimistic. See: President's Committee on Corporate Pension Funds, *Public Policy and Private Pension Programs* (Washington, D.C.: Government Printing Office, 1965); Dan M. McGill, *Fulfilling Pension Expectations* (Homewood, Ill.: Richard D. Irwin, Inc., 1962); Merton C. Bernstein, *The Future of Private Pensions* (New York: Free Press, 1964). The chief hazards to eligibility are large-scale employee job separation from plans before achieving the substantial service required by most, and plan funds insufficient to meet valid claims.

together with other specialists, is also responsible for considering ways in which pension plans may be modified or reconstructed to serve their purposes better. Legislation in this field may well come under active consideration by Congress in the not too distant future.[10]

Certain characteristics of plans, such as the all too frequent absence of provisions for survivor's benefits for a widow or the special conditions for electing such benefits, require attention. Executive and white-collar plans tend to more generous treatment of widows, while blue-collar plans generally provide no such benefits or do so under difficult election conditions. Considering the long years [*see Vol. 1, Chap. 7.A.3.e, p. 166*] and the meager resources [*see Vol. 1, Chap. 4.A.1.a, p. 71*] of widowhood that face the average older woman, such arrangements merit close examination.

SOME NEW ASPECTS OF ESTATE PLANNING

In order to shape an "estate planning" strategy, a legal counselor to an individual must understand, as his client very well may not, the economic and legal arrangements that affect the decision whether to retire; the possible timing of this decision in differing occupations [*see Vol. 1, Chap. 18.C, pp. 442–459*]; the range of possible uses for time in retirement; the interrelationships of earnings and social security benefits; the possible pension arrangements open to self-employed persons; the possible limitations upon employment imposed by private pension plans; the expected period of survival of a wife; and the social security and private plan benefits payable to her as a widow and to the children. In addition, he must be acquainted with the tax consequences of alternative plans for meeting these exigencies and situations in order to permit the client to make an informed choice. But even more is required of the estate counselor. Account must be taken of the possibilities of change, and adaptability should be built into any estate plan. Some changes can be readily foreseen; others, such as prviate pension legislation, seem fairly likely. Major amendments to the Social Security Act should be the occasion for review of estate arrangements. Clients should be advised to report private pension plan changes in cases where the attorney does not himself counsel on the particular plan; where he does, attention must be directed to the Internal Revenue Code provisions and regulations and rulings governing plans.

---

[10] The Labor Section of the American Bar Association established a Committee on Pension, Welfare and Related Plans in 1965. The Section's annual proceedings contain discussions of some pension problems and present analyses of proposed legislation.

As patterns of work and retirement change, so must the financial and legal arrangements for the period when earnings from work cease or diminish. [*See Kreps, Chap. 7 in this volume.*] This is a major area for exploration and innovation by the traditional estate planner. Where formerly only the well-to-do retired, today the great majority of men, almost regardless of economic class, will be retirees, a situation that suggests the desirability of new approaches to retirement and estate planning for those in lower earnings brackets. With more widespread "affluence" but generally modest asset accumulations, readily understood and low-cost probate and administration procedures should be devised.

FINANCIAL ASPECTS OF PARENT-ADULT CHILD RELATIONSHIPS

The law touches parent-adult child relationships in innumerable ways, such as requirements for support of the parent by the child, tax laws governing estates and gifts, and laws governing inheritance.[11] The increase in numbers of the elderly out of the work force increases the urgency of familiarity with the statutes dealing with parental support, gifts, and inheritance. As Professor Rheinstein has demonstrated, these subjects abound with legal issues. They also call for cooperative study by lawyers and other social scientists of the effect that laws in these areas in fact have had upon conduct, that is, whether they promote or retard desired conduct, or affect it very little.

If longevity does increase, the law will be confronted by parents and their adult children all of whom are retired. Although their relationship might be shoe-horned into existing statutes governing the obligation of children to support parents, one may be permitted to doubt that this particular situation was envisaged when such laws were drafted. The possibility that large numbers of future aged may themselves have aged parents calls for serious consideration. Indeed, the whole subject of statutory responsibility of children for parents may be ripe for reevaluation in view of possible shifting social attitudes, exemplified by enactment of Medicare and of the Prouty amendment to the Social Security Act providing cash benefits to those over 72 who do not otherwise qualify.

[11] A provocative essay on the subject is Max Rheinstein, "Motivation of Intergenerational Behavior by Norms of Law," in Ethel Shanas and Gordon Streib (eds.), *Social Structure and the Family* (Englewood Cliffs: Prentice-Hall, Inc., 1965), 241–266. See also Alvin L. Schorr, "Filial Responsibility and the Aging, or Beyond Pluck and Luck," *Social Security Bulletin,* 25 (1962), 4–9; and Social Security Administration, *Filial Responsibility in the Modern American Family,* (Washington, D.C.: Government Printing Office, 1960).

Impairment: problems and proposals

A growing population of older people means increasing numbers of individuals whose physical capacity, and in some instances mental competence, becomes progressively impaired. If, as is possible, the Medicare and Medical Assistance to the Aged programs result in even greater longevity, degenerative problems may be still further increased. In addition, considerable geographical mobility makes probable a growing number of persons of advanced years without the nearby relatives who might otherwise provide attention and services to enable the elderly to maintain substantial independence and avoid institutionalization. [*See Susser, Chap. 5 in this volume.*]

VOLUNTARY ARRANGEMENTS

With foresight, certain difficulties of declining capacity can be forestalled. An attorney familiar with alternatives may advise the adoption, in advance of actual need, of arrangements for financial management to assure informed investment and prudent disbursement. Such voluntary, forehanded arrangements avoid the traumatic experience of a formal incompetency proceeding and also avoid the dissipation of funds that may occur before the requisite formalities can be initiated (often reluctantly) and completed. Moreover, a sensitive adviser can counsel against the tendency for some anxious and inexperienced oldsters to be more frugal than is wise.

Unfortunately, such private arrangements can be more expensive than modest assets warrant. Some states have attempted to simplify procedures and thus to reduce charges against small estates. Moreover, under certain Federal and Federal-state programs, notably Old Age Assistance, OASDHI, and programs for veterans, provision is made for receipt of benefits on behalf of those unable to deal competently with their funds. (Unfortunately, these arrangements are limited to amounts received through the particular programs.) However, further experimentation and innovation are required to meet the important goals of achieving low-cost management of assets (presumably in amounts for which the usual kind of private trustees would be overly expensive) of those not fully able to act for themselves, and providing some individualized counseling to those only mildly impaired but in need of guidance.

Personal services that will enable elderly persons or couples to maintain independent quarters are at least as important as guidance in the management of assets. If anticipated, this need may be planned for. Home assistance to the impaired or infirm may very well be provided by more vigorous elderly persons who, in the process of being useful and providing companionship, can earn some income and themselves receive companionship.

INVOLUNTARY ARRANGEMENTS

Voluntary arrangements to administer an aged individual's affairs, or some of them, may not be possible in some cases, and the question may arise whether an individual can care adequately for himself without endangering the interests of others. In this connection, three cautions are in order. First, one must guard against intolerance of independence and crustiness, which may accompany aging as vanity (and conformity) decrease. Mere inconvenience to others is hardly adequate ground for institutionalizing an elderly person, any more than it is for removing younger individuals from society. We must consider afresh the freedom that should be accorded the individual to live, as the price of privacy and self-determination, under circumstances difficult or even dangerous to himself. In my opinion, independence seems a higher value than safety, if the individual is capable of making a reasonably clear-minded choice. Society should intervene with compulsion only in extreme circumstances. Moreover, as some commentators make clear,[12] incompetence may not extend to all capacities, and guardianship should be limited to the areas of proven necessity with only the degree of supervision that is demonstrably necessary.

In the second place, as larger numbers of the aged will in all likelihood require institutionalization during the remainder of the century, lawyers must assure that commitment procedures insure due process and guard against victimization by interested relatives, business associates, and proprietary receiving institutions (by prohibiting, for example, a physician connected with that institution from being one on whose opinion of incompetence commitment or continued institutionalization depends).

Finally, we must insure that institutionalized persons do not become rightless outcasts. Cures, or at least restoration to reasonable competence, have become more common in the treatment of mental illness, even though degenerative conditions may not have shared in the advance. At the least, ready access to judicial procedures for release should be available, free of interference by the institutional authorities.

[12] Virginia Lehman and Geneva Mathiasen, *Guardianship and Protective Services for Older People* (New York: National Council on the Aging, 1963).

There must be assurance also of both adequate and humane treatment of those whose helplessness makes them the natural prey of others whose own difficulties make them seek victims. To this end, record-keeping of medical treatment for both accidents and illness should be required and private communications to outside friends, relatives, public officials, and institutions should be guaranteed. In addition, disinterested visitors, preferably highly motivated private citizens such as clergymen, lawyers, and doctors, should be a regular (and unannounced) feature of institutional life. My own proposals in this area[13] parallel the more detailed draft of the Institute of Public Administration's proposed "New Mental Hygiene Law for New York State,"[14] reported as a "bill of rights for mental patients."[15] Anyone who has viewed "The Titticutt Follies," a documentary film of existence at Bridgewater, a Massachusetts institution for the mentally ill, will appreciate the urgency of such protection for the institutionalized.

The question of whether and to what extent institutionalized older persons should work in the institution presents special problems of policy and may require accommodations in state statutes. Such work may be financially advantageous to the institution, but for that very reason may lead to exploitation of the elderly and cut-rate competition with noninstitutionalized staff workers. Yet, the opportunity to be useful and to earn money for some amenities is clearly desirable for the aged inmate. [*See Vol. 1, Chap. 25.4.b and 5.d, pp. 588, 593–594.*] Although the full connotations are not intended, the historic struggles over prison labor present a parallel case and may provide a relevant body of experience and law upon which to build.

PROBLEMS OF QUALITY AND FRAUD

The elderly have more concentrated needs than the remainder of the population for certain accommodations and services requiring legal attention. For example, many older people need, or at least desire,

[13] Put forward in an unpublished paper at a meeting of the Walter E. Meyer Research Institute of Law in April, 1967.

[14] February, 1968.

[15] *The New York Times*, March 8, 1968, p. 53, col. 5. I question some provisions, such as 31.03(b) under which a voluntary patient can be held involuntarily by an institution for as long as ten days after he indicates his desire to leave. And I wonder at the utility of 31.25(c) under which if a rehearing on the question of retention of a person is made by someone on his behalf, such as a legal representative or relative, that other person must make a deposit or post bond for repayment of the costs of the rehearing review and determination by a jury if the order is sustained. If the patient moves for rehearing no such costs attach. Conceivably only the outsider may be in a position to contest effectively. This is especially true of indigents for whom a Legal Aid or "Neighborhood law office" attorney may act.

homes designed for declining capacities and particular recreational preferences, often in a "retirement community," or other special types of housing. A recent device to help meet housing needs of the elderly (as well as of others) is the "rent supplement." Such projects may be privately sponsored, and familiarity with Federal law and regulating arrangements is a responsibility of the lawyer.

Private ventures into housing for the aged, especially profit-making ventures, as well as the somewhat similar nursing or retirement homes, present problems. For one thing, these facilities are in short supply so that their proliferation must be stimulated, often by Federal, state, or local public programs. To work out means of establishing particular facilities within the legal framework of such programs requires the talents of lawyers. Equal difficulties of statutory and administrative control are involved in insuring that such facilities will be adequate to the purposes they ostensibly serve and are fairly priced.

Moreover, the elderly may be particularly susceptible to fraud, notably in the purchase of homes or residential units or in long-term-care contracts. Senator Harrison Williams' Senate subcommittee has done extensive investigatory work in this area and has proposed legislation governing interstate sales.

New legal devices may be required. Available data on mental impairment among the elderly suggest the need for systematic study of the definitions and standards of fraud properly applicable to the dealings of the elderly, who may have differing capacities for important transactions. [*See Vol. 1, Chap. 16, pp. 361–406.*] Similar limitations of mental capacity may require study in regard to criminal law.

Conclusions

This essay has selected, for discussion of their legal implications, but a few examples of the problems suggested by the evidence on aging summarized in Volume One, *An Inventory of Research Findings.* It is to be hoped that many different kinds of lawyers will assay the Inventory. The volume represents the efforts of innumerable scholars and analysts, the refinement of their findings, and the organization of these findings in orderly ranks. Delving into the Inventory is not working deep in the mine shaft searching for veins and fragments of ore. Rather, it is like a walk through Fort Knox: It is up to the artisan to take the bullion and convert it into jewelry.

10

Aging and the ministry

PHILLIP E. HAMMOND

Doctor Hammond, a sociologist, brings the conceptual tools of his discipline to bear on an examination of the part played by the church and by church-sponsored activities in the life of the aged parishoner. Although a surprisingly varied list of programs is found to exist, the author argues that there are no clear theoretical bases for evaluating these, which leads Doctor Hammond to an insightful discussion of ecclesiastical strategy for ministering to the needs of older people. This analysis will be of interest to churchmen and laymen alike since Doctor Hammond insists that the church, along with other social institutions, must be sensitive to changes in the social structure. The implications of such responsiveness for the kinds of functions which religious institutions have traditionally performed are traced out in some detail. "It may well be one of history's greater ironies," he says, "that, at the same time society becomes more differentiated, it produces larger proportions of aged persons whose needs appear to be for less differentiation." Both the concerns and the opportunities presented to the church by this dilemma are identified and discussed.

Advisers for this chapter were James M. Gustafson, Divinity School, Yale University; Andrew M. Greeley, National Opinion Research Center, University of Chicago; and Manfred H. Vogel, History and Literature of Religions, Northwestern University.

ON THE RELEVANCE OF VOLUME ONE

One persistent stereotype of older people holds that they become increasingly dependent upon religion and religious institutions. Surprisingly, however, there is little research evidence to support the suggestion of such a tendency in any definitive way, as indicated in Chapter 20 of Volume One. Not only is the concept of dependence upon religion susceptible to many interpretations, but those researches that do indicate such a relationship are typically based upon cross-section data pertaining to only one moment in time. Thus the comparatively high levels of religious conviction and feeling among older people today may simply reflect the greater religiosity of an earlier period in our history.

Apart from the question of religiosity, Volume One contains information relevant to understanding other aspects of the religious roles of older people and to planning the strategy of the church. The social, economic, and cultural factors set forth in Part 1 outline the broader context within which older people relate to religious institutions; while Parts 2 and 3 describe a number of factors at the individual level—health, personality, attitudes—that affect the older person's religious involvement. Part 4 includes chapters on the various other roles—political, economic, familial—that the aging individual must integrate with both his participation in the church as an institution, and his personal religious observances and beliefs.

> For gray hairs are a glorious crown, which
> is won by a righteous life.   *Proverbs 16:31*

But—

> Cast me not off in the time of old age; forsake me
> not when my strength faileth.   *Psalms 71:9*

Idealization of the past is not an uncommon tendency among men, regardless of the society or historical epoch in which they live. Despite speculation to the contrary, however, there is little evidence that the aged in traditional societies experienced fewer anxieties and insecurities than do old people in America today. As the line from Proverbs suggests, senior members of Biblical times were supposed to be venerated, but the plea of the writer of the quoted Psalm indicates that veneration was not always forthcoming. Old age was sometimes accompanied—as it is today—with fears and concerns.

It may be, though, that the basis of those fears and concerns has changed. The argument is sometimes advanced that the aged are of diminishing utility to modern, industrialized societies. As Leo Simmons claims, special possession of knowledge (especially of supernatural powers) has allowed old people in many primitive societies to occupy "key positions in a wide range of social activities. They are esteemed as experts in solving the problems of life."[1] By contrast, "problems of life" in modern society may have become increasingly technological in nature, and the old, relatively lacking in technical education, have no special competence. Written language and the spread of literacy, moreover, have allowed books, which may be read by all, to become the repositories of knowledge. Thus the act of becoming old may have lost much of its traditional functional basis for others in society.

Even if we grant validity to the argument of decreased utility, we still may question whether veneration, respect, or security must therefore automatically diminish. Just as infants are welcomed into different societies despite their uniform lack of immediate utility, so also may the elderly be viewed as worthy of respect despite their possibly decreasing utility in modern society. Moreover, from the standpoint of Western religion, the question of the social usefulness of the individual is in part irrelevant. For one of the most significant themes in the Judeo-Christian heritage is the *inherent* worth of the individual, irrespective of his familial, occupational, or social ties. Thus although his utility may wane, the elderly person is entitled to consideration of his needs and desires. Assuming continued persistence of this theme, then, the only question for religion is *how*, not whether, these needs should be met. Organizations of religion are publicly committed to meeting the needs of old people, and they do direct some of their resources to the aging. The issue to be confronted in this essay is how these resources can be allocated to achieve maximum benefit.

As a social scientific treatment of the issue, this essay is concerned more with strategy than with moral admonition. It must be recognized, however, that decisions of strategy, as choices between alternative courses of action, presuppose certain value positions. Although,

---

[1] Leo Simmons, *The Role of the Aged in Primitive Society* (New Haven: Yale University Press, 1945), 175.

as already pointed out, religious values are basically sympathetic to the aged, commitment of limited church resources requires specification of *priorities* in satisfying the needs of various age groups that are potentially in competition for the same resources. The establishment of such priorities is outside the province of this essay. Whether scarce resources should be made available to the aged in preference to the youthful, for example, is an issue to be decided within particular religious organizations. The purpose of this essay is not to provide a set of directives but to suggest a framework, a set of conceptual tools, by which religious organizations—and individual ministers—may assess their work with the aged.

In developing this framework for analysis, consideration must be given to a number of questions. How much is known about the "religious" needs of old people? What are churches and clergy doing now in their ministry to the elderly? What are the costs of following one path rather than another; that is, what are the values foregone? What is the likelihood of making an impact through various programs?

In the discussion to follow, we shall first examine the relation of older people to the church, paying special attention to a facet of aging —diminution of role playing—which may be of particular importance in planning church programs. Next, we focus on current church practices relating to the senior members of society. Finally, we draw together these elements into an analysis of ecclesiastical strategy and provide illustrations consonant with recommended strategy.

Throughout the essay we shall use such words as "church" and "minister" in their generic sense. We are concerned with all faiths, sects, and denominations that are within the Judeo-Christian tradition.

Older people and the church

What is the relationship of older people to religion? [*See Vol. 1, Chap. 20, pp. 483–500.*] As will become clear in this section, the answer is not at all easy to formulate for two reasons. First, the data—dealing as they do with a "religiosity" concept that is amenable to many definitions—are frequently contradictory and therefore difficult to interpret. And second, even when an answer is formulated, causal connections often remain unclear. Because cross-section researches are conducted at single moments in time, their results could reflect the *aging process*—but they could as well reflect *generational* (cohort) *differences*. If older persons are found to express more belief in God than do younger persons, for example, we may ask whether this difference tells us something meaningful about the way aging and religion interact, or whether it reflects merely a persisting contrast between younger generations and the generation who happens now to be old.

The voluminous research in the area of aging and religion is not worthless, however. At the least it helps present-day clergymen *define* their clients among the older generation, helps them know something of the relative rates of attendance, devotional practices, death concerns, and so on. In this section, therefore, we shall summarize a number of these findings, attempt to relate these to our developing conceptual framework, and then draw implications for church policy.

It is part of the forklore about aging that religious concerns increase with advancing years. Thus:

> Because of the numerous problems older people experience in our society because of the gradual approach of death, because they have more time to think than they have had for decades previously, and for various other reasons, many older people turn to religion in old age with renewed fervor. . . . It is natural for older people to turn to the church.[2]

Is there basis in fact for such folk wisdom? Almost all older people regard themselves as having some religion. Only 3 per cent do not, and only 22 per cent do not report themselves as members of a church or synagogue. [*See Vol. 1, Chap. 20.1, pp. 484–485.*] Church and other religious organizations are second only to lodges and fraternal organizations as voluntary association affiliations for older persons (55+). [*See Vol. 1, Chap. 20.3.a, p. 490.*] Attendance in church, moreover, is maintained into old age, though after the decade of the 60's, special circumstances intervene, such as ill health (which diminishes attendance) and a preponderance of females in the elderly population (which, because females are more active than males in church, inflates attendance rates relative to younger age groups). [*See Vol. 1, Chap. 20.2, pp. 485–490.*]

Some studies report different findings if based on selected populations. Harold Orbach, for example, concludes after an analysis of several large-scale surveys: "The mixed trends observed between age and religious attendance when relevant sociologic variables are introduced, point to the absence of any simple relationship and suggest that the picture of an almost level plateau through the adult life span . . . represents a merging of the various sociologic influences (such as denomination, sex, race)."[3] A similar conclusion is reached by Ruth

[2] Robert M. Gray and David O. Moberg, *The Church and the Older Person* (Grand Rapids, Mich.: William Eerdmans, 1962), 38.
[3] Harold L. Orbach, "Aging and Religion," *Geriatrics*, 16 (1961), 539.

Albrecht who, summarizing a number of attendance studies, remarks that on the basis of them alone, "it is not possible to believe that older people become more religious."[4]

Other conclusions are possible, however, when evidence other than church attendance is used to define religiosity. For example, older individuals are more likely than those younger to: (1) read the Bible at home, (2) pray in private, (3) be able to name correctly selected books of the Bible, (4) believe in immortality, (5) report the personal value of religion, (6) favor teaching religion in school, and (7) feel the world needs religion more than economic security. [*See Vol. 1, Chaps. 20.4, 20.5, and 20.8.c, pp. 490–493, 498.*] Joel Smith, contrasting a sample of "well" older people (65 +) with a sample of adults 21 to 64, found that, though there was some decrease in church attendance among the elderly, they were more involved in "ecstatic religion" as indicated by their greater exposure to emotional radio church services and more primacy given to afterlife than this life.[5] Gray and Moberg conclude that religious beliefs, especially regarding death and afterlife, are more characteristic of the aged.[6] And Milton Barron summarizes his analysis of the subject: ". . . religiosity among older people is a surprisingly modest part of their overt lives. . . . But in the inner or subjective lives of older people, religion . . . does play a larger role and tends to intensify as people grow older."[7]

Such a conclusion is supported in what is perhaps the best synthesis of research reports on religion and age. Using Glock's dimensions of religiosity,[8] as his scheme for classifying a number of studies, Moberg states: "Research to date seems to indicate fairly conclusively that ritualistic behavior outside the home tends to diminish with increasing age, while religious attitudes and feelings apparently increase among people who have an acknowledged religion."[9] A similar conclusion is drawn by R. G. Kuhlen: ". . . in all studies examined,

[4] Ruth E. Albrecht, "The Meaning of Religion to Older People—the Social Aspect," in D. L. Scudder (ed.), *Organized Religion and the Older Person* (Gainesville, Fla.: University of Florida Press, 1958), 69.

[5] Joel Smith, "The Narrowing Social World of the Aged," in Ida Harper Simpson and John C. McKinney (eds.), *Social Aspects of Aging* (Durham: Duke University Press, 1966), 233.

[6] *Op. cit.*, 39–43.

[7] Milton L. Barron, *The Aging American* (New York: Crowell-Collier Press, 1961), 178.

[8] See Charles Y. Glock and Rodney Stark, *Religion and Society in Tension* (Chicago: Rand McNally & Company, 1965), Chap. 2.

[9] David O. Moberg, "Religiosity in Old Age," *The Gerontologist*, 5 (1965), 86.

with the exception of those relating to church attendance, trends indicate an interest in and concern about religion as age increases, even into extreme old age."[10]

An occasional demurrer is found,[11] but the current consensus would appear to be that the elderly are, at least subjectively, more "religious." What is still very much at issue is whether this religiousness *results* from aging or is simply a *correlate* of generational differences. Although a final answer requires further research, the direct implications for church policy should be considered. If the religiosity of old people *results* from aging, then the church must be prepared for succeeding generations of "clients" roughly in proportion to the current older generation. If, on the other hand, the religiousness of the aged is in part a *correlate* of generational differences, then, given what appears to be the present association between religion and age, the church must be prepared for the possibility of relative decline in the size of its clientele with succeeding generations.

Whatever may be the case for the future, the religiosity of current generations of old people, whether measured by church attendance or by religious feeling and belief, indicates that the church confronts a sizable religious "market" in the elderly; the church is, potentially at least, of considerable significance in their lives. We may ask, then, whether religion appears to have a measurable effect; that is, what difference does it make in the lives of older persons?

One frequently cited kind of evidence comes from the "religion and adjustment" area. One study has found, for example, that the more religious (as measured by religious activity and by "fundamentalist" or "orthodox" Protestant or Catholic attitudes) among the aged "look forward to death" more than do others. "Fearful" or "evasive" attitudes were more characteristic of the latter.[12] [*See Vol. 1, Chap. 14.6, pp. 332–337.*] Another investigation found that one-half of an aged sample reported religion to be "more helpful" in old age

---

[10] R. G. Kuhlen, "Trends in Religious Behavior During the Adult Years," in L. C. Little (ed.), *Wider Horizons in Christian Adult Education* (Pittsburgh: University of Pittsburgh Press, 1962), 23. Quoted in Moberg, *op. cit.*, 86.

[11] For example, Nila Kirkpatrick Covalt, "The Meaning of Religion in Older People —the Medical Perspective," in D. L. Scudder (ed.), *Organized Religion and the Older Person* (Gainesville, Fla.: University of Florida Press, 1958), pp. 79 ff. Doctor Covalt claims that in twenty-five years of practice she can recall no patient who brought up religion as a subject, who asked for clergy help, or, when dying, who "called out to God or audibly prayed." Nor had her colleagues reported such experiences to her.

[12] Wendell M. Swenson, "Attitudes Toward Death in an Aged Population," *Journal of Gerontology*, 16 (1961), 51. This study is based on very few cases.

than it had been earlier, while one-third proclaimed it less helpful. [*See Vol. 1, Chap. 20.6.c, pp. 495–496.*] Moberg and Taves, studying a random sample of aged, noninstitutionalized Minnesotans, discovered "church leaders" (very active members) to have better personal adjustment (that is, greater satisfaction with various aspects of life) than did regular church members, and the latter were better adjusted than nonmembers.[13]

Such findings are not unusual; Gray and Moberg summarize numerous others.[14] But as they point out, the frequently observed relationship between religion and adjustment is very likely spurious.[15] It is probably not because such persons go to church or remain religiously active that they exhibit better adjustment. Rather, those who are better adjusted manifest that adjustment in the religious sphere as well as elsewhere. Thus, old people who are organizationally active are also more engaged in occupational and marital roles, informal visiting, Golden Age Clubs, and so forth. [*See Vol. 1, Chap. 21, pp. 501–510.*] Barron, therefore, concludes:

> Without doubt research exposes the shortcomings of religion as an effective geriatric force. Although . . . there are some indications of inner religiosity intensifying in later years, there is little change of interest in the church and synagogue with advancing age and *very little indication that organized religion has succeeded in helping most of the aged adjust to their personal and social situations.*[16]

Where does this state of affairs leave the church in the lives of old people? Shall we conclude that the church either has no special mission to old people or, more discouraging, has failed in that mission? One way of assessing such a question would be to ask what the elderly themselves expect of religion and the church and then to ask whether the "religious" needs of older people, as they themselves perceive them, are currently being satisfied. Research evidence on this point is almost totally lacking. Some suggestive clues are revealed, however, if we reason indirectly from certain aspects of the total situation of the aged in American society. We shall, therefore, in the next section dis-

---

[13] David O. Moberg and M. J. Taves, "Church Participation and Personal Adjustment to Old Age" (Paper presented at the Gerontological Society, Inc., Miami Beach, Fla., 1962).

[14] *Op. cit.*, 43–49.

[15] *Ibid.*, 53.

[16] Barron, *op. cit.*, 181. Italics added.

cuss in some detail the nature of one aspect of aging—decline in levels of activity—which is of special relevance to church policy.

Aging and disengagement

Of critical importance to an assessment of the religious situation and needs of old people in American society is a proper interpretation of the constriction of role behavior which apparently accompanies aging. [*See Vol. 1, Chap. 17, pp. 409–420.*] Unfortunately, much needed evidence is not in hand. Not only the lack of research evidence but the difficulties—of varying definitions, of cross-section versus life-cycle effects, of controls for spurious relationships—encountered in attempting to evaluate existing research findings necessarily impart a high degree of tentativeness to the discussion. Although we shall present a number of interpretative ideas which would seem to be consistent with the available research findings, such ideas are more properly regarded as hypotheses for subsequent investigation than as direct inferences from adequate evidence.

There can be little doubt that old people are in the process of relinquishing significant portions of their prior social worlds. Loss of occupation, of spouse, of old friends who have died, coupled with the infirmities and ill health often associated with old age, imply that old people typically must reduce or radically modify past activities. There is, however, ample room for debate concerning the nature of the change that takes place, change that has a number of implications for church policy regarding the aged.

Research indicates that the older person plays, on the average, fewer social roles, has fewer interpersonal contacts and exhibits a generally lower level of activity than younger persons. Scattered clues suggest a concomitant withdrawal on the psychological level. [*See Vol. 1, Chap. 12, pp. 275–287.*] Although older individuals are no more likely to report worries and insecurities, they are less likely than younger persons to express positive satisfaction with life. They are less likely to report expectations that important events will happen to them. They are more introverted, exhibit generally less affect. It is as though the lives of the aging "flatten out," becoming less dramatic, more benign. Thus it has been suggested that older people might be involved chiefly in what has been labeled "disengagement"—withdrawal from specific roles and from life generally. [*But see Vol. 1, Chap. 15, pp. 341–359.*]

One theological writer refers to the final stage of life, therefore, as one of "achieving simplification of life in its physical, material, and spiritual aspects, so that the soul may, with less and less impediment, progress toward its chosen destiny."[17] Psychologist Erik Erikson claims that the "crisis" during the last "age" of man is one of "ego integrity" versus "despair." Successful resolution of the crisis brings "renunciation and wisdom."[18] And Bernice Neugarten refers to *psychological* disengagement as "increased interiority of the personality," wherein, "with the change from active to passive modes of mastering the environment, there is also a movement of energy away from an outer-world to an inner-world orientation."[19]

Of crucial interest to those planning programs for the aged is whether disengagement is volitional; that is, do old people, given a choice, elect to abridge social ties? Does withdrawal result in greater happiness and adjustment? Or is disengagement an unwanted necessity, thrust upon the aged by the exigencies of their general situation?

Certainly the data in hand indicate that simple *in*activity offers few psychological blessings. For example, general satisfaction is greater among those still working than among the retired. Although individuals vary greatly in activity styles and adjustment, those with low levels of activity tend to be less satisfied with life, have more feelings of loneliness, uselessness, and loss of affection. [*See Vol. 1, Chap. 15, pp. 341–359.*]

Construed simply as a general tendency to withdraw, moreover, the disengagement notion would seem not entirely consistent with some of the empirical findings. It is not clear whether the finding of role diminution in old people reflects change over the life cycle or simply the relatively lower socioeconomic and health status of old people today. Some exploratory findings indicate that given individuals, as they age, tend to maintain a level of activity similar to their younger years. If, despite retirement and the increasing likelihood of conjugal and friendship loss, the elderly manage to maintain given levels of activity, the implication is that relinquishment of some past ties is compensated by other relationships and other kinds of contact with the environment. Thus old people apparently do not decrease participation in religious and political activities. [*See Vol. 1, Chap. 19, pp. 463–482.*] The fact that they do not exhibit a tendency to

[17] Lewis Joseph Sherrill, *The Struggle of the Soul* (New York: The Macmillan Company, 1958), 9.

[18] Erik H. Erikson, *Childhood and Society* (New York: W. W. Norton and Company, Inc., 1963), 268–269, 274.

[19] Bernice L. Neugarten, "Adult Personality: Toward a Psychology of the Life-Cycle" (Paper presented to the American Psychological Association, New York City, 1966), 6.

withdraw from *all* social activities suggests there may be a meaningful pattern to those they give up and those they retain.

Given the American value pattern, the connection between low levels of activity and dissatisfaction with life is not unexpected. Nonetheless, some individuals, given a choice, do elect to withdraw from some social activities, and these are more satisfied than those whose withdrawal is forced. Retirement, for example, offers to some individuals a welcome release from a disliked occupation. [*See Vol. 1, Chap. 18, pp. 421–462.*] Reduction of activity is less closely related to dissatisfaction than whether such reduction is seen as externally imposed. Perhaps, then, successful aging is contingent on a pattern of *selective* disengagement, on the opportunity to relinquish some kinds of activities and to retain others.

Cumming and Henry, the originators of disengagement theory, describe what they regard as the typical pattern of change:

> The reduction in interaction and the loss of central roles result in a shift in the quality of relationship in the remaining roles. . . . There is a wider choice of relational rewards, and a shift from vertical solidarities ("mutual dependence bonds") to horizontal ("bonds of similarity") ones.[20]

The shift from "vertical" to "horizontal" solidarities may be conceived more broadly as a change in emphasis from "instrumental" to "expressive" orientations. We propose that, given a choice, old people would tend to reduce activities that might be called instrumental—endeavors in which persons are expected to achieve, to produce, to withhold emotions, to restrict their range of obligations; but they would retain and seek out expressive relationships and activities—diffuse endeavors in which they can spontaneously "express" themselves, in which their actions are ends in themselves rather than instruments to the accomplishment of other ends. The roles of spouse, of grandparent, of neighbor, of friend are primarily expressive roles, and the aged wish to retain them. By contrast, the work role, the child-rearing role, many roles in voluntary organizations, are instrumental, and old people may be less reluctant to give up such roles.

Although the research evidence is scanty, scattered findings are highly suggestive of a desire on the part of the aged to turn from instrumental to expressive activities. [*See Vol. 1, Chap. 13, pp. 289–313; Chap. 14, pp. 315–339.*] For example, older individuals

---

[20] Elaine Cumming and William E. Henry, *Growing Old* (New York: Basic Books, Inc., 1961), 217. See also Elaine Cumming, "New Thoughts on the Theory of Disengagement," in Robert Kastenbaum (ed.), *New Thoughts on Old Age* (New York: Springer Publishing Co., 1964).

are less oriented to achievement, place less stress on capacity or performance, and give more emphasis to goodness and moral virtue than younger persons. Willingness to continue work beyond age 65 is more pronounced among individuals who stress the noneconomic meanings of their jobs. [*See Vol. 1, Chap. 18.B.3.f, p. 440.*] Among old men who continue voluntary association memberships, the retired are more likely than those still working to belong to sociable rather than occupationally oriented organizations. [*See Vol. 1, Chap. 21.3.c, p. 508.*] Those older individuals taking adult education courses are more likely than younger persons to say they enroll to become better informed rather than for job-related reasons. [*See Vol. 1, Chap. 22.5.b, pp. 526–527.*] And, given large amounts of leisure time, old people spend many hours visiting, watching television, reading, and gardening—all expressive activities for the most part. [*See Vol. 1, Chap. 22, pp. 511–535.*]

Such evidence is not decisive, especially since much of the research does not disentangle cross-section from life-cycle effects. A further difficulty of interpretation arises because most activities have *both* expressive and instrumental components, and it is not always easy to decide which aspects are sought out or stressed by participants. On balance, however, the data would seem consistent with the thesis that older people willingly give up their segmented, specific, task-oriented activity *if* they can retain their diffuse, integrative, socio-emotional activity.

Thus the premise of our remaining discussion is that the aged in American society confront the church as people who (assuming their subsistence needs are met) are more concerned with "being" than with "doing," more interested in being wanted than being useful, more expressive than instrumental. As a surrogate family or point of community, the church remains a factor in their lives; as an agency of instrumental achievement, it declines in importance. To use the title of a recent monograph on parishioner attitudes, old people especially expect the church "to comfort" rather than "to challenge."[21]

In his Long Beach study of 606 elderly persons, for example, Charles McCann found that, when asked what more the church could be doing for them, they put home visitations at the top of the list.[22] A survey of a Catholic parish in St. Louis found exactly the same first

[21] Charles Y. Glock, B. B. Ringer, and Earl R. Babbie, *To Comfort and to Challenge* (Berkeley: University of California Press, 1967).
[22] Charles W. McCann, *Long Beach Senior Citizens Survey* (Long Beach, Calif.: Long Beach Community Welfare Council, 1955), 53.

choice among its aged.[23] A less prosaic and more poignant expression of this attitude is seen in the comments of a dying patient to a hospital psychiatrist:

I was dumbfounded to find that when I requested a chaplain in the middle of the night there was no night chaplain. I mean, this is just unbelievable to me. Because, when does a man need a chaplain? Only at night, believe me. That's the time when you get down with those boxing gloves and have it out with yourself. . . . When does a man need a minister? He needs him about three o'clock, ordinarily.[24]

It is being suggested, then, that in contrast to younger people, who may maintain a variety of orientations toward religion and the church, the aged tend to narrow their religious outlook. Disengaging not in the sense of withdrawing from church but in the sense of bringing simplified expectations to it, they seek from the church a feeling of anchorage, of community, of neighborhood and "location" in their religious activity. Older people, we are asserting, expect the church to be expressive, not instrumental.

Before we turn to a discussion of church practices in relation to such expectations, one more aspect of aging in society needs to be set in context. The secular trends in America of greater industrialization, urbanization, bureaucratization—what has been called increased differentiation—may operate with special impact on old people, who face both increasing differentiation and role loss. Thus, old people in large cities are less likely than those in areas of smaller population to know many families, have most of their friends in the neighborhood, visit with younger neighbors, or have someone stop by regularly. [See Vol. 1, Chap. 6.A.3, pp. 125–128.] The exceptions occur where the elderly are concentrated, as where there are old people's homes or where neighborhoods are deserted by younger cohorts, leaving behind the oldsters. Aged persons in cities are increasingly differentiated *by age*, and their needs are increasingly met by *specialized* services— for example, old people's homes, geriatric hospital wings, retirement communities, Golden Age Clubs—rather than through social structures serving other age groups as well.

Highly differentiated structures, in which social interaction tends to be segmented and impersonal, present a number of barriers to the

[23] Catholic Charities of St. Louis, *Older People in the Family, the Parish and the Neighborhood* (St. Louis: Catholic Churches of St. Louis, 1955), 10.
[24] Elizabeth Ross, "The Dying Patient as Teacher," *The Chicago Theological Seminary Register*, 57 (1966), 13.

development and maintenance of expressive relationships. It may well be one of history's greater ironies that, at the same time society becomes more differentiated, it produces larger proportions of aged persons whose needs appear to be for less differentiation. As an institution in society, the church, too, is subject to trends of increasing differentiation. This fact may, on the one hand, greatly complicate its task of meeting the expressive needs of its parishioners; on the other, used strategically, increased differentiation may facilitate an enlightened ministry to the aged. We pursue that strategy, following a discussion of present church programs for the elderly.

Churches and older people

What, then, is the view churches have of old people? How do they minister to the elderly? Since billboards urging Americans to "worship this week" so frequently picture young married couples and their children, it might be assumed that old people are not very visible to churchmen. That assumption, however, would not be accurate; the range of services performed by churches for the aged is enormous.[25] It has even been estimated that as much as one-third of a minister's counseling and pastoral calling time is spent with old people.[26] If clergymen continue to feel special responsibility for the sick and the dying, and if illness and death continue their trend toward localization in the elderly, the estimate of one-third can probably be pushed upward.

Unfortunately, no systematic data are known to this writer which indicate how clergymen feel about the elderly, and inference yields contradictory answers. On the one hand, clergy probably are more comfortable with parishioners their own age and those younger, especially in a counseling situation.[27] By this reasoning, only "old" ministers may enjoy their contacts with the aged. Correlatively, in a society

[25] Good recent descriptions of these services are found in E. T. Culver, *New Church Programs with the Aging* (New York: Association Press, 1961); White House Conference on Aging, 1961, *Background Paper on Services of Religious Groups for the Aging* (Washington, D.C.: Government Printing Office, November, 1960); Paul B. Maves, "Aging, Religion, and the Church," in Clark Tibbitts (ed.), *Handbook of Social Gerontology* (Chicago: University of Chicago Press, 1960), 714–720; Margaret Frakes, "The Church and Older People," *Christian Century*, 72 (1955), series beginning 1201–1204. A portrait of a local parish's services is found in H. Lee Jacobs, *Churches and Their Senior Citizens* (Iowa City: University of Iowa Press, 1957).

[26] P. B. Maves and J. L. Cedarleaf, *Older People and the Church* (Nashville: Abingdon Press, 1949).

[27] See Robert E. Mitchell, *Minister-Parishioner Relations* (Report of the Bureau of Applied Social Research, Columbia University, New York, 1962), esp. Chap. IX.

where youth and young adulthood are exalted, clergymen, too, may prefer to be in touch with the young, the active, the vital. Ministering to parishioners who are old, then, might be regarded as an unpleasant necessity.

On the other hand, it is quite clear from a number of investigations that ministers enjoy personal calling and counseling, and research indicates that the least amount of minister-parishioner conflict arises from such contexts.[28] If most ministerial contact with the elderly *is* personal calling and counseling, then it could well be that such contact is, in fact, enjoyable. Actually, this conclusion has some basis in theory when one considers the defining characteristics of most minister-parishioner interaction. From the clergyman's point of view, there is generally "business" to transact: persuading a person to take on a committee assignment, or to increase his financial pledge, or to alter his civil rights opinion, for example. But where such business may burden many parish calls, those with elderly parishioners are not as likely to be so burdened. The sense of being involved with people over crucial issues may be missing from contacts with the elderly, it is true, and that absence may take away from the enjoyment of the contact. But the disadvantage brings an advantage also; without business to transact, there is less chance of failure and more room for pleasure.[29]

The fact is, of course, no one knows which of these two contradictory views is the more accurate portrayal of contemporary clergy's orientation toward old people. Parishioners might be assumed to have attitudes toward old people which are roughly parallel with the attitudes of all adults—in or out of the church—but their attitudes are distilled from relationships in economic, neighborhood, and family spheres as well as in the religious sphere. The minister, too, may have one set of attitudes toward the old persons in his own family, but toward the elderly in his congregation, with whom he interacts as clergyman, he very likely has a different set. Without question, the range of ministerial attitudes extends from great dislike of old people

[28] For the second of these points, evidence is available for Protestants only. See *ibid.*, IV–7, IX–7.

[29] Suppose, for example, that churches regularly counted on bequests from most or all dying parishioners. The *nature* of ministerial contacts with older people, we are saying, would be different. In a fascinating, though inadequately documented, paper, Luke M. Smith argues a similar point—that Congregational clergymen are less likely than Episcopal clergymen to have close friendships with parishioners. Episcopalian theology defines a clergyman's priestly, sacramental duties as paramount, whereas the Congregational minister must regard *all* of his contacts with parishioners as "utilitarian." See Luke M. Smith, "The Clergy: Authority Structure, Ideology, Migration," *American Sociological Review*, 18 (1953), 242–248.

and their problems to great affection for and delight in contacts with the elderly. What is not known is the distribution of attitudes along this range.

To some significant degree, however, attitudes of the clergy are only minimally important to churches' programs for the aged. Given their value premises, churches are committed to helping the elderly, and what they do is but a matter of awareness and resources. No doubt a minister whose personal view of the aged is negative will do less for them in his ministry than will his colleague whose personal view is positive. But sociological analysis would argue that factors other than personal orientation are probably far more important. Thus, churches with more resources will do more for older people than will churches with fewer resources. And churches in the inner city with older congregations will do more than surburban churches serving mainly young families. From an array of possible programs, a church will choose those ministries to old people which reflect its level of awareness, amount of resources, and the priority given to the aged relative to other groupings. What are some of those programs, and on what basis will choices be made?

As variegated a list as will be found is contained in the Background Paper, "Services of Religious Groups for the Aging," White House Conference on Aging, 1961. Classified by the type of problem they confront, these programs are cited here in part:

Income and Employment
1. Use of old people for paid part-time jobs in the church.
2. Formal contacts with state employment services.
3. Retirement counseling.
4. Counseling on investment, taxes, wills, budgets, applications for assistance.

Health, Medical Care, Rehabilitation
1. "Library" of sickroom equipment to lend.
2. Counseling on choice of hospitals, doctors, nursing homes, funeral arrangements.
3. Visiting of the elderly ill.
4. Sponsorship of hospitals and nursing homes.
5. Chaplaincy services within hospitals.

Housing
1. Sponsorship of homes for the aged.

Education
1. Library of books relevant to aging.
2. Preretirement classes or forums on aging.
3. Bible classes for the elderly.

Free Time, Recreation
1. "Golden Age Clubs."
2. Care of church gardens.
3. Sale and exhibition of handwork and hobbies.

Religion
1. Pastoral counseling.
2. Facilitating participation in religious services by, for example, earphones, transportation service, and tape recordings.

Confronted by this or a similar list, a church will of course choose not at random but only after asking some questions.[30] Since the effect will be to eliminate some programs, such question-asking amounts to a placing of value on each alternative. The questions, therefore, might be as follows:

1. Is this program commensurate with a church's tradition and theology? Some denominations, for example, do not regard the church building as an appropriate place for "recreation." Golden Age Clubs, therefore, might rank so far down on the list as to be not considered at all. Similarly, counseling on investments may be prohibited among those for whom the stock market is a sinful use of money. Less precise, but no less binding perhaps, is the tradition that places such emphasis on familism that any attempt by the church to usurp the family's responsibility for caring for its elderly would be proscribed. Quite probably in contemporary America, however, strict *theological* prohibitions on any of the above activities would be relatively rare. More likely, some programs would be eliminated on remaining grounds.

2. How effectively can the church conduct a given program? Most churches, for example, have job openings for very few persons other than the full-time clergyman. As worthy as the part-time employment of old people may be, many churches may decide that their resources can better be spent in bringing more old people into contact with jobs *outside* the church. Correlatively, maintenance of an adequate supply of sickroom articles for loan may unduly tax the budget of an average church, especially as it includes more than crutches and bedpans. Clearly, an orthopedic bed is a more important item from the standpoint of the old person needing one, yet the capital outlay and storage facilities necessary probably make such an item unfeasible as part of a *church* program. But this example suggests the importance of the third question.

3. How effective is the church relative to other agencies in conducting a given program? Presumably any program for the aged can be ranked along a continuum from those activities which *only* churches do to those

[30] Perhaps the logical first question is whether the list exhausts the possibilities, whether other programs might be added for consideration. We shall assume here, however, that the realistic alternatives could be fully listed.

activities which *other* agencies do also. The *effectiveness* or, to use an economic term, the "marginal utility" of a particular church program for the elderly will thus be assessed in the context of the church's peculiarity in pursuing it. For example, only the church can supply tape recordings of its worship services to shut-ins; regardless of the quality of the recording or the availability of other tape recordings, therefore, the church is likely to place high value on this activity. Bible classes or pastoral counseling are other programs that might be regarded as "peculiarly" religious and therefore not undertaken except by churches. Contrarily, sponsorship of hospitals, nursing homes, or homes for the aged, though in some instances pioneered by churches, is not uniquely a church activity in the present day.

These three questions would seem to underlie Maves' recommendation that the church's task vis-à-vis older people is twofold: (1) doing those things which it is "uniquely fitted to do," and (2) doing those things which need doing because no one else is or because it is in a better position to do them.[31] Few problems are likely to arise over the "uniquely religious" activities; the marginal utility of installing hearing aids in pews or railings on front steps, of providing radio broadcasts of worship services or rides to church for those who do not drive, and of offering worship and pastoral calling to the elderly is no doubt such that they will readily be done if resources are available. Similarly, at the other end of the continuum there are probably few difficulties, once the church has evaluated its relative effectiveness. Marginal utility for the church declines for those activities which nonchurch agencies do as well or better. Thus, fewer than one-fourth of all older persons living in institutions live in church-sponsored homes [*see Vol. 1, Chap. 6.B.7, pp. 141–142*], and in the years since World War II the proportion of institutions for the aged which are religiously sponsored has been declining.[32] Max Feder cites the National Directory of Housing for Older People for his statement that, "As of January, 1965, 292 church-sponsored housing projects have been completed, with 53 more such developments in the blueprint stage."[33] But even though this number seems large, it is easily surpassed by secular developments.

[31] P. B. Maves, "The Church in Community Planning for the Aged," *Pastoral Psychology*, 5 (1954), 13.

[32] Cf. the 1939 figures cited in Maves and Cedarleaf, *op. cit.*, 251, with those in Samuel W. Blizzard, "Expanding the Role of Organized Religion to the Aged," in D. L. Scudder (ed.), *Organized Religion and the Older Person* (Gainesville, Fla.: University of Florida Press, 1958), 95.

[33] Max Feder, *The Senior Citizens Program in Our Temples*, Synagogue Research, Survey No. 8 (New York: Union of American Hebrew Congregations, 1966), 14. The housing here refers to low- and middle-income retirement communities and apartments.

It is the area between the extremes where policy decision-making agonizingly arises, especially in local parishes. Shall churches give over their resources to Golden Age Clubs? Should another clergyman be hired so that more pastoral counseling can be provided? And to what extent should the church serve as therapeutic counselor for anxious old people, as provider of welfare services, as mediator between older people and secular community agencies? These are not questions easily answered, for, though the values implicit are ones the church readily acknowledges, to allocate resources in these directions is to forgo other values toward which resources might be directed.

One major resource to be included in churches' consideration of their ministry to the elderly is their location and physical plant. With the exception of elementary schools, no other agency in society has followed the neighborhood ecological pattern as closely as have churches. It is a rare community where one or more church buildings are not in the immediate vicinity of every resident. Built generally to include meeting rooms, office space, cooking facilities, and so forth, churches are peculiarly situated to focus on neighborhoods, as well as on congregations of like believers or fellow worshipers.

But despite a neighborhood location and a set of values that clearly support a ministry to the aged, churches have not received notably helpful directives and recommendations. Goals have been clarified,[34] and sources such as those mentioned above have *exemplified* programs that might be carried out. But no particular rationale or organizational philosophy justifies an unambiguous allocation of a church's resources, especially for choosing among alternatives between the extremes. The consequence, as Maves points out, is that "Local churches generally assume that their regular religious services of worship are open to persons of all ages. . . . In this sense they would feel that they are ministering to the aged. . . . [But] it is doubtful if many local churches have gone very far in adapting their programs to the needs of older people."[35]

This is not to deny that change in churches has occurred. The training in counseling which seminaries now give is a significant change with ramifications for ministering to the aged.[36] And some-

---

[34] For example, in the White House Conference on Aging, *Background Paper on Religion and Aging* (Washington, D.C.: Government Printing Office, March, 1960) 13; Barron, *op. cit.*, 166; Maves and Cedarleaf, *op. cit.*, 75–80; Culver, *op. cit.*, 7–20.

[35] Maves, "Aging, Religion, and the Church," 721.

[36] H. Richard Niebuhr, D. D. Williams, and J. Gustafson, *The Advancement of Theological Education* (New York: Harper & Row, Publishers, 1957), 122, refer

thing of a norm seems to have emerged to the effect that "oldsters should not be singled out" but should instead be integrated as much as possible into the parish body comprised of all ages.[37] Maves and Cedarleaf recommend a two-step diagnosis in developing a ministry to the elderly: discovering first the constituency (for example, how many aged in the parish, where, and whether members of a church), and second, determining their patterns of association, their interests, and so forth.[38] Jacobs, moreover, urges that "every congregation" institute a religious education for older persons *beginning with the fortieth year.*[39]

What is missing in such recommendations, of course, is a precise rationale. *What* patterns of association and interests are to be learned, and what is to be done with such knowledge? What is to be the *content* of a religious education that anticipates old age? Persons making the suggestions are not unaware of the gap, but until a rationale is forthcoming, probably any church program for the aged remains "experimental" or, at least, qualifying as a "good thing," unassailable in the abstract but perhaps not the best expenditure of time, effort, and money.

The problem, however, is not unique to the church's stance vis-à-vis older persons; it pervades ecclesiastical strategy. The remaining pages of this essay, therefore, are an attempt both to explicate the general problems of strategy and to suggest how a rationale for "aging and the ministry" may emerge.

An analysis of ecclesiastical strategy

In 1844, Theodore Parker preached "A Sermon of Old Age" at the Music Hall, Boston. He was only 34 at the time but already a renowned preacher and author. What he said—and did not say—about old age is instructive today.[40]

---

to this change as "one of the most influential movements in theological education." A cursory look at a random selection of Protestant seminary catalogues reveals that virtually all now include clinical training in hospitals or other institutional settings. Over 40 per cent offer courses in personality development and 25 per cent offer either a course on aging or include aging as one focus in a course on developmental problems.

[37] Jacobs, *op. cit.*, 6; Feder, *op. cit.*, 12; E. B. Jackson, "Religion, Psychiatry, and the Geriatric Patient," *Mental Hospitals*, 11 (1960), 15.

[38] *Op. cit.*, 164–165.

[39] *Op. cit.*, 17–18.

[40] The quotations and paraphrase to follow are from a pamphlet published by The Fraternity, Boston (1859), and sold by H. W. Swett and Co.

Life is likened to an apple that ripens, sweetens, and then reddens without getting bigger.

Such is the natural process . . . the same divine law is appropriate for every kind of animal. [The old person] thinks the old is better. [He] loves to recall the old times, to revive his favorite old men. . . . The pleasure of hope is smaller; that of memory greater. . . . His affections now are greater than before; yet it is not the mere power of instinctive affection—the connubial instinct which loves a mate, or the parental instinct which loves a child; but a general human, reflective, volitional love, not sharpened by animal desire, not narrowed by affiliated bounds, but coming of his freedom, not his bondage. . . . His religion is deeper, more inward than before. It is not doctrine alone, nor mere form. There is little rapture. . . . His religion is love of God; faith and trust in Him; rest, tranquility, peace for his soul.

[However] the man reaps in his old age as he sowed in his youth and manhood. He ripens what he grew. . . . Here is an old man who loved nothing but money. . . . There is no want so squalid, no misery of poverty so desperate, as the consciousness of an old miser in his old age of covetousness. Pass him by. . . . Here is a woman who has sought chiefly the admiration of the world, the praise of men. . . . Now the audience is tired of her, and laughs at the hollow voice, the bleary eye, the spindle limbs. The curtain falls; the farce is at an end. Poor old butterfly!

The sermon combines, then, a rather sophisticated developmental view of life, an awareness of socially structured differences among people, an almost cavalier disregard for the woes of old age, and, by default, the assumption that the church can preach, can admonish, but need not look out for the welfare of those who lived unwisely. "They ripen what they grew." A disengagement theory—the view that old people selectively withdraw from social life, leaving their instrumental activities but retaining, indeed sharpening, their emotional connections with others—that theory, one surmises, would be very congenial to Theodore Parker. But beyond warning people that "such is the natural process," the church has no obligation. There is no conception of the church as a multifaceted agency, doing some things uniquely and some things that other agencies also do. There is no implicit model of the ministry as existing at national and regional levels and in specialized forms as well as in local parish structures.

Now much of this conception has changed. When the church's ministry to the aged (or to any "problem") is discussed, there is implicit at least the idea that the ministry is more than local parishes. Church bodies at regional and national levels issue statements, carry out research, invest huge sums of money, exert political pressure, and conduct information campaigns. Specialized ministries, with no connection to local parishes other than a financial one, are found in higher education, city slums, hospitals, developing nations, and, of course, in old people's homes. Church strategy for dealing with the aging, therefore, must be set in a context quite different from the context in which Parker preached his sermon.

For example, given the demographic, ecological, and cultural trends whereby older people became increasingly delimited socially, specialized ministries to retirement communities, inner-city parishes, and geriatric hospitals may well increase. Such ministries, however, will reflect the "ministry" of usual parish churches only in the sense that overseas missions do now. Similarly, when the "church" undertakes support of a medical-aid-for-the-aged bill or tries to expand the coverage of social security, local congregations are involved more as aggregations of individual citizens than as corporate bodies.[41]

Therefore, although the "social issue" of aging is far less controversial for churches than, say, war, poverty, civil rights, or criminal rehabilitation, questions remain. Despite the frequency with which they are given lists of goals with respect to aging, ministers do not have to be urged to "help old people confront loss as loss," to "help maintain dignity in our senior citizens," or to "make the latter years of earthly life a time of fulfillment." The questions are *how* to achieve those goals, through *what* social structures, and by *whom*.

An answer, with some logical connection to the preceding pages, begins to emerge with consideration of the following chart:

IMPLIED ORIENTATION TOWARD ACTIVITY:

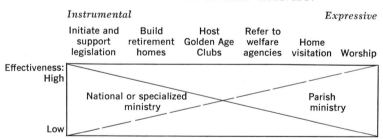

[41] See, for example, Phillip E. Hammond and Robert E. Mitchell, "The Segmentation of Radicalism—The Case of the Protestant Campus Minister." *American Journal of Sociology*, 71 (1965), 133–143, for a discussion of how one specialized ministry, apart from its success in achieving stated goals, influences the larger church organization. The general point is discussed in N. J. Demerath, III, and Phillip E. Hammond, *Religion in Social Context: Tradition and Transition* (New York: Random House, Inc., 1969), Chap. 6.

Across the top of the chart are listed examples of programs for older persons which churches have undertaken or might undertake. As the additional designation indicates, these activities differ in terms of the implied orientation, ranging from the segmented, specific, affectively neutral, instrumental orientations required for legislation to the more diffuse, integrative, socio-emotional, expressive orientations implied in the worship service. To use other examples, when churches build retirement homes (or old people's homes, or geriatric hospitals) the accumulation of capital, arrangements for financing, construction, and managing, and decisions on admission and maintenance require calculation, criteria of success, and a general "hard headedness." But a program of "friendly visitation" or pastoral calling requires almost the opposite orientation—the noncalculating, accepting warmth connoted by the term "expressive."[42]

The chart contains one other assertion which needs to be added: The more instrumental the orientations required by the activity, the more effectively can it be carried out by a regional, national, or specialized ministry; but the more expressive the orientations required, the more effectively can the activity be carried out by a local parish ministry.

Consider now the following statement in the context of the theory implied in the chart:

It is the prophetic business of the church to stand up for human rights. . . . The present concern about aging offers the church one more opportunity to stand in the community as a witness to one basic tenet of both Christianity and democracy—the essential worth of every individual, as a *person*.[43]

It would be difficult to argue *against* such a view, but it can be maintained that to the extent the church effectively "stands up" for human rights, it does so with instrumental methods which do not treat in-

---

[42] It is important once again to realize that the distinction between "instrumental" and "expressive" is an analytic one, that is, there is always the assumption of instrumental for *what* or expressive of *what*. Thus, the clergyman *conducting* worship may view his role as instrumental for the achievement of ecstacy by worshipers, while *their* orientation is expressive of the desire to be in touch with the divine. Similarly, the erstwhile instrumental act of buliding a hospital, with criteria of success, progress, and final operation, could "express" one's motivation to create monuments. The choirmaster obviously plays an instrumental role in providing music which enhances the expressive worship, just as the ribbon-cutting ceremony "expresses" celebration that a building project is completed. Nevertheless, most activities can be classified by the degree of instrumental-expressive balance that is expected of most participants, and it is this classification that is implied here.

[43] Culver, *op. cit.*, 92. Italics in the original.

dividuals as "persons" but as political objects. Insofar as the church treats individuals as persons it does so locally, in face to face contact, through the parish.

A hypothesis presented earlier should now be recalled—that older people selectively disengage, retaining their involvement in the church as an expressive agency but withdrawing their involvement in it as an instrumental agency. Old people, we said, expect the church especially to comfort, not to challenge.

Assuming the correctness of the statements illustrated by the chart, and of the assertion regarding older people's selective disengagement, we can conclude that, as seen by the aged themselves, *the ministry is largely a ministry of the local parish.* Such a conclusion does not deny older people's interest in legislation regarding their welfare or their concern for retirement housing, but it does assert that such concerns are less than the comparable concerns of persons not yet old. And it does assert that the aged, even though churches provide them with "instrumentalities," will nevertheless regard the church as failing unless it also provides them with "moral support." The conclusion suggests, as another example, that older people will more readily participate in Golden Age Clubs than they will organize them or arrange for their location, staffing, and financing. And the conclusion certainly suggests that, when asked "What is the church?", older people will more likely answer that it is the agency where they worship and which visits them at home.

The report from St. Philip Neri Roman Catholic parish in St. Louis conveys this orientation:

> What stands out more clearly than anything else [during periods of illness in elderly parishioners] is the support they received from their children, their relatives, their church, and their neighbors. We are not stressing solely the question of financial support. The support that they looked for mostly was moral support.
>
> This service . . . called for no machinery, no reports, no statistics. Many people have asked us what can be done to extend this personal service without institutionalizing [sic; read "bureaucratizing"] it. This is the eternal question. . . . One thing is sure, they cannot promote it by some of our present highly specialized and mechanized methods.[44]

The fact is, of course, the church's ministry has *had* to bureaucratize or use "specialized and mechanized methods" in order to achieve many of its goals—both instrumental and expressive—in-

[44] Catholic Charities of St. Louis, *op. cit.,* 4, 8. See also H. J. Wershow, "The Older Jews of Albany Park," *The Gerontologist,* 4 (1964), 198–202.

cluding goals furthering the welfare of the aged.[45] But as far as the elderly are concerned, the church chiefly provides "moral support," an expressive act of local parishes. The distinction, though analytically clear, is frequently obscured in empirical reality. Sudnow describes the activity of a Catholic chaplain in "County" hospital:

> His main responsibility, it seems, is administering last rites. Each morning . . . at each ward, he consults a master schedule . . . containing patient's names, religion, sex, and diagnosis. All patients who have been posted [to die] are identified with a red plastic border . . . placed on their cards. The chaplain . . . enters these patients' rooms and administers extreme unction. After completing his round on each ward, he stamps the index card of the patient. . . . His stamp serves to prevent him from performing the rites twice on the same patient.[46]

The impersonality of such action is no doubt shocking to the behind-the-scenes observer. At the same time, the chaplain-specialist's task *is* facilitated. The critical question in assessing his effectiveness is how the activity is presented to and interpreted by the aged individual.

The "social gospel" or welfare orientation of ministers has had its critics and defenders from the beginning. In this day, Fichter suggests that all the nonsacerdotal things the parish priest does may cause him to wonder if his "spiritual" function is being neglected.[47] Contrarily, Fairchild and Wynn ask:

> Is it possible . . . that the constriction of the pastor's interest to family living in the parish has led to an overdevelopment of his "priestly" and "pastoral" roles, wherein he becomes a "father" instead of a "prophet" in his ministry?[48]

But what is not seen, and therefore not questioned, is whether the church might do both these things though segmentally, some at regional or national (and perhaps ecumenical) levels, others at local parish levels. Some, being instrumental tasks, require the impersonality of formal association; others, being expressive tasks, require instead the informal, personal contact.

---

[45] For example, of nearly a hundred news releases from the Housing and Urban Development Agency announcing church-sponsored retirement homes, fewer than one-third indicated sponsorship by a local church, and most of those created separate administrative corporations. The majority were sponsored by regional or interdenominational groups.

[46] David Sudnow, *Passing On* (Englewood Cliffs, N.J.: Prentice-Hall, Inc., 1967), 73.

[47] Joseph H. Fichter, *Religion as an Occupation* (Notre Dame, Ind.: University of Notre Dame Press, 1961), 142–145.

[48] R. W. Fairchild and J. C. Wynn, *Families in the Church: A Protestant Survey* (New York: Association Press, 1961), 17.

It is not difficult, if the foregoing analysis is correct, to locate the desires of older people on this question: They want and "need" the personal contact. Presbyterian parishioners ranked as most helpful about their churches the "sermons and congregational worship" and next the "personal friendships within the congregation." But all together, the investigators conclude, the chief desire is for the church to provide "meaningful relationships, especially involving the whole family."[49] Psychiatrist E. B. Jackson warns clergymen that "the older people become, the more they need explanation, support, encouragement and appreciation."[50] And Newman Biller asserts, "First and foremost, the Synagogue can become a concrete symbol of the idea that life is a continuity; it is a symbol that has existed in the hearts and souls of Jewish people for thousands of years."[51] For all parishioners, perhaps, but certainly for older people, the church is a symbol of "community," of intimacy. It is, in their view, an expressive, not an instrumental, agency.

Should such a point of view not be obvious? One would expect the ministry, say Gray and Moberg, "to emphasize primarily spiritual needs of senior citizens, yet [in] most official publications of major Protestant denominations . . . a 'social-service orientation' is more pronounced than the 'personal religious-experience orientation.' "[52] The church, understandably, finds training and admonishing its ministers to *do* things easier than helping them *be* things. Clearly it is erroneous to assume from this discussion that the older person has *no* interest in what has been termed instrumental activity. Obviously matters of housing, income, and health are major concerns. The question we are raising, then, is not *whether society* need attend to such concerns but *how* the *church* can reasonably share in those concerns. And, more importantly, we are raising the correlative issue of which agencies of the church can best meet which needs of the aged.

It would appear that churches, through their supra-parochial channels, are addressing many of the instrumental needs of America's elderly. They sponsor hospitals and build retirement communities; they support appropriate national legislation and initiate information campaigns. *But the strategic question is a question of its aims for the local parish*—whether the local parish should continue to be the major channel through which the church's programs (instrumental and

---

[49] *Ibid.*, 198, but see all of Chap. 6.
[50] *Op. cit.*, 14–15.
[51] Newman M. Biller, "The Role of the Synagogue in Work with Old People," *Jewish Social Science Quarterly*, 28 (1952), 287–288.
[52] *Op. cit.*, 48.

expressive alike) flow, or whether regional, national, and specialized channels will increasingly be given the instrumental tasks, leaving the parish structure chiefly to discharge the expressive tasks. It might accurately be said that regional, national, and specialized channels *are* on the increase.[53] But it is by no means clear that local parishes are performing their role as intimate centers of "community." Moreover, in the context of a differentiating society, it is not clear just how local church organizations can do so. One thing might be pointed out, however, as an Episcopal report perceptively notes:

> Mass living, with its resultant loss of personal relationships, is one of the most important factors which the churches face. . . . The growth of multiple organizations and units within the congregation has been a response to these needs. *There is a dichotomy, however, between the growth of these organizations which are usually based on age or sex groupings and the drive to minister to the whole family in its new consciousness of unity.*[54]

Granting the viability of a strategy which calls for local parishes to maximize their "community" function, then,[55] certain implications for the church and ministry become clearer. The day is no doubt passed when the parish can be the office of vital statistics for its neighborhood, but some of the following may be functional equivalents.[56]

Implementing the strategy

It was pointed out above that most local parishes share with elementary schools the pattern of following *neighborhood* lines. This fact might, therefore, underlie most local churches' ministry to the aged. They already exist as buildings, for example, and frequently they have a sizable clientele of old people already available. Moreover, churches, however new their physical plants, are established agencies

---

[53] As one example, see Donald B. Meyer, *The Protestant Search for Political Realism, 1919–1941* (Berkeley: University of California Press, 1960).

[54] National Council of the Episcopal Church, "The Family in the United States" (Report prepared for the Lambeth Conference Deliberations on the Family in Contemporary Society, 1958), 14. Italics added.

[55] Lest there be misunderstanding, we repeat what has been implicit before: This is not a conservative call for the church to "stick to religion and keep out of politics." It is rather an acknowledgment that religio-political affairs are most effectively conducted by church agencies other than local parishes, and a further acknowledgment that: (a) people in fractionated society need centers of community, and (b) local parishes may provide such centers. Moreover, if this is true of people in general, it is truer yet of old people.

[56] No claim is made for the originality of these suggestions. Rather, given the rationale, these suggestions seem to follow. See n. 25, above, for sources describing many church activities for old people.

in society; most people know of them, trust them, and are aware of how to behave in them. Timidity and confusion, which may characterize the feelings of the elderly about new agencies, are less likely to arise around churches.

Perhaps the first step a local church should take, therefore, is to determine the number and location of old people in its purview. Not only will the parish then know better how *it* can operate, but also information on housing and health needs can be transmitted to regional, ecumenical, or specialized church agencies.[57] On the basis of such knowledge, a number of "community" or expressive functions might be deemed worthwhile.

For example, given their locations, churches are logical places for hosting Golden Age or Senior Citizens Clubs. [*See the description supplied by Madge, Chap. 8 in this volume.*] To maximize the expressive function for the neighborhood, however, membership in the club cannot be contingent on membership in a specific church; "religious" activities (narrowly defined) must take place at other times.[58] Much self-direction of such clubs by the elderly themselves probably cannot be expected since their aim in participating is largely sociability, not some goal (such as economic gain) for which the club is a means. The church should recognize, therefore, that the instrumental tasks of leadership may have to be met by others.

An analogous program to which local churches can commit themselves is that of hosting adult education courses. Many church buildings are utilized throughout the week, but many are not. As discussed elsewhere in this volume, continuing education through city school systems and university extension divisions is an expanding endeavor. [*See Eklund, Chap. 11, pp. 342–343 in this volume, and Chap. 5, pp. 111–120 in Vol. 1.*] For the older person to benefit maximally, neighborhood sites must be available, and churches can usefully minister in this way.

Whether through a club organization, or more likely through the ministerial office, the church is often nicely situated to direct old people to welfare agencies and services available to them. There would seem to be no excuse for a minister's failing to know the range and limits of such agencies; an important part of his ministry to the elderly can be a referral system. [*See the discussions by Morris and by Schwartz, Chaps. 2 and 4 in this volume.*]

[57] For local parishes to accent an expressive ministry, in other words, does not absolve them from involvement in the instrumental activity of other church agencies.

[58] Frakes, *op. cit.*, 1329.

Separation of the elderly in the church, many observers agree, can go too far. Parishes large enough to sustain religious education or study classes for older persons are put in a dilemma, therefore, because large size calls for dissection, and age-grading is a standard dissecting technique used in churches as well as elsewhere. The use of "family nights," or potluck suppers, and family observance of holidays in the church have been suggested as multigenerational devices, but it is significant that these activities, too, are socio-emotional. In activities where educational background, occupational interrelationships, or other instrumental characteristics intrude, age-grading appears to remain important.

The minister can play a role of intermediary between generations, however. "The filial responsibility for the care of parents has become so ingrained in Jewish family life," says Newman Biller, "that even today many Jews have a sense of guilt, if not shame, when they are compelled to place a parent in a home for the aged."[59] And though Jews, Catholics, and Protestants are known to differ with respect to this norm of "filial responsibility,"[60] nevertheless the process of aging in modern society may well bring emotional strains between generations for which the ministry can be a help.

Certainly programs of "friendly visiting,"[61] whereby members of a congregation regularly call on the homes of older persons, are commensurate with the strategy identified here. So too, of course, is the increasing conception of the minister as a counselor, a trend which not only is seen in seminary education but also conforms to elderly parishioners' wants. [*See Vol. 1, Chap. 14.3.b and 14.6.e, pp. 327, 337.*] The titles of "father," "rabbi," and "pastor" connote guidance and advice; old people especially would have the ministry maximize this aspect of its work.

One area of gerontological counseling, the increase of which shows no signs of leveling off, is that of dying patients in hospitals. [*Cf. the discussions by Lasagna and by Schwartz, Chaps. 3 and 4 in this volume.*] We observed earlier that death is becoming increasingly "age-specific," occurring more and more among the aged, and more such deaths occur in hospitals. Thus, the ministerial time with death preparation increases as more individual deaths can be anticipated and as they take place under medical supervision. Glaser and Strauss imply, from their research into the matter, that ministers, chaplains,

[59] Biller, *op. cit.*, 285.
[60] Robert M. Dinkel, "Attitudes of Children Toward Supporting Aged Parents," *American Sociological Review*, 9 (1944), 71–83.
[61] Frakes, *op. cit.*, 1234.

nuns, etc., are not only very evident in "terminal" cases, but also their presence is very useful for doctors and nurses as well as for patients and their families.

A chaplain whom we observed derived great satisfaction . . . from his ability to converse with dying patients about their oncoming deaths as well as about their postdeath affairs. His satisfaction is highly instructive for two reasons. He could respond to patients' invitations to talk and, indeed, draw them into conversation better than could the nursing and medical personnel. And he was wonderfully able to wed his professional standards, with their emphasis on giving spiritual and psychological comfort rather than medical care, with his sense of the humane—of what was a proper human death.[62]

Related to the counseling of the dying person is the changed task of ministering to the survivors. Blauner estimates that, unlike citizens of yesterday, Americans today attend only one or two funerals a decade through their middle-age.[63] Death, then, though less wrenching for society, since it more often occurs among the elderly, can be more wrenching for the "inexperienced" survivors; the clergyman ministers to the aged by ministering to his family.

And finally in this brief list of recommendations which seem to flow from the strategy as elaborated in this essay, why should churches not own and operate funeral homes? Not only is the cost of dying inordinately high when operated by a profit-making enterprise, but also death remains the example *par excellence* of a religious event. Yet the religious overtones of funerals conducted by secular businesses are not automatic but must be planned. If churches can buy bakeries, hotels, even girdle factories, which have no "intrinsic" religious meaning, why can they not buy mortuaries, which do? To maximize the community function, funeral homes in neighborhoods might even be mutually owned by the various churches in those neighborhoods.[64]

Conclusion

Readers might be surprised that more or different recommendations were not forthcoming in this essay. It is this writer's belief, however, that ministers and others interested in church practices do not need

[62] Barney G. Glaser and Anselm L. Strauss, *Awareness of Dying* (Chicago: Aldine Publishing Company, 1965), 98–99.

[63] Robert Blauner, "Death and Social Structure: A Functional Analysis," *Psychiatry*, 29 (1966), n. 43.

[64] Many of the "funeral insurance" clubs are sponsored by churches, it is true, but these are not necessarily neighborhood based, a fact that would seem to be of considerable significance if the analysis here is correct.

additional specific suggestions. Numerous sources, including a number cited above, provide a rich assortment of ideas and programs for ministering to the aged. What is needed, rather, is a rationale and a specification of organizational ideology, which permits choices to be made in a nonrandom way. Sociology, of course, is only one source of help in this regard; theology is an obvious other source of help, but so also might cost accounting, psychiatry, or political science have relevant theory for advancing the church's understanding of its posture toward the aging.

So it is that we have been speaking more about church strategy than about ministerial behavior. And so it is that many important considerations—whether the ministry is conducted in a rural or urban setting, for example, or whether a congregation is liberal or conservative in economic outlook—are ignored. Exclusion of these considerations should not be taken to mean their unimportance, any more than theology is unimportant in a ministry to the aging, but each of these factors permits refinements, or sets limitations, on the operation of the others. The social scientific limitations have been the focus here. It may well be one of history's greater ironies, we said near the outset of this essay, that, at the same time society becomes more differentiated, it produces larger proportions of aged persons whose needs appear to be for less differentiation. The gerontological strategy of the church should, it would seem, be directed toward easing the strains of that differentiation.

11

Aging and the field of education

LOWELL EKLUND

*In this chapter, Dean Eklund examines the biological, physio-
logical, and psychological factors pertinent to education for the
aged and concludes that the traditional stereotype of older people as inherently uneducable is largely false. He argues that the
negative and discriminatory position often taken in relation to
the aged impedes intellectual progress of this group, and that
many of the decrements of aging could be remedied or delayed
by properly designed educational programs for the postretirement
years.*

*Since the learning ability and motivation of older individuals
is significantly affected by their past educational experiences, such
programs should aim at intervention early in life to generate and
maintain motivation to learn and to continue the educational
experience past the period of formal schooling. The implementation of these programs, however, will require extensive changes
in our educational systems and priorities. Although "catch-up"
remedial programs are necessary to narrow the educational gap
between current generations, more basic solutions, it is argued,*

require the involvement of all levels of the educational hierarchy in order to create a system of continuing education as complete as the system which now exists for youth.

Advisers for this chapter were Ernest E. McMahon, Dean, University Extension Division, Rutgers University; and Thurman White, University of Oklahoma.

ON THE RELEVANCE OF VOLUME ONE

The education of older people, not unlike their health or income, affects their position in society. Throughout Volume One education is seen to be correlated with income, occupational and employment experience, and community status as well as with many types of behavior and attitudes. The older person's educational attainment (though only a crude index of his intellectual background and talents) has implications for the values he holds, for his occupational and cultural concerns, for his political and economic views, and for his competence in relationships with family and friends. In particular, Chapter 5 shows how the older person of today, whose formal schooling was completed many decades ago, is strikingly disadvantaged educationally. He is surrounded by successive younger generations each one of whom is better educated than the one before. In the future, of course, older people will have had a more extensive and intensive education than their present counterparts, for tomorrow's older people are simply today's younger, more advantaged, generation. But despite such advances, as long as the country's level of educational attainment continues to rise, and the amount of knowledge to be disseminated increases daily, the older person will remain perennially behind because his formal education cannot keep pace. In the light of this trend, the plea of Dean Eklund for a system of continuing education has special cogency.

"Man is never too old to learn—
he only becomes old when the process of learning stops."[1]

As Volume One of this series on aging and society amply attests, the characteristics of old people, the assets and liabilities which each cohort brings to old age, are profoundly influenced by the educational

---

[1] Attributed to Cecil B. DeMille.

attainment of its members. A fundamental source of knowledge and understanding, education serves as the principal modifier of attitudes, behavior, and skills. Educators, therefore, have a special obligation to the aged as well as to the young. This obligation, however, must both chasten and challenge members of the profession; chasten, because education has not provided the answers that the problems of aging require; and challenge, because the need for educational remedies is increasingly urgent.

Gradually, the education of mature adults is being recognized as an obligatory function of most educational institutions. The previously heretical idea that no individual, however generously endowed intellectually, can learn in twelve, sixteen, or even twenty years of formal schooling all he may need for a lifetime of effective living is today gaining increased support in the profession. The involvement of educational systems with adults, however, though relatively intensified, remains basically remedial rather than preventive. Education has only begun to recognize the importance of education for the life cycle, of the principle that the education of adults cannot be simply remedial, that it must be both cumulative in its effect and anticipatory of later stages in the life cycle. Because the education of the mature, *middle-aged* adult has so recently become a legitimate concern for extensive academic programing in institutions of learning, most of today's aged and even many middle-aged individuals have never experienced the benefits of *continuing* adult education. Moreover, the profession's problems are exacerbated by the need to work both ways from the middle: Although the needs of many adults for remedial or catch-up education are being met, more fundamental concerns require intervention at earlier stages. [*See Vol. 1, Chap. 5.4, pp. 116–119; also Chap. 3.B.3c, p. 59, on retraining of workers.*] If current patchwork programs are to be supplanted by systems of continuing education, youth must be provided curricular experiences that will impart an impulse to lifelong learning. Yet educational development is severely inhibited by established patterns and policies.[2]

While the acknowledgment and service of the remedial needs of adults is already underway, the provision of education for the life cycle would require revolutionary redesign and overhaul of the existing educational system. If education is to cope with the dynamics of radical change embracing all age groups, not just the oldest, it must create

[2] For a particularly relevant discussion on education's problem of working both ways from the middle, see Margaret Mead, "The University and Institutional Change," *Oakland Papers*, Notes and Essays on Education for Adults, No. 51 (Boston: Center for the Study of Liberal Education for Adults, 1966), 53.

new curricula and methods stimulating interest in *learning as a process* in place of an exclusive emphasis on information accretion.

The professed objective of the traditional liberal arts education—to impart an insatiable curiosity for knowledge—has unfortunately rarely been achieved. If, however, this remains the goal—and, in the writer's view, it must—our educational establishment must overcome the inertia of the status quo, of vested interests and entrenched defenses, to permit drastic modification of its traditional practices and cherished principles. As a beginning, the phrase "liberal education" might be redefined to convey the notion that the liberally educated man is one who is both *equipped* and *motivated* to free himself from constraining ignorance throughout life in *any area* of intellectual need. He should not be confused with one who has happened to be exposed in his youth to that segment of the academic spectrum referred to as the humanities or the liberal arts.

The formal educational hierarchy must recognize that its curricula should aim at the development of a process, rather than the infusion of content. Emphasis needs to be placed upon learning, unlearning, and relearning; as well as learning to learn and upon learning to want to learn. In this view, education becomes a vital continuum in which at any given phase one is already preparing for the later stages. Certainly, the notion of a terminal education should be expunged from the profession's lexicon. The duration of education needs to be seen in biological terms, ceasing only when the human organism stops functioning. Perhaps, and not altogether facetiously, the only meaningful terminal degree will be granted by the mortician. The alternative, apathy in the face of encroaching ignorance, has as one consequence a growing number of old people who may function physically but who are dropouts from life with its promise of continuing self-renewal and fulfillment.

Thus the emphasis given in this essay to education's neglect of the nation's aging and aged is intended to highlight the urgency of meeting the educational needs of older adults as *primus inter pares*. Immanuel Kant may have voiced the appropriate challenge over two hundred years ago when he wrote, "Man becomes man through education; he is what his education makes him." Simply, yet profoundly, Kant underscored the indivisibility of educational process and individual progress.

It is therefore not only with cognizance of education's past deficiencies, but more particularly with faith in its immense potential, that this essay will examine some of the philosophical and practical relationships of aging and the field of education.

The challenge

Formal education appears at many points in Volume One to be significantly correlated with the income, occupation, and community status of older adults. One's occupational and cultural concerns, values, political and economic views, and to a very considerable extent, the degree of success enjoyed in one's family and community relationships are all closely related to one's educational level.[3] Indeed, of all the indexes of social status, educational level seems to be the most powerful.[4] Even geographic mobility is clearly related to years of formal education. Quite obviously the educationally advantaged enjoy positive achievement in those areas of living and making a living that our society views as effective or successful.

However, that segment of the population categorized as aged (those 65 and over) is characterized by relative and absolute deficits in educational attainment [*as described in Vol. 1, Chap. 5, pp. 111–120*]. For example, almost 70 per cent of this group have had no more than an eighth-grade education.[5] This limitation would be sobering enough in *current* educational terms, but in this instance, we are speaking of education received in the early 1900's. Save for the basic skills of reading, writing, and arithmetic, the great majority of the aged may be said to be scholastically handicapped. When this 70 per cent with but eight years of early schooling is contrasted with only 17 per cent of the age group 25–29 so limited, the deficiency becomes even more striking. (Furthermore, in 1960 only 9 per cent of the 65+ against 23 per cent of the 25–29 group had had some college experience.)

Thus from the single viewpoint of formal schooling upon which they can draw, our older people are disadvantaged in relation to succeeding generations and most especially in relation to today's youth who enjoy unprecedented exposure to formal education and the rising expectations incidental to it.[6] The deficit gap widens with each passing day as the education of the aged tends to remain static while advances in knowledge and technology levels generally favor the young. In economic terms, as a dynamic technology inflates the value of education, the fixed earlier schooling of older persons is effectively devalued in a downward spiral.

[3] Church, library, theater, and movie attendance; participation in civic affairs and hobbies also correlate positively with education.

[4] Coolie Verner, *Adult Education* (Washington, D.C.: The Center for Applied Research in Education, Inc., 1964), 29.

[5] 1960 Census: 16.7 million.

[6] Another very significant social and political consideration of this condition is the fact that over half of the population is now *less* than 25 years of age.

But even these data do not reveal the complete extent of educational handicaps among old people. The full impact of early educational patterns is revealed by two additional facts:

(a) One-fifth of those 65+ are considered functional illiterates (that is, four years or less of schooling), constituting one-third of the nation's population so classified.

(b) Seven per cent of the aged have had *no* schooling at all!

Thus a substantial proportion of our aged population is virtually devoid of any formal education, superimposing the burden of illiteracy on those already experiencing the debilitating effects of age, and hence compounding the liabilities with which many old people confront their society, their family, and ultimately themselves. Although some remedial and basic education may still be possible with a portion of this group, their situation of relative disadvantage should generate a resolve to prevent such disadvantage among succeeding generations.

The conditions

In approaching the task of serving the educational needs of old people, professional educators require knowledge of conditions of mind, body, and environment which influence educability at older ages. These factors are numerous and complex and a comprehensive review would necessarily duplicate Volume One of this series. Therefore, only the most salient aspects of biological, physiological, psychological, and sociological factors will be considered. In this summary it will be noted that some of the conditions of decrement characterizing the aged under these headings are themselves susceptible to educational remedies. The profession needs, therefore, not only to be cognizant of these factors but also to assume leadership in stimulating the research and educational programs necessary for their effective amelioration. Moreover, a comprehensive understanding of these factors will also facilitate the no less important educational task of orienting the larger community to the needs of its older citizens.[7]

BIOLOGICAL FACTORS

Basic to the understanding of any aspect of aging is an awareness that, biologically, the human organism ages from the moment of

[7] Among many who underscore this need are: David O. Moberg, "Life Enrichment Educational Needs of Older People," *Adult Leadership*, 11 (1962), 162; and Joseph Drake, *The Aged in American Society* (New York: Ronald Press Company, 1958), 397.

fertilization, characterized by the parallel processes of growth or evolution, and atrophy or involution. Certain cells or tissues of the body die or degenerate to permit or sustain growth of others; such as the placenta at the time of birth, or a sloughing scab upon the healing of an abrasion. Body cells are thus in a continual process of death and regeneration. [*See Vol. 1, Chap. 8, pp. 187–194; Chap. 10, pp. 221–239.*]

At that point in life when the balance between growth and atrophy tips in favor of the latter, the decrements usually identified with "aging" become evident, but this subtle and gradual shift takes place at varying rates among individuals, and differentially along the several dimensions in any given individual. Thus, some persons are physically older at 45 than others at 65. Or an individual at age 85 may have a cardiovascular system functioning as well as the average of age 50, while other organs may have lost much of their reserve capacity. Though muscle vigor usually decreases with age, coordination may increase with significant resulting compensations.

This wide variability between and within organisms is an important factor in understanding and effectively serving individuals of advanced age. Biologic aging is an uneven process that may have little, if any, relationship to chronological age. Maturation takes place in irregular, episodic, but relentless phases. As one perceptive educator describes it:

We grow by leaps and bounds, and fits and starts and long-waiting pauses on plateaus. . . . Our interests seem to have changed overnight and our philosophy too—but not by themselves or altogether of our own volition. A large part of our response depends upon our ability to readjust to the realities of our "new bodies."[8]

Sensitivity to the discrepancies between chronological age and functional capacities, admittedly desirable in programing for the young, is of crucial importance in dealing with older people. Continuing education of an adult is a highly individualized pursuit serving the unique needs of a unique set of human experiences and conditions. Therefore, the educator must, in particular, avoid stereotyped thinking and be prepared to adapt educational programing to the profound and numerous differences among individuals of the same age, and between cohorts of older persons.

[8] Milton Stern, "Grow Old Along with Me," *Pleasures in Learning* (New York: New York University Press, 1961), Vol. IX, No. 2.

Closely related to these biological considerations are certain physiological and health factors. Of prime significance is the increased life expectancy of individuals, so that persons reaching 65 today may expect to live some 13 to 16 more years [*see Vol. 1, Chap. 2.3, pp. 24–35*], most of these in sufficient good health to permit continuance of major activity. [*See Vol. 1, Chap. 9.2, pp. 204–218.*]

Thus, the need and opportunity exists for education to equip individuals for continued productive and satisfying roles during years of relatively high potential, both to the benefit of the individual and the society which utilizes his contribution.

Nevertheless, the potential is ironically in contrast with current reality. Decline in health, for example, is a serious problem for a great number of old people and eventually becomes a limiting factor. [*Cf. Susser, Chap. 5 in this volume.*] Poor health is not only a handicap in itself, but also affects the ability and motivation to learn, thus creating a self-debilitating cycle.

Closely related to the acute and chronic illnesses which cause debilitation, disablement, and death are other physical losses which impair the organism's ability to function in the learning situation, and which must be taken into consideration in efforts at educating old people. Volume One [*Chap. 10, pp. 221–239; Chap. 11, pp. 241–272*] has documented their vision and audition decrements, impairment of psychomotor skills and manual dexterity, other sensory (touch, taste, and smell) decrements, and decreases in physical mobility, strength, and ability; declines in basal metabolic rate, cardiac output, respiratory capacity, and estrogen output in women (which is believed to be associated with some decline of intelligence); increases in reaction, movement, and reflex time; losses in time perception, weight discrimination, perception of dimension and direction, and perception of incomplete, concealed, or ambiguous form; and, finally, a general decline in complex sensorimotor coordination, which is reflected in one's ability to perform complicated tasks such as automobile driving or to learn a new skill.

Significant to the educator in relating many of these factors to the learning process is the finding that they do not necessarily reflect age-related differences in motivation or ability to learn. Loss of self-confidence, unwillingness to risk failure in the learning situation, and wariness stemming from self-assumption of a negative stereotype of old age may all depress the test results on many of the above measures. That old people may tend to reflect the societal evaluation of their capabilities has led one medical expert, Halbert Dunn, to observe that:

Once society begins to emphasize maturity instead of aging, education will respond. Educators will join forces with colleagues in mental health and public health education, will give more and more attention to the idea that achievement and maintenance of a high level of health and well-being are every man's due. They will be increasingly concerned about the public's understanding of the principles of nutrition and environmental health. They will do more to prepare each person for his struggle against the deterioration of his body and to help him learn how to compensate for the limitations the years may eventually impose on him.[9]

He reinforces the life-cycle concept of education in declaring that, "Education for maturity is a lifelong process." The "processes of aging are so intertwined with the processes of growth and maturation that aging cannot be considered as a thing apart."[10]

Quite obviously, then, education for better physical health is a broad area of need and opportunity. Understanding of the limitations and capabilities of the human organism in the late years of life is essential to its conservation. Therefore, programs in physical hygiene, body care and exercise, nutrition, intake moderation, safety, and various areas of "replacement therapy" fall under the appropriate aegis of adult education. Insight into the "aging process" may counter the prevailing emphasis on negative features of physical losses with age by reminding us that time is a measure, not a force, and that the effects of environmental stresses and trauma on the human body are not always chronologically measurable.[11] Significantly, no disease entity or physical or mental condition can be attributed *only* to the passage of time nor, "is there any condition that can reasonably be expected to occur in anyone after the passage of so much time."[12] [*Cf. Lasagna, Chap. 3 in this volume.*]

In summation of the case for health education, Frederick Swartz declares that, "medical attention applied preventively in the form of emphasis on better nutrition, higher standards of physical exercise and posture, better habits of mental activity, along with periodic health

---

[9] Halbert Dunn, "A Positive View of Aging Asks Much of Education," *School Life,* U.S. Department of Health, Education and Welfare (Washington, D.C.: Government Printing Office, 1964).

[10] *Ibid.*

[11] Frederick C. Swartz, "Health Education for the Aging" (Paper presented at Conference on the Aging, University of Michigan, Ann Arbor, Mich., 1967).

[12] American Medical Association Committee on Aging, *A New Concept of Aging* (Chicago: American Medical Association, 1963).

appraisals, could postpone or eliminate all of the now-accepted stigmata of aging."[13]

PSYCHOLOGICAL FACTORS

Intelligence   A number of physiological decrements—as well as behavioral manifestations of supposedly physiological changes—have been briefly referred to in the previous section. The topics of motivation and intelligence, however, require more extensive discussion, not only because presumed losses in these areas form the stubborn core of the "senescent" stereotype, but also because relatively little conclusive investigation has been done in this significant area. [*See Vol. 1, Chaps. 11.3 and 11.4, pp. 255–258; Chap. 12, pp. 275–287.*] There are few firm answers to some very simple but crucial questions regarding the mature individual's ability to remember, to learn, and to respond with intelligence—the vital factors in programing continuing education of adults. It is not known, for example, whether test findings of change in many of these areas do in fact reflect an ebbing of mental powers themselves, or may be attributable to physical deterioration of sensory functions due to aging.

In studies relating age to intelligence, the most frequently encountered limitation is lack of longitudinal designs holding constant innumerable background variables. The alternative cross-section studies have obvious weaknesses, especially in intelligence testing, since the test factors correlate highly with education and related social variables, and the younger cohorts enjoy not only a more recent and better education, but also one which is probably more directly applicable to the tests used.

Some efforts at longitudinal testing have been made, however, and those, along with the more scientifically administered and controlled cross-section studies, suggest a rather consistent pattern. All tests confirm the long-held assumption that intelligence as measured by the ability to learn increases rapidly from birth to young adulthood (approximately twenty years). Many researches show continued increments, though at a less rapid rate (or at least no general decline) up to the sixth or seventh decade. Several studies indicate definite increases in measured intelligence up to age 60 and attribute such age variations as exist not to age-related declines in any innate intelligence factor but to the relevancy and recency of the individual's educational experience, health, socioeconomic status, and other extrinsic variables. The Bayley and Oden study of 1955 concludes that the variation

---

[13] *Op. cit.*

in ability to learn associated with *age* per se is so slight in comparison with the effect of intelligence and prior experience (including educaton) "that up until age 60 it is of little significance. . . ."[14]

In some instances the older adult whose experience has exposed him to a variety of learning experiences has an advantage over younger persons;[15] but in tests requiring speed or new learning with which the old person's stored information might interfere, the younger adult is advantaged. The older person is generally at his best in tests depending upon vocabulary, general information, verbal reasoning, experience and judgment, but he does less well than younger persons in non-verbal tasks and those with speed limits or which involve manual skills. In situations where accuracy is preferred to speed, the older person may be considered more "efficient."[16]

To summarize briefly the available research findings, an individual's age and his test performance are neither clearly nor consistently related, while there is substantial evidence that: (a) Intelligence level, education, and socioeconomic status at early adulthood (which also correlates with childhood advantages and educational opportunities), constitute the most consistent cluster of variables associated with learning abilities; (b) poor health is a dominant inhibitor; (c) different motivations underlie the learning of older people as compared with young people or with themselves at younger ages [*see Vol. 1, Chap. 22.5.b, pp. 526–527*], and (d) when other factors are held constant, apparent declines in learning ability and motivation may be the consequence of disuse and lack of opportunity to practice relevant skills. [*Cf. also Vol. 1, Chap. 18.B.4, pp. 440–442, on occupational learning.*]

This latter finding is particularly significant. Both frequency and recency of educational experience have been shown to correlate with learning ability and interest in learning, that is, the more education one gets, the more one seeks and the more easily one learns. No less an authority than Thorndike, while carefully qualifying any claim that ability to learn continued to increase after early adulthood, acknowledged that "adult learning is itself a partial preventive or cure for the inability to learn."[17] Thus the positive dimensions of continuing edu-

[14] Nancy Bayley and M. S. Oden, "The Maintenance of Intellectual Ability in Gifted Adults," *Journal of Gerontology*, 10 (1955), 91–107.

[15] Indeed, individuals differ so greatly that the scores of some well-educated, healthy older people are higher than the scores of younger people and their own scores at an earlier age.

[16] A. T. Welford, *Skill and Age* (London: Oxford University Press, 1951), 161.

[17] Howard Y. McClusky, "The Relevance of Psychology for Adult Education," in Gale

cation and learning ability are apparently self-accelerating and mutually enhancing.[18]

Commonly encountered fears of loss of mental capacities with age might be allayed by the realization that, as Doctor Swartz notes, such decline "could largely be prevented if we will all continue to encourage some habits of study learned in school. Some serious reading and thinking should be a part of each one's daily life. As muscles are strengthened by proper physical exercise, the wits are sharpened only by regular and systematic mental activity."[19]

In essence, the older person need no longer accept the assumption—largely fallacious—that he cannot, like the old dog, learn new tricks. Similarly, the educational hierarchy of our society can no longer sidestep the challenge of need and opportunity that this fact presents. The significant relationship of both the ability to learn and level of interest in educational pursuit (motivation) to the recency of educational experience itself, constitutes a powerful argument for the commitment of resources to the continuing education of adults, on a scale second to none in its array of programs and aimed at the widest possible audience.

Motivation Although findings to date are somewhat inconclusive, of critical concern to professional educators is the identification of consistent, dependable motivational factors that could guide effective programing for continuing adult education.

Expectation of success in the proposed task must be high for the adult, if he is to approach the educational experience with confidence, and if he is to persevere in the face of diverting interests and anxieties often experienced by those for whom education is no longer a full-

---

Jensen, A. A. Liveright, and Wilbur Hallenbeck (eds.), *Adult Education* (Chicago: American Education Association, 1964), 168.

[18] This conclusion and other summary thoughts in the foregoing are derived from Alan B. Knox, "Older People as Consumers of Education" (Paper presented at Conference on the Aging, University of Michigan, Ann Arbor, Mich., 1967).

[19] *Op. cit.* Additional documentary support for mental as well as physical vitality as requisites to successful aging is contributed by Sir Richard Livingston of Oxford University: "It would be disastrous if men were physically old in their fifties . . . but it is an even greater national loss if most of them lose their intellectual and spiritual energy by that age. In the physical realm we have solved the problem . . . and our attention needs to be given to the even more important question of preserving his intellectual vitality, if not intact, at any rate in good repair. It can only be done in one way. The body will not remain fit if its owner leads a sedentary life; nor will the mind. But what is the regimen necessary for preserving its youth? I can put the answer into two words—Adult Education . . ." From "The Future in Education" as excerpted by Cyril O. Houle, *Continuing Education Report*, No. 12 (Chicago: University of Chicago Press, 1967).

time activity. If, moreover, the educational experience is associated "with past defeats and failures, the adult will stay away or be too busy."[20] Humiliation and failure impede the learning of the adult perhaps more than that of the child because the adult is much more fearful of revealing his inadequacies.[21] As his self-image as mature master of his world becomes threatened, he must be reassured that the game is worth the candle. [*Cf. Vol. 1, Chap. 13, pp. 289–313; Chap. 14, pp. 315–339.*]

In general, motivation factors implicated in adult education are substantially different from those associated with formal education at younger ages. Elementary, secondary, and even collegiate curricula are relatively standard and prescribed; programs are viewed as either prerequisites to further formal schooling or as terminal. In short, they are designed to provide at least the minimal necessary cultural underpinnings for dealing effectively with one's environment. For adults, however, educational experience must serve another classic purpose, considered almost a cliché in the profession, a "felt need." This need usually consists of a more or less pragmatic objective for which the adult requires information beyond his intuitive, or experiential, capacities at the moment.

As one specialist in adult education describes the problem of motivating older individuals:

I would like to see an emphasis on the voluntary nature of adult education. Although there is some compulsion on the part of employers and professional groups, the captive audiences of adult education are a minimum element contrasted with the almost 100 per cent captive enrollments of the elementary and secondary schools. Further, parental pressure as a substitute for legal obligation provides compulsion for a high percentage of college enrollments. The adult, conversely, becomes a student on his own volition and remains a student only so long as he finds satisfaction.

The lesson for the professional educator may be drawn from Houle's three categories of learners: goal oriented, activity oriented, and learning oriented.[22] Much of adult education is designed for the goal-oriented in the bread and butter sense of job-improvement. Much additional adult education is goal-oriented for those who are seeking to be better Sunday School teachers, Scoutmasters, or other volunteers. The goal-oriented are

[20] J. Roby Kidd, *How Adults Learn* (New York: Association Press, 1959), 96.

[21] Jane C. Zahn, "Differences Between Adults and Youth Affecting Learning," *Adult Education*, 17 (1967), 67.

[22] Cyril O. Houle, *The Inquiring Mind* (Madison: University of Wisconsin Press, 1961), 15 *et seq.*

generally those with economic and social goals ahead of them; young people or the early middle-aged. Adult educators need to turn their attention to imaginative and effective ways to appeal to the activity-oriented and the learning-oriented. By so doing, they will also serve the aging and aged.[23]

Adult interests are highly specific and differentiated, and motives for pursuing education vary among individuals. Although some may deliberately seek to avoid intellectual poverty and mental apathy, most act to compensate for recognized deficiencies in their social or professional lives. A desire for constructive use of leisure time and assumption of family-community responsibilities are also catalysts to educational pursuit. In any event, awareness of these sources of motive-power are important to the educator, providing insights into the subject matter of current significance to adults, and also fixing the "teachable moment" for their education—a most crucial element in successful organization and administration of learning experiences.

One theory of stimulating positive motivation in adults rests upon the concept that the life cycle is punctuated by significant milestones or transitional experiences which create awareness of changing need and thereby provide incentive for further education. For example, Paul Essert mentions such specific "stress points" in adulthood as: the transition from youth to family maturity in the twenties and early thirties; transition from family emancipation in the late forties and early fifties; and thence to retirement in the sixties and seventies.[24] Similarly, Robert Havighurst speaks of "developmental tasks" in adult life which include "setting adolescent children free," "reaching the peak in one's work career," "achieving mature social and career responsibility," etc., which provide special learning occasions and opportunities.[25] Howard McClusky notes the "observable and overlapping" stages of adulthood.[26] Alan Knox cites several major changes in life circumstances such as the first job, marriage, moving to a new community, retirement, death of spouse, etc., as experiences that prompt a heightened readiness for participation in adult education which he describes as "educative coping behavior."[27] Other schema of this

[23] Ernest McMahon in an advisory comment on this essay.

[24] Paul Essert, "Conclusion," in Wilma Donahue (ed.), *Education for Later Maturity* (New York: Whiteside, Inc., 1955), 316–317.

[25] Robert J. Havighurst, *Adult Education and Adult Needs* (Chicago: Center for the Study of Liberal Education for Adults, 1959), 6 *et seq.*

[26] *Op. cit.*, 173.

[27] *Op. cit.*

nature have been conceptualized by thoughtful scholars who support the theory of transitional needs of adults.[28]

Awareness of need   Awareness of need is, of course, the prerequisite to basic motivation toward adult learning. A serious and prevalent problem, however, is the absence of such cognitive awareness on the part of those for whom a need may objectively exist. Recognition so often comes after the fact that a major contribution of education lies simply in encouraging the inward look that leads to awareness of needs. If, however, education is to function preventively, such awareness must anticipate future stages of the life cycle. If the earlier conclusion that educational activity is a principal impetus to further education has any validity, the tendency for older people to lack interest in further education is predictive of maladjustment and impaired achievement in later years. In fact, research reveals that even those whose interests were engaged in earlier years may show diminution of such motivation after age 50 as their sense of futurity wanes.[29] Again education's inadequacies in providing sources of stimulation and renewal of interest throughout the life cycle become evident and humbling to the profession.

Finally, among the ingredients of motivation of particular significance for older people whose occupational, parental, and social obligations have diminished, is what may be described as the "need to be needed," a concept much in evidence in the gerontological literature. [*See, for example, Vol. 1, Chap. 15, pp. 341–359.*] Psychiatrist Lawrence Kolb indicates that a person's greatest want is "to be sought," and declares that millions are hospitalized or under custodial care simply because they think nobody wants or cares about them.[30] Huxley's classic assertion that "uselessness is the severest shock the human system can endure" serves as a stern warning to those concerned with the welfare of old people. Again education cannot disclaim its responsibilities. The insights and understanding, as well as the skills, learned through education can serve to enhance a sense of self-worth in old people, offering interests and outlets for engagement in useful activity, of which fulfilling one's own potentials must surely be included among the most rewarding. The need to be needed can be served, but most effectively only if older people do in fact

[28] See, for example, Jess Burkett, "Comprehensive Programming for Life-Long Learning," *Adult Education*, 10 (1960), 116–121, and Thurman White's chart, 116.

[29] John W. C. Johnstone and Ramon J. Rivera, *Volunteers for Learning* (Chicago: Aldine Publishing Company, 1965), 171.

[30] Harold Seymour, "What We Need to Know About People," *Alma Mater*, 34 (1967), 16.

possess the skills, knowledge, and personality characteristics that claim the respect and affection of others; in short, if they earn the right to be needed, through ability to serve themselves and others; if they are able to function effectively. "To live," says Lerner, "is to function—not to retire to apathy, to idleness, to vegetation, to trivia of living—but to function."[31] This condition is the essential goal of education.

SOCIOLOGICAL FACTORS

A basic tenet of psychology is that motivation, to be sustained, must be rewarded. A related and equally basic tenet of sociology is that effective functioning of the individual requires appropriate social structures, providing opportunities to assume socially valued roles. The efforts of educators to motivate and equip old people to perform more effectively can generate only frustration and, ultimately, less effective functioning, if the larger society is not prepared to accept the potential contribution of older individuals and to allocate to them an adequate share of social resources.

One of the most intriguing factors in the educability of old people may be society's attitude toward them. Many behavioral and personality characteristics, it is now recognized, are shaped by the expectations of others, and members of any age group tend to conform to the stereotype into which society casts them. Stereotyped "senescence" imposes the burden of an image unrelated to actual debilitation of mind and body, deleteriously affecting old people's sense of personal worth and well-being. Thus it may occur that old people yield passively to the self-fulfilling prophecies their social image projects such as conservatism, preoccupation with health, loss of memory, inability to learn, and withdrawal from social activities. [*See Vol. 1, Chaps. 13.11 and 13.12, pp. 306–311.*]

Moreover, older people suffer discrimination in relation to the young. The primacy we place on youth, occupational identity, beauty, and vitality is implicitly a detrimental standard when applied to the aging. As hostages to the future, our young people are systematically favored in areas of educational opportunities as well as in innumerable private and publicly supported welfare, recreational, and improvement programs. Perhaps because they represent both our finest hopes and gravest threat to whatever accomplishments we have wrought, the young are more likely to engage the concern and sympathies of all

[31] Max Lerner, "The Five Revolutions in American Life" (Proceedings of the Fifth Annual Governors Conference on Aging, New York City, 1966), 17.

older age groups. They are in a much more favorable position than old people to bargain for the material and emotional resources of society.

By contrast, older people are, in many areas, relegated to less significant roles. [*Cf. Vol. 1, Chap. 3, pp. 39–68; Chap. 17, pp. 408–420.*] John Gardner cites as a serious defect in our social structure the absence of relevant and useful things for older people to do.[32] Their influence is diminished and their opportunities for contribution curtailed. They tend, at best, to be tolerated; at worst, deliberately rejected and neglected. Isolation from society becomes the pattern for many. For those fortunate enough to remain in the social mainstream, the degree of engagement is largely independent of a society that makes no attempt to encourage such involvement. Consequently, that portion of the nation's human resources represented by this expanding group are less than fully deployed in important economic and social areas.

The evolving combination of earlier retirement (and a tendency for more individuals to retire out of personal choice), on the one hand, and increased life expectancy, on the other, challenges the field of education to provide intellectual enrichment to large numbers of persons over periods of from ten to twenty years. Enjoying relatively good health, assured of minimal financial security, exposed to cultural experiences, and provided with talent outlets, the older people of the nation *could* become a new leisure class in the most literal and constructive sense of that phrase; a leisure representing entrance into a period of reward, and fulfillment for a lifetime of service and achievement.

Significantly, the negative stereotype of aging may be exposed and modified by the educational process. The attitudes and understanding of society in regard to the aging, the personal insights of older people into their own social attitudes, and, also important, the *real* degree of decrement in their condition which *must* be accepted—as distinct from that which can be avoided, delayed, or remedied—are very legitimate and logical concerns of education. The fact that the stereotype is composed of educationally modifiable and intellectually malleable conditions should challenge the ingenuity and resources of the profession in providing adequate information about aging to *all* age groups.

The basic challenge to the professional educator is to become sufficiently expert regarding the numerous and complex facilitators of and barriers to educational pursuits that old people encounter, and

---

[32] John Gardner, "What Self-Renewal Can Do for Retirement," *Think*, 33 (1967), 4.

then to exploit the facilitators sufficiently to neutralize the barriers. The need for the educator's own continuing education in this process is implicit. "Adults," writes Jane Zahn, "are the workers, parents, and shapers of a nation. To teach such as these is an honor and an ever-new challenge that calls for the highest abilities of the teaching profession."[33]

Education's dilemma: allocation of resources

Having reviewed the salient needs, opportunities, and problems affecting education of the aging, the sequel would seem quite naturally to be a treatment of specific programs, hopefully ingenious, innovative, and effective, aimed at meeting these needs and solving these problems. But it is at this point that education encounters the more fundamental concerns touched on briefly in the introduction of this essay.

On the one hand, there is the demand for the business-as-usual approach involving patchwork, episodic, and crash-basis efforts to meet the immediate situation as adults encounter questions never anticipated in their schoolhood days. Great gaps in educational experience create more need for *remedial* and *updating* efforts than for *continuing* education in the literal sense. Even where programs exist, prodigious amounts of time and resources must be devoted to promotion and marketing to stimulate positive response from the "audience create more need for *remedial* and *updating* efforts than for more effort and ingenuity than the creation of programs to serve them. Moreover, education confronts the so-called knowledge explosion virtually paralyzed by frustration with the seeming hopelessness of even sifting out, let alone ordering, all the *new* knowledge considered necessary to human effectiveness in living and making a living.

Education finds itself thus overwhelmed by the diverse demands upon it, and dismally inadequate to the task. Its failure to anticipate, much less meet, the needs of adults who have some degree of readiness for and interest in continued learning is the inevitable consequence of its half-hearted commitment to adult education. The absence of universal, coequal, systematic programs and facilities for the education of adults, as complete as that for youth, has left this vital area to scattered institutional effort born more of voluntary largesse than of philosophical obligation. Consequently, the tremendous and unsolved need for catch-up education is the first horn of the dilemma upon which education finds itself firmly impaled. To the degree that

[33] *Op. cit.*, 76.

scarce resources are diverted to remedial programs, the seamless fabric of life-cycle education may never leave the designer's atelier.

Although episodic, stopgap programs may be education's most feasible entering wedge in any general effort to remedy deficiencies in serving the needs of the aged and aging, a massive commitment to continuous adult education must be the next step. All echelons of the educational hierarchy must respond, especially the universities, which admit increasing proportions of succeeding cohorts of youth. The very nature of their professed objectives permits nothing less. Universities can no longer purport to teach their graduates answers to questions to be encountered five to ten years in the future, since even the questions are obscured by the rate of social change. Perhaps the most valuable service a university can perform for society is to make that society humbly aware of how inadequate a university education *really* is. As John Mason Brown suggests, it must be recognized as "part of the American myth that we expect the skin of a dead sheep to keep the mind alive forever."[34]

Such a commitment by our institutions of higher education must rest, however, upon an unqualified philosophical base which attests to the merit and justification of adult education, and which influences Federal and state legislatures, college and university governing boards, administrations, and particularly faculties to accept and demonstrably support the coequality of continuing educational services.

Although it is probable that increasing proportions of future cohorts will enter universities, there will remain substantial segments who do not receive a university education, at least in the current sense of the phrase. The question arises, then, of how the need for adult education of this group is to be served.

Colleges and universities may not be the most appropriate structures for providing continuing education to those without prior university experience. Even though special programs may be offered, the "audience" may tend to feel intimidated by lack of familiarity and may fail to take advantage of such programs. Furthermore, many aged individuals may find it difficult to travel the distance necessary to attend classes at the nearest college or university.

Alternatives to the university for the continuing adult education of noncollege educated adults include, among others, employers, unions, local secondary schools, community arts and recreation cen-

[34] For elaboration of this idea, see Lowell R. Eklund, "The Alumni University—Education's 'New Frontier,' " *Adult Education*, 11 (1961), 161.

ters, and churches. In addition, there remains the vast educational potential of the mass media to bring formal education into the home. [*See Vol. 1, Chap. 22.4, pp. 518–526, and Schramm, Chap. 12 in the present volume.*]

But whatever structures for adult education may develop either within or outside of universities, professional educators within these structures will face, for some time to come, the dilemma of how to allocate resources to provide both remedial and continuing education.

The merit and justification for reform, however, rests upon a few simple irrefutable facts: There are more adults in the nation than children; adults are adults longer than they are children; the period of adulthood is lengthening; the number of old adults is rapidly increasing; adults, not children, run the nation (though this fact may at times appear in doubt); the education of childhood and youth is not sufficient to serve a dynamic lifetime of need for intellectual enlightenment; adults' needs for education may be greater than youth's in scope and quality; an ignorant adult is more dangerous than an ignorant child; adults are deficient in most areas of intellectual activity; adults have the capacity to continue to learn and society has urgent need for their learning.[35]

Thus, the objective of perpetual inquiry is crucial to our social and political survival. Only *lifelong* learning can serve man's uniquely human capacity to be better than he is, to become all that he can become. Only through continuing education, made readily available, generously flexible, effectively designed, and vigorously administered can the problems of responsible adulthood—young, middle-aged, or aged—be even partially solved. The illusion of education being "completed" at some early phase of life is no longer tenable. Education must be seen as lifelong and life-wide—to be pursued throughout adulthood and into "creative senescence." John Gardner sums it up:

No matter how firm an intellectual grasp the young person may have on the idea that education is a lifelong process, he can never know it with the poignancy, with the deeply etched clarity, with the overtones of satisfaction and regret that an older person knows it. The young man has not yet made enough mistakes that cannot be repaired. He has not yet passed enough forks in the road that cannot be retraced.[36]

[35] List includes specific points from Theodore P. Gnagey, "The Coming Revolution in Education," *Adult Education*, 15 (1964), 9; and Jack Crabtree, *Adult Education: A Social Imperative* (Trenton: New Jersey State Department of Education, 1965), 1.

[36] John W. Gardner, "The Servant of All Our Purposes" (Annual Report, Carnegie Corporation of New York, 1958), 4.

Education's dilemma: learning to learn

The educational establishment has an obligation to produce the continuing learner. (Subject matter, though important, is but the incidental grist for the student's learning mill.) Yet in pursuit of this goal the profession has been trapped in the stereotyped thinking toward the human developmental process noted earlier in this study. Human life is seen as comprised of three basic phases: first, the period of physical and intellectual maturation (birth to age 20–25); second, the period of functional maturity (to age 65); and third and finally, the period of senescence characterized by physical and mental decline.

Correspondingly, the mind is tacitly seen to have a period of growth, a period of mature application, and a period of inevitable decline. This model so dominates our society that it governs the very character and flow of our educational process. Consequently, we have molded an educational system that crowds intensive formal education into the first third of a person's life, is then content to entrust the middle segment to occasional and chance exposure to programs of varying quality ostensibly designed to meet "felt needs," and then serves the final phase with, if anything, remedial programing intended to assist the aged in achieving a passive and hopefully pleasant, but orderly, withdrawal from society and life. An educational system so ordered can hardly be expected to offer the aged more than repair service for obsolete social machinery or some cultural embroidery for the finite fabric of the twilight years.

The dynamic needs of many of today's old people, and certainly of an increasing proportion of future cohorts, do not conform to the simple three-phase life cycle upon which education is currently patterned. Coming generations will enjoy relatively sound physical health until late in life, will tend to be relatively secure financially, and will not be illiterate. They should be ready for and expectant of increased opportunities for novel and broadened experiences as society provides the means for personal achievement and fulfillment in the later years. Remedial, patchwork education cannot serve these augmented and upgraded intellectual interests. Will we then have exhausted education's potentials for service to an increasing segment of the population?

Unless there is vigorous effort along the lines advocated on the preceding pages, education can do little more than it is doing now, although it might collect its institutional wits and do the remedial job a little better. But the total output will undoubtedly fall short of the need, if not the demand. Though retired from his job, the healthy older person never retires from an innate, uniquely human trait with which he has been blessed, a continued search for meaning and purposefulness in his life. Aware or not, he will pursue this quest in a world in which established bench marks of meaning and purpose undergo abrupt shifts. He will experience sweeping sociological and technological changes which affect his society. But in spite of his desire for understanding, his inadequately trained capacities are likely to collapse under the challenge, and he may find it easier to forsake the search and to retire to the comfort of a manageable past, quietly letting "interests" in life ebb away.

The problem of today's older person, even of the college graduate, is that he was typically "taught" an education—a prepackaged collection of confirmed knowledge—but was not ordinarily provided with the skills necessary to seek the new knowledge required by his own changing needs and development. He was trained in the passive ingestion of information, taught disconnected "facts"—often of only topical interest—rather than ideas and concepts to be used in recalling or inferring specific data that the memory cannot independently construct or retrieve. He was not generally encouraged to explore, or challenged to expand, his own competence in learning. Lacking skills required for questioning and ordering a changed environment, he may view profound change in his environment as a threat rather than an opportunity for creative adaptation. Thus, in the very process of being "taught" he may have been deprived of the opportunity to "learn."

To the older person of today, "terminal education" was a pleasantly connotative phrase in his academic experience; "completing one's education" was a virtuous goal approaching a social norm. Even the Ph.D. degree was referred to as the *terminal* degree. Only at commencement was there a vague allusion to the implicit need for continuing education but with no recognition that the impulse toward education was the most precious and decisive accomplishment any educational institution could render to its alumni. The promise that he would acquire an insatiable curiosity in exchange for four years of attendance at an institution with a "liberal arts emphasis" failed utterly. Predictably, the tools and motivation by which he was to continue to learn proved tragically inadequate to the demands of his time.

His alma mater's postgraduate contacts were limited to announcements of athletic and social events, and exhortations to contribute to the annual fund drive. At no time did the alumni relations office suggest participation in his or any other university's educational program for adults as a logical and necessary sequel to his undergraduate phase. Such cultural pursuits as he engaged in were generally limited to those which only occasionally and intuitively struck his undefined fancy.

Present educational forms and institutions are products of an age which understood learning as a partial rather than a total life function, and which perhaps were adequate to the times. However, as the pace of societal change has quickened and learning needs increased, the mediating function of the teaching institution has become more cumbersome. There is less time for the institution to serve as interpreter of change; more demand that it shift from communication of prestructured knowledge toward the development of the individual's own knowledge-generating abilities. Learning, today, is recognized as no longer the exclusive province of the classroom. The individual learns throughout life. He learns *how* to learn in the classroom. From this realization, we may now envision a society capable of an educational continuum from youth through old age, with the various institutions serving the stations of this spectrum dedicated to developing the competent, self-motivated inquirer rather than the certified terminal graduate.

Institutional restructuring toward education for the life cycle

For the educational planner there is no task as important, difficult, threatening, and as unattended as that of charting realistic goals toward which the mammoth machinery of our educational system should be directed. To venture even a minor modification is to risk being ground by gears set with the inertia of centuries. Knowledgeable observers decry the inflexibility and neophobia of entrenched educational interests—David Riesman and others have pointed out, for example, that the very people whose life work is to question and to differ—namely, the faculty—are usually the first to challenge innovation.[37] Paradoxically, educators often seem little disturbed by the impact of radical change in other spheres of the society they ostensibly serve and lead. Thus, the continued existence of an education system based on learning as preparation *for* life, rather than upon learning as the fundamental process *of* life.

The extensive institutional restructuring required by an educational system capable of making a preventive or anticipatory response to the problems of the aged involves near-revolutionary measures, a

[37] Seymour, *op. cit.*, 18.

much more sophisticated understanding of how people do learn, and the devising of techniques suitable to students of various ages and interests. Distinctions as to the type of content—cultural or technical —are not pertinent to this process. Focus must be upon developing a set of capabilities enabling the individual to cope with any body of content. The lifelong student will function in a world containing an infinite number of units of information, each unit representing some coherent fact or observation, of which only a small fraction can be assimilated and employed by any single person in his lifetime. Given his unique capabilities and purposes, each person faces the task of filling his limited capacity with optimally useful information. Consequently, his early education must stress the development of two sets of skills: (1) those required to scan his information universe efficiently; and (2) those needed to use the acquired information effectively.

To this end, researchers are now engaged in early-stage experimentation and testing of new methods. One such arrangement involves small group seminars, in connection with large lecture sessions pursuing a particular topic, with assignments requiring each student or group, given the same topic and raw data, to develop comprehensive lesson plans and lectures. The student's experience should demonstrate that given the same topic and resource material, each work group will produce a different solution, that is, that in spite of the highly structured, carefully organized packages used to capture insight and perceptions—books, articles, lectures—there is no "last word" about anything. He will learn that knowledge can only fill memory and should only serve inquiry. To emphasize this point he may engage in some courses that build on no content save his own experience and his own image of things. Employing the tools (and language) of the behavioral sciences, he will strive to generate meaningful knowledge from his own and his fellow students' unstructured experiences.

He will thus be equipped with a working knowledge of the conceptual tools enabling him to explore and map out any area of subsequent concern. In this process he may be introduced to the potential of a simple binary matrix in predicting the relationships of seemingly disparate units of information. In approaching a subject he will not be "lectured at" concerning its content, but will be asked to discover for himself its latent design and pattern, with the assistance of a skilled counselor.

Educational technology will become part of the student's tool kit, placing at his fingertips the means for exploring quickly and precisely an information universe for those units of knowledge that his question requires. Through participation in one of many computerized information services, he can be kept up to date in areas of professional, civic or cultural, and personal concern. His interests will have been first determined by generating a profile of key descriptor words which, when weighted according to the systems dictionary, will be processed against a document population scanned for information relevant to that profile. Where effective, a simple coordinate index system provides the employed retrieval. When necessary, however, other systems sensitive to the associative bonds of "synonomy" and "contiguity" which exist between words can search a total cross-disciplinary body of literature identifying areas of information previously unknown to the participant.[38]

The foregoing are but examples of the techniques and procedural models that educational institutions could apply to the learning process. Approaches such as these should dominate the future design of educational curricula at all levels. Each institutional unit in the educational system from kindergarten through programs for the aged would focus upon what might be called *meta-learning* concerns; that is, conceptual model building, information use, and problem solving skills. The heuristic concepts common to the many disciplines would be analyzed and applied. Aesthetic, analytic, organizational and predictive conceptual tools would be refined and employed by students dealing with unstructured experience and data since these are exactly what the mature adult must confront in his real world.

Motivational ingredients would be generated by the learning process itself, since as one achieves competence in learning, the rewards and satisfactions of mastering these tools and processes should kindle the desire to pursue their use in many areas. Out of this set of factors should emerge open-ended continuing universities providing stimulus, counsel, subject matter and information units, and concepts for their *lifelong* students—never alumni.

In addition, and functionally related to these innovations, the orientation of young people toward continuing education should become an integral part of the curricula at all levels of formal education, so that the student "normally" expects to pass into systematic and largely self-directed postgraduate continuing education as readily as he moved from elementary to high school, then to college or some

---

[38] The associative matrix concept has been experimentally tested under Oakland University's Knowledge and Information Dissemination System. The experience on this and related activities has been extensively, but informally, documented.

other post high school institution of learning.[39] Throughout the school system, a new norm of continuing education will replace our current emphasis on fixed units of education. In practice, the norm implies that "the individual becomes habituated to living as a matter of systematic cumulative seeking and finding" and requires a program which "seeks genetically to provide for the full education continuum of the individual's development from childhood on through adulthood."[40]

In this schema, institutions of higher learning should be viewed not as four-year undergraduate colleges but as perpetual universities that assume a responsibility, not just for four years, but for forty-four or more years of educational pursuit by their lifelong students. The traditional four-year program thus becomes a period in residence during which students will learn both that they must learn and how to continue to learn. They should emerge with an awareness that learning is a lifetime rather than a classroom process, and is the only viable means to effective action in an age of radical innovations.[41] The postcollegiate years should be served systematically and comprehensively by all institutions of higher education in the country as they provide continuing learning opportunities for each other's alumni.[42] A nationwide network of colleges and universities vigorously united to serve the common cause of education of all alumni could implement this concept. Mobile and transient graduates could be readily integrated into the alumni education programs of any other university much as under-

[39] Houle, for example, asserts that ". . . from the moment a student registers as a freshman, he should be made aware of the pervading belief of the faculty that it is preparing him for a long life of continuing education." Taken from Cyril O. Houle, "Education for Adult Leadership" (Address at Inauguration Exercises, University of Pittsburgh, Pittsburgh, Pa., 1957).

[40] Maxwell H. Goldberg, "Continuing Education as a Way of Life," *Adult Education*, 16 (1965), 6.

[41] Peter Drucker provides a cogent statement of this position: "Finally there is a tremendous need to build into the entire teaching and learning process, and especially in college, the ability and motivation to keep on learning. The most important thing any student can acquire in college today is not this or that knowledge or this or that skill. It is to learn how to learn—and the desire to keep on learning.

"First of all then, colleges and universities have an obligation to teach the discipline of learning; the vigor and method of analysis . . . ; the ability to define the knowledge needed; and the capacity to acquire new knowledge fast. These things can be learned. . . . But they are not being taught if the emphasis is on learning what is already known rather than on finding out what one does not know and needs to know." Peter Drucker, "The University in an Educated Society," *Oakland Papers*, Notes and Essays on Education for Adults No. 51 (Boston: Center for the Study of Liberal Education for Adults, 1966), 14–15.

[42] For a plan of implementation of this concept, see Lowell R. Eklund, "The Oakland Plan for the Continuing Education of Alumni," *Adult Leadership*, 15 (1966), 154–156.

graduates currently transfer from one institution to another as, in Blakely's words, "Continuing education becomes the growing and the harvest for which formal schooling is only the planting and cultivation."[43]

These are only suggestive of the numerous innovations requiring urgent evaluation and adoption if current, to say nothing of future, demands are to be met; if continuing education of adults—young, aging, and old—is to become the rule rather than, as at present, the exception.

Conclusion

Education is, in fact, implicated in every problem of the aging. The question today is the degree to which the educational hierarchy is willing to commit resources to solutions.

In this regard, there will not be unanimity of support for all the measures urged in this polemic; exceptions will be taken to philosophy and method. So be it. If everyone agreed, little would be accomplished save the euphoria of sterile mutuality.

One objective must, however, receive the concerted support of all: Older adults *must* be served through education by *whatever* philosophy and method. Old people deserve it; society needs it. Old people's ever-increasing numbers and days represent a growing resource whose potential is too precious to neglect; and, conversely, whose neglect is too great a social and economic loss to countenance.

The challenge belongs to education, through which, Kant said, "Man becomes man." The word "becomes" is the crux: Man is always in the state of becoming. From the moment of conception, his life is open, tentative, ever-changing. The quality of those changes depends upon the quality of his education, the degree of enlightenment by which he orders his environment and behavior, at every age. Man's capacity, and thence obligation, to improve—to be better than he is, to be all that he can become—is more than rhetoric, it is the imperative of human progress and survival; it is man's brush with divinity. Education can and must presume to serve this high calling, and to provide every man with the means to a productive, useful life. Equipped with the ability and will to learn, he will engage in the process of habitual inquiry; he will glory in the realization that, ". . . there is no

---

[43] Robert J. Blakely, "What Is Adult Education?" in Malcolm S. Knowles (ed.), *Handbook of Adult Education in the United States* (Chicago: AEA, 1960), 6.

point at which you say the book is finished, the chapter is closed, I know, now I know."[44]

With such an impregnable philosophy as his arsenal, he may approach senescence with zest and expectancy. Self-indulgence, self-pity, and conformity to self-fulfilling prophesies will be replaced by a conviction of the worth of life and living. With confidence born of intellectual competence he will see his own life's essential purpose through the eyes of the venerable nonogenarian, Pablo Casals, who, when asked why he still persisted in practicing several hours each day, replied simply, "Because I think I'm improving."

[44] Lerner, *op. cit.*, 19.

12

Aging and mass communication

WILBUR SCHRAMM

In contemporary society, the mass communicator may be a policy-maker, an editor, a publisher, an entertainer, a politician, an adviser, a newscaster, a therapist—indeed, he might be any one of the professionals whose role, vis-à-vis older persons, is discussed in one of the foregoing essays; for the mass media represent an important means of facilitating the policies, plans, and counsel of all individuals and agencies concerned with the situation of the aged. Doctor Schramm's essay, consequently, should be of interest to the wide range of practitioners who communicate with older people, and about older people's problems and opportunities.

Doctor Schramm focuses our attention on the potential of mass communications for reintegrating the older person into the ongoing social order. First, he takes the mass media to task for poor coverage of the dramatic story of the changing age structure of our population, for perpetuating biased stereotypes of old people, and for being insensitive to the great policy issues posed by an aging population. Second, he gives us a highly sophisticated analysis of the age composition of mass media audiences, emphasizing both the importance of the mass media to the aged population and the challenge presented by the continuing interest, even dependence, of the older audience on these sources of information and entertainment. Doctor Schramm then raises the basic question of how, in fact, the media function in the lives of older people and suggests that a special function may be that of maintaining engagement with the larger society. Finally, he points to ways in which the mass media might assess and improve their services to the large and loyal audience represented by older people.

The adviser for this chapter was W. Phillips Davison, Public Opinion Quarterly.

ON THE RELEVANCE OF VOLUME ONE

Parts 1 and 2 of Volume One detail the social-cultural contexts within which older people live and specify some of the limiting conditions which the processes of aging seem to impose. In one sense, important audiences for the mass media are thus identified. Chapters 12 through 15 discuss the personality needs and life attitudes of older people; while Chapters 19 and 20 report on their political and religious roles. In all these materials, implicit questions as to the nature and content of mass communications are raised. The final chapters of Part 4 which deal with leisure time and family and neighborhood relationships suggests a framework for assessing the role that mass communications may play in the lives of older people.

The argument of this paper is that the mass media are called upon more and more to build a bridge between old people and the rest of American society. On the one hand, they are challenged to report in depth and breadth one of the great societal stories of our time—the emergence of old people as a major segment of the population. On the other hand, because the media have a large and loyal audience among old people, they are in position to maintain for these people a link to the larger society, and thus to combat the loneliness and progressive disengagement that may come with time.

Implications of an aged population: the story behind the news

In the last week I have noted four stories about old people in my morning newspaper. I have disguised these stories so that no one would be embarrassed, but readers will recognize the types of subject matter.

Samuel A. Throckmorton did not stand on his head today, as expected, when friends gathered to celebrate his 90th birthday. "I did it on my eighty-fifth," he said, "but that's kid stuff. I'm growing up now! . . ."

This is the façade of the news. The story lies behind it.

Between 1900 and 1960, the number of Americans 65 and older grew from 3.1 million to 16.7 million. It is expected to be 25 million by 1985. This is a rate of growth more than twice that of the American population as a whole.[1]

In ancient Rome the average life expectancy was 20 to 40 years. It was 40 in the United States in the mid-nineteenth century, and 49 in 1900. In 1962 it was 70 years.[2]

This is the story [*set forth in Vol. 1, Chap. 2, pp. 15–37*] that the mass media are challenged, needed, to report—the emergence of a sizable segment of the population who, contrary to their wishes, in many cases, are no longer working and earning, whose children in most cases have grown and made their own lives apart from their parents, and who are typically living in reduced financial circumstances and in leisure that has not been sought. And beyond that, what it will mean to the American economy and culture to have a "mature" population, in which there will be many aged people contributing neither goods nor services, and increasingly disengaged from social contacts and activities.

Another story:

Doctor James and Senator Crabapple charged today that the alleged $200 million deficit in state funds for medical care of the aged was a product of fiscal juggling, and had been created for political campaign

---

[1] See U.S. Bureau of the Census, *Historical Statistics of the United States, Colonial Times to 1957* (Washington, D.C.: Government Printing Office, 1960), 8. Projection by Conrad Taeuber, *Data Relating to the Population of the United States*, U.S. Bureau of the Census (Washington, D.C.: Government Printing Office, 1964), 1.

[2] Louis I. Dublin, Alfred J. Lotka, and Mortimer Spiegelman, *Length of Life* (New York: The Ronald Press Company, 1949), 42. See also Mortimer Spiegelman, "Significant Mortality and Morbidity Trends in the United States since 1900" (Bryn Mawr, Pa.: American College of Life Underwriters, 1964), 2.

purposes. They opposed the plan to transfer patients to state institutions after eight days of hospital care. . . .

Old people are in an unfavorable financial situation as compared to younger ones, and perhaps always will be. Social security, retirement plans, medical plans have helped keep the disparity from getting worse, but with inflation and generally rising incomes the old people are relatively as deprived as ever. Therein lies the real story.

In 1900, 68 per cent of the men 65 and older were working. This percentage had dropped to 32 per cent in 1960, and is expected to be 25 per cent or less by 1975.[3] Most of the salaried workers will have dropped out of the labor force by 65. Most of those continuing to earn will be in the self-paid professions, a few of the crafts, and some of the low-paid service occupations where it is difficult to recruit younger people. [*See Vol. 1, Chap. 3, pp. 39–68; Chap. 4, pp. 69–109.*]

Fewer old people welcome retirement than the early idealists expected. The research shows that, even among old persons with good health and adequate income, morale tends to be higher among employed than retired people.[4] There is increasing fear of financial problems as retirement approaches,[5] and the apprehension of retirement grows as people pass from the 30's through the 40's into the 50's.[6] [*See Vol. 1, Chap. 18, pp. 421–462.*]

Men and women often react differently to retirement. The man who lives longer than his forebears usually spends many of those additional years away from his work group. The woman, on the other hand, does not have to retire from housework. She can look forward to a longer life than her husband, without such a traumatic break at 60 or 65 or 68, and her social relationships will tend to change less because she will not be removed from occupational friendships and contacts.

But old people tend to evaluate leisure less highly than do the people who put them into it. The proportions increase by age who say, for example, on public opinion polls, that "A four-day work week would

---

[3] Donald Bogue, *The Population of the United States* (New York: Free Press, 1959), 426. Data for 1960 and 1975 from *Manpower Report of the President* (Washington, D.C.: Government Printing Office, 1963), 88.

[4] See Seymour L. Wolfbein, "Changing Patterns of Working Life," *Monthly Labor Review*, 88 (1963), 820–823.

[5] Bernard Kutner *et al.*, *Five Hundred over Sixty: A Community Survey on Aging* (New York: Russell Sage Foundation, 1956), 72. See also Gordon Streib, "Morale of the Retired," *Social Problems*, 3 (1956), 270–276.

[6] George Katona, *Private Pensions and Individual Savings*, Monograph No. 40 (Ann Arbor: Survey Research Center, University of Michigan, 1965), 15. The proportion who say they "dread" retirement is still less than the proportion who say they "look forward" to it.

make people soft and lazy," or that "Tax money should not be used to support exhibitions of statues and other art."[7]

This is the story. We are imposing leisure on more people than are seeking it. Can we afford to lose so much talent and experience and willingness to work? If so, how can we share the wealth of an affluent society equitably with them? If early retirements are necessary to maintain high employment, how can we manage them so as to bridge the gap between work and retirement and avoid the discontinuity of having leisure suddenly imposed? Is there any "moral equivalent" of work in the late years? To make retirement generally desirable at an early age is it necessary to counteract our traditional "work ethic," and if so, what will that mean for the productivity of *younger* workers?

A public opinion poll says that old people know more than young adults about politics. More of them can name their Senators and Congressmen. . . .

One-fifth of our old people (65 +) at the present time are functional illiterates—meaning they have had four years of education or less.[8] Only 28 per cent of persons over 75 in 1960 had gone beyond the eighth grade, as against 83 per cent of the present 25–29-year-old group.[9] Their education was completed many years ago, and what they learned is therefore less easily applicable to modern developments. As the presently young generations become older, the average level of education among old people will rise; but old people will always be disadvantaged to some extent as long as the level of education keeps rising. [*See Vol. 1, Chap. 5, pp. 111–120.*] Needless to say, this forms a barrier to communication between the generations, and makes it harder for old people to march along with technology.

Yet, many old people remain intellectually keen and active. Without citing Cato who began studying Greek at 80, or Bertrand Russell who wrote a history of philosophy at 85, we can note how active and interested many less famous old people remain politically. They tend to be more conservative than young people except in the politics of social security—where they are more radical than young people.

---

[7] The first of these is from a Roper poll reported by David Reisman, "Leisure and Work in Post-Industrial Society," in Eric Larrabee and Rolf Meyersohn (eds.), *Mass Leisure* (New York: Free Press, 1958), 369. The second is a Swedish poll reported by Hadley Cantril (ed.), *Public Opinion, 1935–1946* (Princeton: Princeton University Press, 1951), 20.

[8] U.S. Bureau of the Census, *Current Population Reports*, P–20, No. 138 (Washington, D.C.: Government Printing Office, 1964), 9.

[9] U.S. Bureau of the Census, *1960 Census of Population*, Vol. I, Part 1 (Washington, D.C.: Government Printing Office, 1961), 404.

Voting does not fall off among men until in the 70's; among women, a little earlier.[10] Fifteen per cent of the population who voted in 1960 were 65 or over, and the proportion is rising. Public opinion studies, as the newspaper said, do indeed show that people over 50 are at least as likely as people in their 20's to keep up with political information (for example, the names of their Senators), although less likely to remember the political science they studied in school (such as the first ten amendments to the Constitution).[11] [*See Vol. 1, Chap. 19, pp. 463–482.*]

What kind of adult education would keep these older people mentally alive and in touch with changing technologies and societies? [*Cf. Eklund, Chap. 11 in this volume.*] What kinds of programs and opportunities can be provided to serve and maintain their intellectual interests, as programs now try to take care of their physical needs?

Henry P. Jones, 83, was married Friday to Cynthia Lowenberg, 79. "I've had my eye on her for 60 years," he said. . . .

Old people, most of them, are not as happy as they have been. The sense of happiness seems to decrease from the years of young adulthood on. The best years are typically placed in the 30's and 40's.[12] Of course, this judgment varies greatly by individuals, and some people feel they are happiest toward the end of their lives. But this is not typical. As most people grow older they suffer increasing disengagement from social contacts and activities. This is forced on them by failing health, retirement, reduced finances, and the gradual disappearance of friends and loved ones in their own generation. [*See Vol. 1, Chap. 15, pp. 341–359; Chap. 17, pp. 409–420.*]

Yet, when one studies the old people themselves, one finds that most of them make rather remarkable adjustments. They typically do not consider themselves old, at least as long as they maintain reasonably good health, and especially if they can maintain some of their major life roles, including the work role.[13] An old person tends not to

---

[10] See U.S. Bureau of the Census, *Current Population Reports*, P–20, No. 143 (Washington, D.C.: Government Printing Office, 1965), 1, 9.

[11] Reported by Hazel Gaudet Erskine, "The Polls," *Public Opinion Quarterly*, 27 (1963), 137–139.

[12] In the Batten, Barton, Durstine, and Osborn, Inc., *Report: An Investigation of People's Feelings on Age* (BBD & O Research Memorandum, 10/1966). The most often mentioned decades were the 30's and 40's, and only 10 per cent named the 60's.

[13] In one sample, 49 per cent of people 60 and over said they regarded themselves as "middle-aged," and 65 per cent said they felt younger than most people their age. (See Kutner *et al., op. cit.,* 94, 98. Corroborative information comes from a 1966 telephone survey by Batten, Barton, Durstine, and Osborn, Inc., *op. cit.*)

stress, or perhaps to suppress, what he notices of his failing health or appearance. He is, on the average, no more likely than a young person to grouse about his troubles, or talk of his worries and insecurities.[14] [See Vol. 1, Chap. 13, pp. 289–313.]

In many ways, old people remain astonishingly active and effective. Many of them remain physically active for many years after retirement. To be sure, exercise such as gardening and walking tends to replace more active sports.[15] They have less energy in reserve, bounce back less quickly, and their medical histories show declines in physical functions.[16] [See Vol. 1, Chaps. 9 to 11, pp. 195–272.] But they like to play what they can play, and if they have been socially active before retirement they like to maintain friendships and activities. A "senior citizens club" is usually a gay and active place. Some older people do marry again at an advanced age. Old people who remain in the labor force beyond the usual years of retirement are typically reported to be as accurate and productive as younger workers, except in jobs where considerable physical strength is required.[17] And their employers often report that the elderly workers seem more committed than younger ones to the work they do.[18] [See Vol. 1, Chap. 18, pp. 421–462.] In San Mateo County, California, a 94-year-old man has just been retired at the polls, while seeking a tenth four-year term as sanitation commissioner; he is being used as consultant to his successor.

How do aging persons come to terms with changes in themselves and their life styles that would earlier have disturbed them greatly? How do they manage, when they do, to combat disengagement and loneliness? What policies and arrangements will help them in that

[14] See Gerald Gurin, Joseph Veroff, and Sheila Feld, *Americans View Their Mental Health: A Nationwide Interview Study* (New York: Basic Books, Inc., 1960), 19–47.

[15] For example, see the reports of old people's activities in Glenn H. Beyer and Margaret E. Woods, "Living and Activity Patterns of the Aged," Research Report No. 6 (Ithaca, N.Y.: Center for Housing and Environmental Studies, Cornell University, 1963), 13–16.

[16] One of the best sources of evidence of this kind is the U.S. National Health Survey, conducted since 1957.

[17] No significant difference is found in the productivity of office workers (U.S. Bureau of Labor Statistics, "Comparative Job Performance by Age: Office Workers," Bulletin 1273 [Washington, D.C.: Government Printing Office, 1960], 18–23) and only a slight decline at age 60 or over in the amount of work done by mail sorters (James Walker, "The Job Performance of Federal Mail Sorters by Age," *Monthly Labor Review*, 87 [1964], 296–301). But notable declines occur after the middle years among factory production workers in whose work physical effort was a factor (Jerome A. Mark, "Comparative Job Performance by Age," *Monthly Labor Review*, 80 [1957], 1468–1471).

[18] Gurin, Veroff, and Feld, *op. cit.*, 170.

effort? For example, what kind of housing is really most likely to contribute to a happy old age? Increasingly, old people are living apart from their children. There is usually a long period in which husband and wife are alone, and then a time when the surviving partner is alone. Is the old people's community the best solution, or is it better to try to keep old people in closer touch with younger ones? [*Cf. Madge, Chap. 8 in this volume.*]

The question is, at what depth have we a right to expect the media to cover this story? We have suggested some of the dimensions of the development that has been covered largely in terms of the politics of Medicare and social security, and the feature news of old people who have done things not expected of them—for example, married at 80, or stood on their heads at 90. Behind this type of news are a great human story and a great national problem. Tomorrow's old people and today's policymakers have every reason to be deeply concerned with them. Do they not deserve better than "Gee whiz!" coverage?

Behind this news lies also a social science literature of considerable size. Most of the data in the preceding pages have been drawn from it. Yet the social scientists' findings about the problems and situations of older people have been represented very imperfectly in the mass media. If the problems of aging in America do indeed deserve better coverage, then writers for the mass media will have to inform themselves about the research on aging, and interpret parts of it for the general public. Fortunately, Professor Riley and her colleagues have made this task easier for them by summarizing all the relevant social science research on this topic, in Volume One of this series. Throughout this paper we have bracketed references to this remarkable review of research, and those references will provide good starting points for any mass media persons who are interested in telling this story in depth and breadth.

The aged population as an audience

So far we have talked of the emergence of an aged population and its problems as something to be interpreted by the mass media to the rest of the American public. Now, let us look at old people as *users* of the mass media.

The tendency has been to play this audience down. The entertainment media have concerned themselves with teenager tastes, and the advertisers have focused on the young adults with their high buying power. The audience of older people, less affluent and less active, has demanded and attracted less attention. And yet, for two media at

TABLE 1 *Use of leisure time by 5,000 persons over 65*

Activity	Per cent engaging in activity on preceding weekday	Median hours given to activity
Watching television	70	3
Radio and records	17	1.5
Visiting	68	2
Reading	61	1
Napping and idleness	56	2
Entertaining	9	2.5
Club and church-related activities	4	3
Gardening	19	2
Meditation and worship	9	1
Walks and sports	10	1
Rides and outings	9	1
Handiwork	15	2
Writing	8	1.5
Crafts and collections	1	2

Source: Glenn H. Beyer and Margaret E. Woods, "Living and Activity Patterns of the Aged," Research Report No. 6 (Ithaca, N.Y.: Center for Housing and Environmental Studies, Cornell University, 1963).

least, this aged generation provides an audience of many millions, loyal, concerned, and, as we shall point out later, dependent for a kind of service that younger audiences do not need. [*Cf. Vol. 1, Chap. 22, pp. 511–535.*]

IMPORTANCE OF MASS MEDIA IN USE OF LEISURE TIME

In 1958 interviewers visited over 5,000 social security beneficiaries in four areas of the United States. These respondents were asked for a full chronological account of how they had spent the previous day (excluding Sunday). The results of this study are worth looking at because they provide about as good a picture as we have of how people over 65 spend the new hours of leisure that have been forced upon them. Table 1 gives, first, the percentage of all these old people who engaged in a particular activity during the day before, and then the median number of hours spent on that activity by those who engaged in it at all. Note that this is not the median time for *all* 5,000 respondents: only for those who chose to use some of their time for the particular activity being studied. Thus, the table should be read: 70 per cent of all respondents watched television during the preceding day, and half of those who did watch it devoted more than three hours to it.

This table demonstrates quite clearly that watching television was the most frequent leisure activity of this large sample of old people, and the one on which they spent the most time. Indeed, this sample

TABLE 2 *Proportion of different age groups who used each medium "yesterday"*

Medium	Age 15–19	Age 20–29	Age 30–39	Age 40–49	Age 50–59	Age 60+
Newspaper	84	85	84	87	86	83
Radio	77	74	71	74	77	75
Magazines	51	44	38	36	35	35
Books	34	27	19	17	16	18
Movies	27	16	11	8	9	6

Source: Henry C. Link and Harry Arthur Hopf, *People and Books* (New York: Book Manufacturers' Institute, 1946).

alone represents more than three million man-hours of television viewing in a single year. Since the number of television sets has considerably increased since 1958, the use of television among people of this generation may be still greater today than it was at the time of the study.

Reading is another common activity, and radio and records also get considerable time. In fact, if we can assume that the median is somewhere near the arithmetical average of time, then we arrive at the somewhat startling figure that almost 45 per cent of all the leisure hours available to these old people were spent on media activities—television, reading, radio, and records.

AGE PATTERNS IN USE OF VARIOUS MEDIA

The time devoted to movies, books, and possibly also to magazines drops fairly steadily from young adulthood on into old age, whereas the use of television and newspapers remains fairly constant and may even increase in the years after middle age. These patterns are fairly well known, but the evidence has seldom been gathered together, and it may be useful to present some of it here.

A national study of 4,000 adults, in 1946 when radio occupied much the same position as television today, and when audiences of movies had suffered less from the competition of television, asked which media respondents had used "yesterday"—see Table 2.

The Opinion Research Corporation found a similar leveling of book and magazine reading in a national study in 1957, although with an upturn after 60.[19] They found that movie attendance dropped steadily

[19] 1957 national survey of 5,000 American adults 15 years of age and over, by Opinion Research Corporation. For comparable data, see E. B. Parker and W. J. Paisley, *Patterns of Adult Information Seeking* (Stanford: Institute for Communications Research, Stanford University, 1966).

TABLE 3 *Use of television and newspapers by different age groups*

		Teens	Age 20–34	Age 35–49	Age 50+
Mean daily television viewing time[a]	M	3:14	3:00	2:58	3:58
	F	2:52	4:08	3:53	4:49

	Age 15–16	Age 17–19	Age 20–29	Age 30–49	Age 50+
Read newspaper within last six days[b]	72	78	80	82	82

	Age 15–17	Age 18–20	Age 21–29	Age 30–39	Age 40–54	Age 55+
Read daily newspaper in United States[c]	69.4	74.9	74.2	81.9	83.0	77.8

	Age 10–19	Age 20–29	Age 30–39	Age 40–49	Age 50–59	Age 60+
Proportion of news read in daily paper[d]	9.3	18.3	21.8	21.2	21.4	19.4

Source: (a) A. C. Nielsen Co., January, 1965 (unpublished).
(b) Canadian Newspaper Publishers, 1962; national study, $n = 3,222$.
(c) Newsprint Information Committee, 1961; national study, $n = 2,449$.
(d) Wilbur Schramm and David M. White, "Age, Education, Economic Status: Factors in Newspaper Reading," *Journalism Quarterly*, 26 (1949), 149–159; $n = 746$.

from the teen years on, with *no* upturn in old age.[20] This reflects, among other things, decreasing attractiveness of leaving one's home for entertainment. Rolf Meyersohn computed results from three previous studies, in 1945, 1947, and 1957, and found in all of them the same decline in movie attendance throughout the adult years; therefore, it seems not to be characteristic of any one generation.[21]

There is additional impressive evidence of the continuing popularity of newspapers and television throughout life. For example, in Table 3 are some figures assembled from different sources.

In his careful study of the television audience in the early 1960's, Gary Steiner found that the number of television programs viewed per week actually increased among persons 55 and over.[22] In the 1957 study previously mentioned, it was found that 39 per cent of respond-

[20] Similar declines have been reported by age in theater and concert attendance, and outdoor sports events, in other countries as well as in the United States. (See Vol. I, Chap. 22.4.c, pp. 523–524.)

[21] Rolf Meyersohn, "A Critical Examination of Commercial Entertainment," in Robert W. Kleemeier (ed.), *Aging and Leisure* (New York: Oxford University Press, 1961), 243–272.

[22] Gary A. Steiner, *The People Look at Television* (New York: Alfred A. Knopf, Inc., 1963), 176–177.

TABLE 4 *Ownership and use of television sets*

Age	Per cent who had television sets	Per cent of set owners who watched television on preceding weekday
65–69	90	82
70–74	85	83
75–79	80	84
80+	77	81

Source: Glenn H. Beyer and Margaret E. Woods, "Living and Activity Patterns of the Aged," Research Report No. 6 (Ithaca, N.Y.: Center for Housing and Environmental Studies, Cornell University, 1963), 14.

ents 60 and over said that they viewed television *more* often than they did a few years ago, whereas only 19 per cent said they viewed it *less* often. This heavy increase in viewing, among persons who had never even been exposed to television in their early years, casts doubt on the shibboleth that old people are reluctant to adopt new practices!

The findings are very much the same for newspapers. The Television Bureau of Advertising found in a 1961 survey of 3,000 households that more time was spent reading daily and Sunday newspapers among people 50 and over than among younger groups.[23] Beyer and Woods reported that reading actually appeared to increase beyond the 60–65 age period, especially among men, who at that time usually have added leisure for reading.[24] Amount of reading is closely related to education, and therefore we may expect even greater use of printed media among older people as the average level of education increases and better-educated younger generations move into old age.

All available evidence seems to indicate that the heavy use of newspapers and television, among people who have access to them, tends to persist undiminished until changes in health make it difficut to read or view. For example, the 1958 survey of 5,000 persons receiving social security payments, reported the figures by age groups shown in Table 4.

A study made in 1960 of 925 members of a senior citizens' club in the San Francisco area, and 245 persons of comparable age and economic status who lived in the area but did not belong to the club, has furnished detailed information on the leisure activities of older people. All the people in this study were over 60, and 71 of them were over 80. Almost all of them were extraordinarily active in their use of

[23] This study was reported by Meyersohn, *op. cit.*, 265.
[24] Beyer and Woods, *op. cit.*, 15. They found that the proportion who read was especially high among persons over 80.

TABLE 5 *Use of information programs compared with use of entertainment programs on television, by different age groups.*

Age	Per cent of information programs versus entertainment	Average no. of information programs viewed per week
Under 25	20	5.2
25–34	33	8.9
35–44	31	8.8
45–54	35	11.2
55–64	44	16.4
65+	48	22.4

Source: Gary A. Steiner, *The People Look at Television* (New York: Alfred A. Knopf, Inc., 1963), 178.

media, and this activity declined very little between 60 and 85 unless ill health intervened. On the average these people over 60 devoted a little more than two hours a day to television, and about one hour to radio. More than 80 per cent of them read a newspaper every day or almost every day. They read an average of three magazines regularly. The educational level in this area is above average, and therefore the amount of reading may also be above average. But the important finding is the persistence of these habits through the years of old age. There was practically no difference between the club members and the community sample in their use of mass media; and both groups valued the media highly.[25]

AGE DIFFERENCES IN PREFERRED CONTENT

What do they read? What do they view?

There is a steady trend through the years of aging toward more "serious" use of the media. This may come as a surprise to readers who think of leisure time as synonymous with entertainment or relaxation. The leisure of old age does not seem to be a time of *mental* relaxation, and old people's use of media is less likely to be for entertainment than in earlier years. See, for example, Table 5 from Steiner's study, reported in *The People Look at Television*, of over 250 persons who kept detailed viewing diaries in 1959–1960.

A similar trend emerges from one of the few detailed studies of the movie audience by age and content preference. Leo Handel in 1942

[25] The study was reported in Wilbur Schramm and Ruth A. Storey, *Little House: A Study of Senior Citizens* (Stanford: Institute for Communication Research, Stanford University, 1961). The figures on mass media use, however, were not presented in any detail in that book, and are actually gathered here for the first time.

TABLE 6 *Changing tastes for different types of motion picture stories, by age*
Per cent who like or dislike each type

Age	Slapstick	Mystery, horror	History, biography	Serious drama
12–16				
Like	4.0	8.5	3.8	5.1
Dislike	4.4	7.6	8.7	6.4
17–29				
Like	2.4	5.4	5.8	10.3
Dislike	10.8	8.3	7.3	3.9
30–44				
Like	2.9	4.5	6.3	10.8
Dislike	11.0	10.4	4.5	2.9
45+				
Like	1.1	5.3	7.1	12.2
Dislike	12.6	11.3	3.7	5.3

Source: Leo Handel, *Hollywood Looks at Its Audience* (Urbana, Ill.: University of Illinois Press, 1950), 125. This table is based on a 1942 survey of 2,000 persons in 45 cities and towns.

asked 2,000 respondents in 45 cities and towns to fill out ballots expressing their preferences among a long list of story types prepared by the Motion Picture Association of America. Respondents were asked to pick out the story types they liked (or disliked) to see in movies, then to select the five types liked most and the five they liked least, and finally to indicate the two types most liked and the two most disliked. The percentages in Table 6 are extracted from the large table that resulted, and represent the proportions of persons of different ages (though unfortunately persons over 45 are all grouped together) who chose each of these types as one of the two they most liked or most disliked.

Parker and Paisley in their 1966 publication[26] report the same trend toward increased use of serious content, with age, in their studies of television and radio use in two California communities. Interestingly enough, however, although reading of magazines holds up fairly well, in their sample, into the 60's, the same trend toward increased use of informational content is not found in magazine use. Whether magazines are fulfilling a different role, or are failing to include serious information of the kind older people desire, is not evident from the data.

This trend toward informational as opposed to entertainment content is apparently reflected also in the increasing proportions of

[26] *Op. cit.*

old people who say that the newspaper is the most important of the mass media to them. Steiner's figures suggest that television is typically cited as most important by larger proportions of teenagers and young adults, but there seems to be a turning toward newspapers by age 60, if not before. The figures in Table 7 are from Steiner's national study of the television audience in 1960.

It is entirely possible that some of the difference between old and young may arise from the different experiences of older and younger generations with television. Even so, however, the data are consistent with the trend toward serious content.

What do older people read in newspapers?

Public affairs news, for one thing. The older the individual, the more likely he is to read a given story on public affairs.[27] Local news. Among a California sample of people 60 to 90, local news ranked highest in readership.[28] In a recent readership survey in North Carolina, steady increases were found by age in the proportion of adults who read obituaries, births, deaths, engagements, weddings, church bulletins, and city hall news.[29] On the other hand, the reading of comics decreases steadily by age.[30]

Among old people, as with younger ones, these media habits and preferences are powerfully affected by education. That is, the more education a person has had, the more likely he is to prefer information programs on television, read public affairs news, and use print relatively more than television.

We have noted that many old people remain intellectually alive and interested in learning. One set of data that bears on that is the enrollment in adult education courses. The Bureau of the Census reported in 1958 that a little over 10 per cent of people aged 20 to 29 were enrolled in adult courses, and the percentage fell steadily to just under 3 per cent of persons between 60 and 75.[31] Perhaps twice as many more are engaged in independent study without enrolling formally in courses. These figures are more impressive when one considers that

---

[27] Wilbur Schramm and David M. White, "Age, Education, and Economic Status: Factors in Newspaper Reading," *Journalism Quarterly*, 26 (1949), 150.

[28] Unpublished material from the Little House surveys, previously cited.

[29] Chilton R. Bush, *News Research Bulletin*, No. 3 (New York: American Newspaper Publishers Association, 1966), 67.

[30] *Ibid.*, 66–67. Parallel to this trend is the finding reported by Meyersohn, *op. cit.*, 260, that studies in both 1948 and 1957 found that popular music was named as a favorite radio program decreasingly in older age groups.

[31] U.S. Bureau of the Census, *Current Population Reports*, P–20, No. 80 (Washington, D.C.: Government Printing Office, 1958), 4.

TABLE 7 *"Most important" media to people of different ages (percentage distribution)*

Question: Which is the most important to you?	Age under 20	Age 20–24	Age 25–29	Age 30–34	Age 35–39	Age 40–44	Age 45–49	Age 50–54	Age 55–59	Age 60–64	Age 65–69	Age 70+
Newspapers	32	29	38	31	35	37	49	38	41	45	45	44
Magazines	7	8	5	10	9	8	7	3	5	4	2	6
None or don't know	0	3	4	2	4	3	2	4	5	4	4	2
Radio	24	18	15	16	16	16	10	16	11	14	11	15
Television	37	42	38	40	36	37	33	39	39	33	38	33
Number	(84)	(180)	(294)	(267)	(280)	(253)	(212)	(211)	(193)	(130)	(138)	(174)

Source: Gary A. Steiner, *The People Look at Television* (New York: Alfred A. Knopf, Inc., 1963), 344.

TABLE 8 *Proportion of persons of different ages able to name at least one symptom of each of three diseases*

Education	Age 20–29	Age 30–39	Age 40–49	Age 50–59	Age 60+
Less than high school	33	54	42	27	32
High-school graduate	53	65	71	63	63
More than high school	80	79	88	70	87

Source: National survey made in 1958 by National Opinion Research Corporation; James W. Swinehart, *Voluntary Exposure to Health Communications* (mimeographed; report on this study to the American Public Health Association, November, 1966).

enrollment in adult education courses rises with level of previous education, for people presently over 60 have had, on the average, much less education than young adult groups and also have had much longer to forget the habits and strategies of formal learning. Moreover, those at or near the age of retirement no longer have reason to take job-related courses. With advancing age, people tend to enroll in courses of a general rather than a specific nature—courses on history, current affairs, art, foreign language, and the like, rather than accounting or computer programing or mechanical drawing, or others that might advance them in a career.[32]

KNOWLEDGE-LEVEL OF THE AUDIENCE

What information we have about the level of knowledge of old people indicates that they are a relatively well-informed audience. On studies of public knowledge, people over 60 typically score lower than younger adults, but most of these differences disappear when the effect of education is eliminated. Table 8, for example, is taken from a survey of public knowledge of health information.

As one reads across the rows of this table for each level of education, it becomes evident that the differences by age are rather small and insignificant, in striking contrast to the large differences by education that are observed by reading down the columns.

Might it be that age differences do not show up in a table of health knowledge, such as this one, because older persons are more preoccupied than younger ones with health problems? In that case we should expect such age differences to show up, despite education, in

[32] John W. C. Johnstone and Ramon J. Rivera, *Volunteers for Learning* (Chicago: Aldine Publishing Company, 1965), 155, 166, 170, 181–183.

studies of other kinds of knowledge. But a recent reanalysis[33] of a number of national surveys of science and public affairs knowledge finds that age contributes less than 1 per cent of the variance in the prediction of public knowledge, whereas other variables, notably education, make very large contributions. Overall, when education is controlled, there is little if any difference in knowledge by age. When groups within the population are studied closely, some differences by age are found, despite a control on education, but these differences are almost always in the lowest educational group: Older people who have had less than high-school education sometimes have less knowledge than younger people with the same education. Interpreting this interesting finding, the investigators conjecture that these less-educated persons may not have learned the skills and acquired the habits of seeking information for themselves, and therefore after their school years have fallen farther and farther behind.

This conclusion should be a provocative one for the mass media. Obviously, most of the knowledge these surveys are measuring has been acquired after the school years. In school one learns the skills and language, and acquires (or does not acquire) the motivation for further learning. Then it is up to him. He is thrown into an environment in which the amount of scholarly publishing doubles in approximately ten years' time, in which recent school courses are soon out of date, and courses taken thirty to forty years ago may be almost irrelevant. Even the skills needed to understand modern science and modern social problems are changing constantly. Where, then, does a person go to keep up with what he needs to know of the world around him? To his friends and acquaintances, for some of the needed information; to adult courses and independent study, in the case of a minority of adults [see Eklund, Chap. 11 in this volume]; but overwhelmingly one depends on the mass media to keep him informed. And if there is little falling off in knowledge with age, when education is taken into account, then that is indeed a tribute to the efficiency of mass media science writing, health writing, and public affairs reporting. But at the same time it is a challenge. With knowledge increasing at an exponential rate, and a citizen's need to know also increasing

[33] The conclusions in this paragraph are from Wilbur Schramm and Serena Wade, *Knowledge and the Public Mind* (Stanford: Institute for Communication Research, Stanford University, 1967). Among the surveys reanalyzed—all with samples of 1,500 or over—were the CBS Science Survey (1967), the Survey Research Center pre-Sputnik Science Survey (1957), the NORC Health Survey (1958), and the several Survey Research Center studies of public affairs knowledge and opinions during campaigns (1952, 1956, 1960, 1964).

swiftly, the media have increasingly more to report and interpret, and their audiences will have to depend on them for more and more.

The special function of the mass media: combating disengagement

It is evident, then, that the mass media can count on a large and loyal audience, and a surprisingly well-informed one, among people in the years of old age. Responsible publishers, editors, and broadcasters will ask how well they are serving it.

For old people the media must perform many different functions, as they do for audiences of all ages. They provide entertainment and tension release (as in the Westerns, the situation comedies, magazine fiction, music). They furnish a continuing survey of distant environment (as in the network newscasts and documentaries, the news magazines, and the interpretive articles and commentaries). They offer a daily record of the events, the people, and the opportunities that a person cannot cover by himself (births, deaths, marriages, sale prices, meetings, and local news in general). They furnish some of the informational tools of daily living (weather forecasts, television and radio programs, lecture schedules, and so forth). In addition to specific services, they offer a pleasurable activity, an alternative to boredom, a part of life that comes to be expected like meal hours and bedtime. One's schedule is disarranged, and one feels vaguely uneasy, when the newspaper does not come or the television set does not work.[34]

But over and beyond all these things, there is reason to think that the mass media perform a special function for old people which will become clear if we say a little more about the situation into which the media enter.

To most persons the last decades of life are a process of gradual or swift relinquishment of roles and activities. One by one, a person

[34] There is no doubt that William Stephenson's concept of mass media use being a kind of "play" (see his *Play Theory of Mass Communication* [Chicago: University of Chicago Press, 1967]) does in part explain the attractiveness of the media. Similarly, both Innis and McLuhan have pointed out the general effect of the media, as distinct from the effect of the content; and Berelson and others have reported that people missed the media, when they were not available, for nonspecific, as well as specific, reasons. See Donald Creighton, *Harold Adams Innis: Portrait of a Scholar* (Toronto: University of Toronto Press, 1957), which is clearer and more readable than either of Innis's own books on communication, *The Bias of Communication* and *Communication and Empire*. See also Marshall McLuhan, *Understanding Media* (New York: McGraw-Hill Book Company, Inc., 1964); and Bernard Berelson, "What Missing the Newspaper Means," in Paul F. Lazarsfeld and Frank N. Stanton (eds.), *Communication Research* (New York: Harper & Row, Publishers, 1949), 111–129.

gives up his role as parent of young children, his role as head of a household with two or more generations in it, his work and his work companions and their daily routine and exchanges of information and ideas, many of his friends, many of his activities, and his spouse. [*See Vol. 1, Chap. 17, pp. 409–420.*]

There has been a noteworthy increase over many decades in the length of time that old people maintain their own household without the presence of children. Children used to stay longer in the parental home, and parents more frequently went to live with their children when they grew old.[35] Among couples born in the 1880's, the death of one spouse typically occurred about the same time as the marriage of the last child. Among couples born in this century, however, the increased length of life has left, on the average, more than a decade between these two events, often *much* more than a decade.[36] During that time, most of the parents maintain their household alone. The wife survives the husband in about 70 per cent of marriages, but even so there is usually a long period in which both partners are living, after the children have departed to make their own homes. [*See Vol. 1, Chap. 7, pp. 157–184; Chap. 23, pp. 537–560.*]

A recent study shows approximately one-fourth of all people over 65 living with their children. Altogether, about 70 per cent are living with a relative (usually wife, husband, or children), while about 25 per cent are individuals living alone.[37]

During the years when people are gradually being disengaged from family relationships they usually have less and less social interaction of any kind.[38] The degree of happiness they express seems to be fairly closely related to this declining amount of interaction. The less active they are, or the more isolated, the more likely they are to express feelings of loneliness or uselessness or lack of affection.[39] [*See Vol. 1, Chap. 15.6, pp. 353–356.*] Recent studies show one-third to one-

[35] Paul C. Glick and Robert Parke, Jr., "New Approaches in Studying the Life Cycle of the Family," *Demography*, 2 (Chicago: The Population Association of America, 1965), 187–202.

[36] Paul H. Jacobson, "The Changing Role of Mortality in American Family Life," *Lex et Scientia: The International Journal of Law and Science*, 2 (1966), 117–124.

[37] U.S. Bureau of the Census, *Current Population Reports*, P–20, No. 144 (Washington, D.C.: Government Printing Office, 1965).

[38] The activities of several hundred old people have been studied in detail and interpreted in a provocative way by Elaine Cumming and William E. Henry, *Growing Old: The Process of Disengagement* (New York: Basic Books, Inc., 1961).

[39] Arthur H. Richardson and Howard E. Freeman, "Behavior, Attitudes, and Disengagement Among the Very Old" (unpublished); and Kutner *et al., op. cit.* See also George L. Maddox, "Activity and Morale: A Longitudinal Study of Selected Elderly Subjects," *Social Forces*, 42 (1963), 195–204.

half of people in their 60's and beyond saying that they feel the need of "more friends."[40] And it is these people—the people who feel the lack of friends, who are retired from their jobs, or who are widowed—who are most likely to admit to "feeling old."[41]

Of course, this is not necessarily true for every person beyond 65. There are notable and heart-warming exceptions. It may become less often true in the future, as today's cohorts of younger people approach their old age better prepared in education, health, and finances. [*Cf. Vol. 1, Chap. 1, pp. 1–11.*] But the general pattern is as described: a progressive decline in activity and fewer social contacts with retirement and the gradual separation from family and friends; and along with this a growing sense of loneliness, uselessness, old age, and alienation. Increasingly what *comes into* the home is responsible for social satisfaction, rather than what is accomplished by *going out from* the home. And as the years go on, one of the more important visitors to the home of old persons is the mass media.

It is easier to say that the mass media can combat loneliness and alienation in old people than to prove that they are doing so. Yet such evidence as we have fits that proposition.

We have mentioned the intense interest of old people in local news of the kind that they might earlier have heard on the streets or at work. Studies of behavior during newspaper strikes have reported that old people complain that during the period when the newspaper was not available they were unable to find out "who has died," and were embarrassed by not knowing it.[42] We have also recorded the great concern of old people with public affairs news. Informal interviews suggest that writers and newscasters like Walter Lippmann, Lowell Thomas, Huntley and Brinkley, and others have become familiar and welcome personalities in the homes of older people. Hobbies, too, are learned from and encouraged by the media. A number of older people were among those who took up Japanese brush painting, when that

[40] Woodrow W. Hunter and Helen Maurice, *Older People Tell Their Story* (Ann Arbor: Institute for Human Adjustment, Division of Gerontology, University of Michigan, 1953), 45. See also Irving Rosow, *Social Integration of the Aged* (New York: Free Press, 1967), 103–104, 117. It is not only friends who are missed. Recall the wry remark of James McNeil Whistler: "I am lonesome. They are all dying. I have scarcely a warm personal enemy left."

[41] For example, see Bernard S. Phillips, "A Role Theory Approach to Adjustment in Old Age," *American Sociological Review*, 22 (1957), 212–217. See also Zena Smith Blau, "Changes in Status and Age Identification," *American Sociological Review*, 21 (1956), 198–203.

[42] A number of instances of this kind were found during a study of audience reactions to the San Jose, California, newspaper strike by Merrill Samuelson, *Some News-Seeking Behavior in a Newspaper Strike* (Ph.D. dissertation, Stanford University, Stanford, Calif., 1960).

was being taught on educational television, and many of them are in the audiences of garden programs and televised bridge lessons.[43] In general, studies of older audiences lead us to believe that the mass media—with some people more than others, in some situations more than others—help to keep old people in touch with environment, combat the progressive disengagement, maintain a sense of "belonging" to the society around them. And thus they are helping to counteract the loneliness, the boredom, the feelings of uselessness and alienation that must come to many aged people in our present society.

This is the special function which we believe mass media can perform, and to some extent are performing, for old people. As the proportion of older people in the population continues to grow, and as the family members move farther apart and retirement comes earlier, this kind of service is likely to become more and more essential.

Policy change and innovations

What can the mass media do that they are not already doing about this challenge? Let us suggest a few questions they might consider.

Are the media making sufficient effort to reach and serve the older audience? There has been such a marked trend toward "youth" in the mass media—advertising to young adults, teenage styles in entertainment, and so forth—that little attention has been concentrated on the people who live in what some of the media call the "sunset years." And yet, is there not good reason to concentrate more on this senior audience? Admittedly, older people do not have the purchasing power of young and middle-aged adults, nor do they set styles in buying and entertainment; but they are a fast expanding segment of the population, and they have more leisure than any other part of the population to use the mass media. They contribute a few points to the rating of a general audience program; more important, they offer a base for a number of special programs or publications. Indeed, if older people are to be served adequately by the media, it may have to be done in considerable part by the media that are concerned with specialized rather than general audience—for example, public television, special magazines, and local newspapers. But on the whole there would seem to be sound commercial reason for paying more attention to this audi-

---

[43] See Wilbur Schramm, Jack Lyle, and Ithiel de Sola Pool, *The People Look at Educational Television* (Stanford: The Stanford University Press, 1963). See also Wilbur Schramm, *The Audiences of Educational Television,* a report to NET (mimeographed; Institute for Communication Research, Stanford University, 1967).

ence (which will soon be 20 million people), even if public responsibility were not sufficient reason to do so.

For another thing, what do the media really know about the tastes and needs of this audience? I am afraid we must admit that little is known. Advertising studies have tended to focus on younger people, and rating reports have directed attention to maximum and general, rather than to special, audiences. A stereotype has been handed down from the earlier days of audience study: Older people make up a rather sheltered audience that resists engaging itself with current problems, is no longer interested in new things, likes religious programs, seeks out conservative commentators, seeks relaxation and escape in light entertainment and light (but not modern) music, and so forth. But the evidence presented in this paper suggests that we need to take another look at that stereotype. For example, the continuing political interest and activity of people over 60 challenges the idea that they are seeking escape rather than involvement. Their interest in new hobbies and continuing study challenges the idea that they are no longer concerned with learning. Furthermore, we are reminded that the present generation of older people is being succeeded by a new generation that is better educated, more accustomed to lifelong learning, and characterized by different tastes in entertainment. Only by reassessing this audience and keeping up with it as it changes can we hope to know what kind of mass communication older people really want and need, give them the kind of programing and publishing they need to remain engaged rather than isolated.

Finally, how can the media make their services physically—as opposed to programmatically—more appropriate to the older audience? We have recently seen a trend toward fewer columns and larger type in newspapers, which makes both for better appearance and easier reading. *The New York Times* is now publishing an entire edition in large type for readers who see poorly. This suggests one way to retain a reading audience through the years of failing eyesight. W. Phillips Davison, of the Columbia Graduate School of Journalism, has suggested a number of other things the media might consider in trying to meet the physical changes that come with old age.[44] How about some adaptations of very small transistor radios that people could carry around unobtrusively with them—for example, eyeglasses with tiny radios built into them—so that the hard-of-hearing can enjoy their private programs without interfering with conversations going on around them? How about making headphone attachments more gen-

[44] Personal communication.

erally available for radios, record players, and television sets, to compensate for deafness without blasting other people out of the house? What kind of recordings would be most useful and interesting to an older audience? Recordings are now typically oriented toward young tastes, but is there possibly a considerable market in recorded literature for those who find reading difficult, or recorded music and radio programs for people who want to enjoy again some reminiscent favorites of previous years? Is there a market for self-teaching devices and programs to serve the general education interests of the elderly rather than the vocational and specialized interests of younger users? What Doctor Davison is really asking, in questions like these, is whether engineers and designers, programers and publishers, have seriously considered the communication problems of a large elderly population, and what ingenious and useful innovations they might come up with if they were to do so.

To sum up, it seems to us that enlightened self-interest as well as public responsibility recommend that the mass media devote some special attention, some of their very special imagination and talent, to the older audience. It can do something for them; they can do a great deal for it. For, as we said at the beginning of this paper, mass communication stands in a position of unique importance between millions of people who are trying to work out a new way of life for which there is no real precedent in history, and a larger society that is trying to understand and cope with a situation in which, for the first time in history, the aged segments of the population have been increasing relatively faster than the younger ones.

Detailed table of contents of volume one

Part 4 Social roles   407

Subject index

61–62, 331–333
prevention, 143, 147
variability, 55, 61–62
SEE ALSO Biological aging; Maturation; Physiological changes in older people
Alarm systems, and housing, 258
Allocation of resources, 9–10, 20, 21–23, 341–343
Anxiety of older job-seekers, 171
Apartments for older people, 241–242, 245–247
SEE ALSO Housing
Architecture, 229–273
Arteriosclerosis, 58–59, 134
SEE ALSO Coronary heart disease
Arteriosclerotic heart disease, 135
Assets, 203, 206–207, 275, 283–284

Bereavement. SEE Widowhood
Biological aging, 329–330
SEE ALSO Aging; Maturation; Physiological changes in older people
Boarders in oversized house, 234
Book reading, 361
SEE ALSO Reading

Cancer of the lung and bronchus, mortality rates, 140
Causality, and priority of services, 12–13
Children, 232, 247–248, 288
Chronically ill, nursing needs, 94–99
Church attendance, 297–298
Churches, 306–312
bureaucratization and, 316–319
as community facility, 311, 319–320
needs of older people and, 295–296
expressive versus instrumental activities, 314–319
funeral home ownership, 322
relation of older people to, 296–301
welfare referral function, 320
SEE ALSO Church programs; Clergy; Ministry; Religion
Church membership, 297
Church programs, 308–312, 319–322
national versus local programs, 313–319
need for personal contact, 318–319
rationale, 293, 309–319, 322–323
Clergy
attitudes toward older people, 306–308

as counselors, 14, 306–307, 321–322
dying patient and, 321–322
responsibilities toward older people, 314–318
SEE ALSO Churches; Church programs; Ministry; Religion
Club activities, 360
Clubs for older people, 248–250
SEE ALSO Golden Age Clubs; Senior Citizens' Clubs
Cohort analysis
of labor force participation, 185–186, 187–190
of morbidity and mortality, 137–143
of unemployment, 192–195
Comfort, and housing design, 254–256
Communal facilities in housing, 242–243, 258–259
Communal living arrangements, 260–267, 281
SEE ALSO Homes for the aged; Institutionalization; Nursing homes
Communities, retirement. SEE Retirement communities
Community, types of, 269–272
Community activities, for retiree, 33–34, 249, 279–280
Community care of aged ill, 36–47
Community care of mentally disordered, 40–42
Community facilities, 248–252
churches, 308–309, 311, 319–320
location of housing and, 244–245
retirement communities and, 240
SEE ALSO Clubs for older people; Health facilities; Health services; Recreation centers for older people; Senior centers; Transportation
Community integration of older people, 13, 235–237, 312, 321
Community nursing care, 79, 94–99
Community planning for older people, 235–237, 250–252
SEE ALSO Community facilities
Condominium arrangements in housing, 241–242, 282
SEE ALSO Home ownership
Consumption level. SEE Spending
Cooperative apartments, 241–242
SEE ALSO Condominium arrangements in housing; Home ownership
Coordination of services. SEE Integration of services
Coronary heart disease, death rates, 133–136

industry distribution, 190–192
occupational distribution, 190–192
retirement communities and, 239
social work and, 18, 33–36
versus leisure, 13
SEE ALSO Labor force participation;
Re-employment; Unemployment;
Work experience
Employment opportunities, 33–36,
274, 278–280
Employment problems of older workers, 165–174
Employment services, 14, 161, 172–174
Employment specialists, and older
workers, 163–165
Entertaining, 360
Environmental assault and aging, 55,
57–59
Environmental needs and housing,
272–273
Epidemiologist, definition, 119
Epidemiology, definition, 119–120
Estate planning, 275, 287–288
Ethical standards, 10–12
Euthanasia, 11, 72–77, 103–104
Expenditures. SEE Spending
Expressive activities of churches, 314–319
Expressive orientation in aging, 303–305
Expressive versus instrumental needs,
13

Family relationships, 18, 28–31
SEE ALSO Children; Relatives
Family responsibility for aged members, 29–31, 288
Family service agencies, 22
Federal revenue sharing and income
maintenance, 285
Female labor force participation, 184,
187, 188
SEE ALSO Labor force participation
Financial assets. SEE Assets
Financial management, 16, 201–228
SEE ALSO Income maintenance programs
Financial situation of older people,
204–212
Formal organizational participation,
31–32
Foster grandparent programs, 280
Fraud, legal protection against, 291–292

Freedom of choice as professional
value, 8–9, 13
Friendship relations, 10, 235–236, 305

Gardening, 360
Geriatric hospitals, 267–268
Geriatric nursing. SEE Nursing
Golden Age Clubs, 248–252, 309, 311,
314, 316, 320
SEE ALSO Clubs for older people;
Senior Citizens' Clubs; Social clubs
for older people
Group housing. SEE Communal facilities in housing; Communal living arrangements
Guaranteed annual income, 203, 285–286
SEE ALSO Financial management;
Income maintenance programs

Health, 10, 13
definition, 118
environment and, 114
labor force participation and, 187,
189, 190
learning and, 331, 334
potential of older people, 6
SEE ALSO Disease; Illness; Morbidity; Public health
Health care
church programs, 308, 309
demand for, 117
determination of needs, 117–119
measurement of needs, 117–119,
120–123
preventive care, 81, 114, 128–147,
147–159
SEE ALSO Health facilities and community planning; Health services;
Medical care; Nursing care; Public
health
Health education, 332
SEE ALSO Health information
Health facilities and community planning, 250–252
SEE ALSO Health services
Health information, 368–369
SEE ALSO Health education
Health services
community, 42–45
interdisciplinary nature of, 15–16,
67, 112–113
social work and, 36–47
use of, 117

SEE ALSO Health care; Health facilities and community planning; Medical care; Nursing care
Home equity, 206–207, 283–284
SEE ALSO Home ownership
Home health aide, 43, 97
Home nursing care, 94–99
Home ownership, 233, 241, 281–282
SEE ALSO Condominium arrangements in housing; Home equity
Homes. SEE Housing
Homes for the aged, 22, 45–46, 260–267
SEE ALSO Institutionalization; Institutional living arrangements; Nursing homes
Hospitals
care of older people, 64–66, 93–94
community health services and, 37–39
day hospitals, 251
diagnostic procedures, effects on older people, 64–65
extension in community, 38–39
geriatric, 267–268
social workers and, 37–39
SEE ALSO Mental hospitals
Household composition, 157–158, 232, 280–281
House size
boarders and, 234
community integration of older people and, 236–237
housing needs and, 233–237
Housing, 14, 229–273, 280–282
church sponsorship of, 308, 310, 314
communal facilities in, 242–243, 258–259
departure of children and, 229, 232
dependence and, 230, 259–268
design for older people, 254–259
disablement and, 230, 253–259
environmental needs, 272–273
interaction with relatives and, 247–248
legal aspects, 280–282
life-cycle needs, 231
location requirements, 244–245
number of units, 245–246
ownership of, 233, 241, 281–282;
SEE ALSO Home equity
public, 242–244
rental, 233–234
retirement and, 229–230, 237–252;
SEE ALSO Retirement communities
safety of, 67, 257–258

social insulation and, 240–244
space requirements, 233–237, 254–255; SEE ALSO Apartments
widowhood and, 230, 252–253
Housing complex, size of, 245–246
Hypertension and aging, 57–58

Illiteracy among older people, 329, 356
Illness, 29–30
chronic, 10, 94–99
multiple conditions, 63–64, 66
SEE ALSO Disease; Health; Morbidity; Sickness
Impairment, legal aspects, 289–292
Incidence study of disorder, 121–123, 125
Income, 12, 201, 203, 204–206
effect of converting assets on, 206–207
effect of economic growth on, 7, 203–204, 215, 222–223
growth and education, 214–216
occupation and, 207–209
production and, 10
sources, 206
spending and, 210–212, 217–220
worklife estimates, 203–204, 212–217, 220–221
SEE ALSO Earnings
Income distribution
cross-sectional comparisons, 207–209
over life cycle, 10, 202–204
Income-maintenance programs, 9, 11, 16, 18, 23, 30, 47–49, 201, 203–204, 226–228, 275, 282–288
SEE ALSO Financial management; Pensions; Social security
Income transfers, 224–228
Independence, 8, 157–158, 251–252
SEE ALSO Dependence
Independent households, 157–158
Individual development, 21–28
Industrial gerontology, 163, 165
Industries employing older persons, 190–192
Information services, 49–51
SEE ALSO Health information; Mass media
Institutionalization, 8
of impaired, legal aspects, 290–291
isolation from kin and, 157–159
social dependence of older people and, 157–159
SEE ALSO Protective services
Institutional living arrangements, 259–268, 310

Marital status
  labor force participation of older
    females and, 187, 188
  morbidity and, 132–133
Mass communication, and aging, 353–
  375
Mass media, 5, 353–375
  adaptation to older audience, 353,
    373–375
  content preferences, 364–368
  coverage of situation of older people,
    352, 353–359
  disengagement and, 370–373
  knowledge level of audience, 368–
    370
  leisure time and, 360–364
  preferences, 367
  social integration of older people and,
    353, 370–373
  as source of information, 353, 369–
    370
  use of, 359–370
  SEE ALSO Book reading; Magazines;
    Movies; Newspapers; Radio; Tele-
    vision
Maturation, 330
  SEE ALSO Biological aging; Physi-
    ological changes in older people
"Meals on wheels" service, 251
Medicaid, 84, 87
Medical care, 55–78, 150–151
  barriers, 55, 62–67
  church programs, 308, 309
  community planning and, 250–252
  of dying patient, 70–71
  facilities, 55, 66–67
  research needs, 77–78
  services, 22
  SEE ALSO Health care; Nursing care
Medicare, 38, 43, 67, 84, 90, 151, 159,
  224, 285, 288, 289
Mental health services and social work,
  22, 39–42
  SEE ALSO Protective services
Mental hospitals and social workers,
  39–42
  SEE ALSO Hospitals
Migration of older people, 237–238
  SEE ALSO Moving; Residential mo-
    bility
Minimum standards for older people, 9
Ministry, 293–323
  attitudes toward older people, 306–
    308
  national versus local responsibility

for aged, 313–319
  SEE ALSO Churches; Clergy; Reli-
    gion
Ministries, specialized, 314–315
Mobility. SEE Physical mobility; Residential mobility
Morbidity, 129
  as cause of dependency, 149–150
  cohort versus cross-section analysis,
    137–143
  incidence rates, 125
  marital status and, 132–133
  prevalence rates, 124
  sex differences, 150
  socioeconomic status and, 132
  treatment, 150–151
  variability in causes, 114, 133–136
  widowhood and, 156
  SEE ALSO Disease; Health; Illness
Mortality, 129–130
  cohort versus cross-section analysis,
    137–143
  environmental variation, 129–132
  rates, 131, 141–146
  variability in causes, 114, 133–136
  widowhood and, 156
  SEE ALSO Death; Dying patient;
    Life expectancy; Longevity
Motivation and education, 324, 331,
  334–339
Movies, 361–362, 364–365
Moving
  in late middle age, 232–233
  in retirement, 237–248
  size of house and, 233–234
  SEE ALSO Residential mobility

Needs and services, balance, 12–14
Negative income tax, 285–286
Neighborhood
  church programs and, 319–320
  friendships, 235–236, 305
  planning for older people, 235–237
  SEE ALSO Community
Newspapers
  content of reading, 366
  as preferred mass medium, 367
  reading of, 361, 362, 363
  SEE ALSO Reading
Noise, and housing design, 255
Nurses
  dying patient and, 79, 99–111
  educational responsibilities, 99
  functions of, 79, 82–85

Space requirements in housing, 233–237, 254–255
"Spare parts surgery," 60
Spending, 209–212, 217–220
Standard of living. SEE Spending
Standards for allocating resources, 9–10
SEE ALSO Priority of needs
Standards of professional services to older people, 8–12
Stereotypes of aged, 339–340, 374
SEE ALSO Social definitions of old age
Subjective age and re-employment, 171–172
Subprofessional workers in social work, 53–54
Suicide rates, 146
Surgery, 60, 65

Tax policy, effect on income maintenance policy, 227–228
Television
content preferences, 364
as preferred mass medium, 367
set ownership, 363
viewing, 360, 361, 362, 363, 366
Terminal illness. SEE Dying patient
Therapy versus prevention, 3, 34–35, 81, 114, 128–159
Training, nurses, 79, 85–86, 112–113
Training of older workers. SEE Retraining
Training, social work, 19, 23, 53–54
Transportation, 244
Tuberculosis, mortality rates, 141

Unemployment of older workers, 166–169, 192–196
SEE ALSO Employment; Labor force participation; Re-employment
Union programs, 34, 278
Urbanization, and needs of older people, 305

Values, social and professional practice, 8–12
Visiting, church programs for, 314, 315, 321
Visiting nurses, 96–99
Voluntary association participation, 31–32
Volunteer work, 33–34, 249, 279–280

Wages. SEE Earnings; Income
Welfare. SEE Public assistance; Public welfare services; Social welfare; Social work
Widowhood
housing needs and, 252–253
morbidity and, 156
mortality and, 156
public health and, 114, 155–157
Work. SEE Employment; Labor force participation; Occupation; Unemployment
Work experience of older persons, 162, 186–187, 200
SEE ALSO Employment; Labor force participation
Worklife income projections, 203–204, 213–217, 220–221

Name index

Belbin, R. M., 179, 180, 181
Belitsky, A. Harvey, 167, 168, 171, 172, 173
Bell Telephone System, 34
Benjamin, B., 156
Benjamin, Ilva, 113
Benjamin Rose Institute, 23
Bentham, Jeremy, 230, 231
Bentley, Canon G. B., 76
Berelson, Bernard, 370
Berkson, J., 156
Bernardin, J., 85
Bernstein, Merton C., 2, 5, 14, 30, 36, 41, 62, 233, 252, 274, 275, 280, 286
Beyer, Glenn H., 230, 233, 254, 257, 260, 265, 358, 360, 363
Biller, Newman M., 318, 321
Birren, James E., 25, 26
Blackburn, John O., 223, 228
Blakely, Robert J., 350
Blau, Zena Smith, 372
Blauner, Robert, 322
Blenkner, Margaret, 42
Blizzard, Samuel W., 310
Bloom, M., 42
Blue Cross Home Care Program, 84
Bogue, Donald, 355
Boquet, R. F., 40
Bott, E., 158
Botwinick, Jack, 26
Boucher, C. A., 257
Bowen, William G., 284
Boyd, R. V., 64
Brady, Dorothy S., 208, 216
Brass, W., 136
Breen, Leonard, 26
Brim, Orville G., Jr., xvii
Brinkley, David, 372
Bristol, Ralph B., 219
British Ministry of Health, 251, 257, 261
British Ministry of Housing and Local Government, 236, 245, 246, 255, 259
British New Towns, 237, 238, 244
British Royal College of Nursing, 88
Brockington, C. F., 154, 160
Brodt, Dagmar, 93, 94
Brookings Institute Conference Study on Housing for the Aging, 245
Brotman, Herman B., 202, 205
Brown, Esther Lucile, 56, 80, 84, 86
Brown, John Mason, 342
Brumberg, Richard, 219
Burkett, Jess, 338

Burns, Eveline, 227
Bush, Chilton R., 366

Cambridge University, 59
Canadian Newspaper Publishers, 362
Cantril, Hadley, 356
Carey, Ione, 85
Carp, Frances Merchant, 242, 246
Cartwright, A., 150
Cartwright, G., 136
Casals, Pablo, 351
Case, R. A. M., 138, 140
Case Western Reserve University, 97
Catholic Charities of St. Louis, 305, 316
Cato, Marcus P., 356
CBS Science Survey, 369
Cedarleaf, J. L., 306, 310, 311, 312
Chamberlain, Neil W., 279
Chen, Yung-Ping, 283
Children's Bureau, 43
Cicero, 71
Clarke, Edward Hammond, 70
Clarke, Margaret, 92
Cleland, Virginia, 92
Collins, S. D., 124, 125
Columbia Graduate School of Journalism, 374
Columbia University, Bureau of Applied Social Research, 306
Columbia University, College of Physicians and Surgeons, 63
Comfort, Alex, 129, 130, 131
Community Service Society of New York, 23
Conference on the Aging, University of Michigan, 332, 335
Conference on Economic Progress, 244
Cornell University—New York Hospital School of Nursing, 81, 112
Coser, Rose L., 94, 158
Council on Social Work Education, 53
Covalt, Nila Kirkpatrick, 299
Crabtree, Jack, 343
Creighton, Donald, 370
Crutcher, Hester, 40
Crocetti, Guido, 38
Culver, E. T., 306, 311, 315
Cumming, Elaine, 239, 303, 371
Cummins, J. F., 121

Davison, W. Phillips, 353, 374, 375
Demerath, N. J., III, 314

McKendrick, A. G., 137
McKeown, T., 132, 149
McKinley, P. L., 137
McKinney, John C., 250, 298
McLuhan, Marshall, 370
McMahon, Ernest E., 325, 337
McNamara, Walter J., 162
Macgregor, Frances Cooke, 80, 86, 91, 92, 93
Mack, Ruth, 219
MacMahon, B., 123, 136, 138, 140, 143, 146, 156
Madge, John, 2, 9, 13, 14, 22, 30, 36, 46, 52, 67, 85, 98, 229, 280, 320, 359
Maddox, George L., 371
Maloney, Elizabeth, 83
Maltese, Dee, xvii
Mangum, Wiley P., Jr., 159
Manpower Development and Training Act of 1962, The, 175, 176, 177, 178
Manpower Report of the President, 185, 193, 194, 355
Mansell, Ellen, 85
Mark, Jerome A., 358
Marris, P., 156
Mathiasen, Geneva, xvii, 41, 162, 290
Maurice, Helen, 372
Maves, Paul B., 306, 310, 311, 312
Mead, Margaret, 326
Medawar, P. B., 147
Medicaid, 84, 87
Medical Assistance to the Aged, 289
Medical Society for the Care of the Elderly, 257
Medicare, 38, 43, 67, 84, 90, 151, 159, 224, 285, 288, 289
Menlo Park Retirement Apartments, California, 243
Mental Retardation Division of the Bureau of Health Services, 43
Merriam, Ida C., 202
Meyer, Donald B., 319
Meyerson, M., 238
Meyersohn, Rolf, 356, 362, 363, 366
Miller, Helen Hill, 74
Miller, Herman P., 213, 214, 215, 216, 217, 220, 221
Ministry of Housing (England), 259
Mitchell, Robert E., 306, 314
Moberg, David O., 297, 298, 299, 300, 318, 329
Modigliani, Franco, 219
Moerwijk, The Hague, 266
Moore, Mary E., xvii
Morgan, James N., 215

Morris, Robert, 2, 5, 9, 11, 14, 18, 23, 32, 52, 62, 67, 85, 112, 127, 159, 280, 320
Motion Picture Association of America, 365
Muller, J., 159
Murray, Janet H., 206, 207, 284
Musson, N., 254

Nadler, Samuel, 40
National Bureau of Economic Research, 219
National Council of the Episcopal Church, 319
National Council on the Aging, 41, 177
National Health Interview Survey of 1964–1965, 187
National Health Service (Britain), 121, 250
National League for Nursing, 87, 88, 97
National Old Peoples Welfare Council (Britain), 246
National Opinion Research Corporation, 368
National Safety Council, 257
Neighborhood Health Services Centers, 52
Neighborhood Service Centers, 52
Neugarten, Bernice L., 26, 302
Newsprint Information Committee, 362
Newton, Kathleen, 105
New York Hospital–Cornell Medical Center, General Medical Clinic, 97
New York State Department of Mental Health, 40
New York Times, The, 291, 374
Nie, Phyllis, 100
Niebanck, Paul L., 242
Niebuhr, H. Richard, 311
Nielson, A. C., Company, 362
Nierstrasz, F. H. J., 254, 260, 265
Nightingale, Florence, 83, 109
NORC Health Survey, 369
Norris, Catherine M., 100, 106

Oakland University, Knowledge and Information Dissemination System, 348
OASDHI, 221, 284, 285, 286, 289
Occam, 63
Odell, Charles E., 162